BOOKS BY

GEORGE MILLAR

A CROSSBOWMAN'S STORY (1955)

A WHITE BOAT FROM ENGLAND (1952)

These are Borzoi Books, *published in New York*

by ALFRED A. KNOPF

A CROSSBOWMAN'S STORY

George Millar

A CROSSBOWMAN'S STORY

OF THE FIRST EXPLORATION OF THE AMAZON

1955 ALFRED A. KNOPF NEW YORK

L. C. catalog card number: 55-5611

THIS IS A BORZOI BOOK,
PUBLISHED BY ALFRED A. KNOPF, INC.

PUBLISHED FEBRUARY 14, 1955
SECOND PRINTING, FEBRUARY 1955

Originally published in Great Britain under the title ORELLANA, by William Heinemann, Ltd., in 1954.

TO

ISABEL

"Una de las mayores cosas que han acesçido a hombres."

—OVIEDO

INTRODUCTION

THE RIVER WAS KNOWN AS EL MAR DULCE (THE FRESH-Water Sea), then as the Marañón, then some called it the Orellana, then it was the Amazons. Today we call it the Amazon, and this is a story about the first journey down it by white men—an astonishing journey. It seems to me that history has been a little harsh with the sixty men who made it, and I hope it will not annoy them if, after the lapse of four hundred and twelve years between the doing and the writing, I take the matter up once more. Many of the historians pacing by on their wide themes have paused to brand Francisco de Orellana "traitor" without bothering to remark on him as a man. This book records the story of Orellana's separation from his commanding officer in, I believe, a truthful fashion; it also records the names of those who made history with Orellana. Like most people who make history, they did it incidentally, because circumstance forced them to do it or die.

This, I said, was *a* story. . . . When I sat down to write I learned to my surprise that I wanted one of Orellana's company to tell the story. And because I write for my own enjoyment I embraced this desire, choosing for my narrator a Biscayan named Isásaga, who was Orellana's scrivener. I make no apologies for doing so. The questions I asked myself were: How did those men make their journey? What kind of men were they? What would it have been like to be with them? In evolving my answers I have incorporated the dates, names, times, distances, adventures, of the expedition that have come down to us through the filter of the years.

If I pretend—and I do—that the framework of my story is accurate, I must give some indications of my sources and acknowledge my debt to them, and for this reason, although I have tried to avoid footnotes except where they explain or amplify the text, I give a bibliography. I shall also feel my time well spent (this is another thing than enjoyment, but there may be a connection between the two) if this book encourages a reader or two to taste some of the books on which this one, with all due deference, is founded.

There are two types of accuracy in the writing of history, factual accuracy and imaginative accuracy. Asked to judge between the two, many would say that the second was by far the more important. That is why I am so greatly attached to the work of Prescott. He makes gorgeous reading.

The robust conquistador Bernal Díaz del Castillo achieved more than he dreamed of, or perhaps cared about, when, irked beyond patience (and he was not a patient man, thank God) by the florid yet mean inaccuracies of the official historians, he wrote his *True History*, which tells so much so well about the Spanish soldier in those turbulent and daring times. Bernal Díaz is splendid stuff, alive with truth, experience, and direct wordage; and he seems as good in the English translation by A. P. Maudslay (for the Hakluyt Society) as in the original volumes, whose ponderous weight is not lightened by the almost complete lack of punctuation. Impossible to believe that any man who has soldiered could fail to be enthralled by Bernal Díaz. How fiddling my own reminiscences of the second German war seem, and are, by comparison! It is true that Bernal Díaz never went near the river with which much of this book is concerned, though he had heard of its great size because a friend of his who had a stammer and who was no horseman, Diego de Ordaz, went on an expedition to the Marañón and was killed. Bernal Díaz wrote about the Spanish soldier, however, and the Spanish soldier is the core of my subject.

Girolamo Benzoni from Milan, who saw something of the Spanish conquests and wrote a book about them that was published in 1572, is interesting because he hated the Spaniards, just as so many people in our world—either from choice or by order—hate the Russians or the Americans. Hatred in a writer breeds lies, and Benzoni lies his head off. Still, he can be very entertaining, and his appetite was always getting him into trouble. . . . "Having killed a dog . . . he roasted a quarter of it, and invited me to partake of it with him, because I had given him a little cheese. . . . And while I was eating with relish, thinking I had never tasted anything so well flavoured, he took it from me, saying: 'Brother, you eat too much; I am old and infirm, you are young and strong; rise, and may God go with you, but I will not allow you to eat any more of my dog.' "

Many writers, some admirable, some despicable, have described their experiences on the Amazon. Of the sojourners perhaps the best is H. W. Bates, who lived on or near the river for eleven years, paying his way by sending specimens of unknown bugs, butterflies, flowers, and birds to London at fourpence a specimen. Bates, short-sighted and very frail in appearance, is the antidote to later travellers who went to the Amazon to describe how they faced death from the decks of river steamers. Wallace is very good too, and so is the careful Mrs. Agassiz, labouring under the watchful eye of her omniscient husband. Of the travellers, I have a particular affection for the Frenchman Marcoy and for the American W. H. Edwards, who exclaims joyfully (and literally): "There are no flies, on the Amazon," and who laps up with enthusiasm the yellowish water—". . . extremely pleasant to the taste, for bathing it is *luxurious*"—water held by more recent writers of his race to be so noxious that they boast of having refused to eat off plates that had been washed in it. . . . I have fought against Italians, and though they greatly appeal to me, both individually and as a race, I found them to be choleric and trigger-happy enemies. Osculati was a choleric and trigger-happy traveller, but his book is all the more enjoyable for that, and because he was an inefficient traveller who got more than his share of trouble and danger. At the other extreme was Lieutenant H. L. Maw, R.N., who left Truxillo on the Pacific coast on December 10, 1827, rode over the Andes on mules and horses, embarked on the upper waters of the Amazon, and reached the Atlantic on April 19, 1828—very good going. From Maw's laconic book we see that he knew exactly what he was after and that he had in him the right mixture of energy, patience, ferocity, and gentleness to get the most out of his few Indians. An intriguing feature of Maw's *Journal* is its brief acknowledgement that the writer made his immense journey in the company of "an English gentleman of the name of Hinde." After this introduction monkeys, urubus, jaguars, and boas take the stage; "Mr. Hinde" is not even noises off. Those of us who have experienced rough travel will be inclined to wonder what dramas this silence conceals, and perhaps to regret the inexorable reticence of a very naval traveller.

In 1894, when it was generally thought that Orellana had been a cad if not a coward, a Chilean scholar, Don José Toribio Medina, obtained new evidence on which he founded his book *Descubrimiento del Río de las Amazonas.* Our world will always be readier to absorb and spread slander than to redeem it, and Medina's book (only two hundred copies were printed) had a lesser effect than he had anticipated. But in 1934 the American Geographical Society published *The Discovery of the Amazon,* a translation of Medina's work together with invaluable appendices and clarifications. Translated from the Spanish by Mr. Bertram T. Lee, and edited by Professor H. C. Heaton, this book is a monument of perseverance and thoroughness in a field where so many of the other authorities prefer the avalanche rumble of a phrase to the tinkle of a fact. I take pleasure in here expressing my gratitude and my indebtedness to the compilers and to the Society. In the same volume are to be found English translations of the two accounts given by Father Gaspar de Carvajal of his journey with Orellana, the first account taken from Medina's *Descubrimiento,* the second from Oviedo's *Historia General.*

The Hispanic Council in 1944 republished in Madrid a part of Medina's book. Perhaps the chief value of this work lay in the additional footnotes supplied by Capitán de Navío Don Julio Guillén, director of the Museo Naval in Madrid. Captain Guillén evoked a clearer picture of the "brigantines" built, sailed, and fought by Orellana's party, and it was indeed time that an expert and a sailor put the historians right on this matter, for most of them went pitifully astray, being landsmen, and each inclined to follow a leader who was himself lost.

Medina discovered his version of Carvajal's story in manuscript in the library of Johan T'Serclaes, Count of Tilly. Oviedo's version requires some explanation. . . . When Orellana's small expedition had reached the pearling island of Cubagua, off-lying what is now the Venezuelan coast, most of his men rested there and eventually drifted back to the fighting and civil war in Peru. But Orellana, intent on returning to Spain to exploit his success by obtaining from the King the right to colonize the lands he had discovered, chartered a ship and arrived on November 22, 1542 at the city of Santo Domingo on the eastern end of the island of Hispaniola (now the Dominican Republic). Orellana and the few men with him found Oviedo, the official historian, living in Santo Domingo, and to him they recounted some of their adventures. It seems likely that Oviedo, who always had a nose for a good story, sent a message to Father Carvajal, still on Cubagua, asking him to provide a full account of the journey. This the friar did. That there are some differences in his two accounts need not worry us unduly because Father Carvajal probably wrote the first (Medina's) version at Orellana's request shortly after the arrival at Cubagua, whereas he must have taken more trouble with the second version, which was going to the distinguished Don Gonzalo Fernández de Oviedo y Valdés. Also Oviedo may well have made insertions or changes to suit whim or ear, and may—as he claims—have added details given him orally by those of the expedition whom he had met at Santo Domingo.

My story is a simple one in that it concerns a strange, perhaps man's strangest, journey, which I follow from departure to arrival. But there is one complication: I do not care to leave Gonzalo Pizarro stranded with his men and his horses in the hostile forests through which the Napo runs to meet the Amazon. Therefore, as a convenience to any reader who may wish it, I add in the form of a short appendix a description of Pizarro's efforts to save himself and his followers. My sources for this description are often the same as those relating to the main narrative. The most important, however, is Pedro de Cieza de León, one so far ahead of his contemporaries that he was capable of exclaiming: "I have sometimes thought that, when one people and nation succeed another, as time rolls on the first is forgotten, and that same fate may overtake us [Spaniards] as has befallen others, which may God forfend." Cieza de León is both clear-headed and factual, and he claims, as seems likely, that he had his information direct from the survivors of Gonzalo Pizarro's expedition when they at last reached Quito. Rather less helpful is Gonzalo Pizarro's own report on the expedition, which is contained in his letter to King Charles V, dated Tomembamba, September 3, 1542. No Pizarro could ever bear failure, and it is natural that Gonzalo should accuse Orellana of desertion. At least his letter, which is preserved in the Archivo General de Indias at Seville, affords proof that some of the charges against Orellana—and particularly one (repeated by Prescott, who in this followed Zárate and Garcilaso) that Orellana marooned in the forest a loyal caballero named Hernán Sanchez de Vargas, who refused to go on downstream in the brigantine, and that this Vargas succeeded in rejoining Pizarro—are, to put it very politely, inventions.

There must be many references in such a book as this one to

the Christian faith as then taught by the Holy Catholic Church. Most Spaniards of the sixteenth century had the good fortune to "know" that allegiance to their faith and a scrupulous regard for the Church's daily program of worship gave them the certainty of a life after death that was (as certainly) denied to heretics. From this state of mind they drew some—by no means all—of the strength that enabled them, few though they were, to overturn the Indies (as Christopher Columbus had, in error, named the American continent and the West Indian islands). They, the soldiers of the Spanish conquests, may well have been superior as fighting men to any who were before them and to any who have followed after; and whatever we may say or pretend, until there be a resurgence of faith in one religion or another among whole masses of practical, intelligent, and hardy people, we are unlikely to have again among the white races of the world men of such steely spirit, such invincible confidence in destiny. In order to give point to the above assertion, and not from any sense of self-importance, I mention that I am not a Catholic; nor, I am happy to say, do I note any resurgence of religion in myself.

I should like to thank Don Alvaro Bertran de Lis for all the help he has so enthusiastically given me; Rear-Admiral Don R. F. de Bobadilla, S.N., and Captain Don Julio Guillén, S.N., for their courtesy and generosity in replying to my importunate queries; the American Geographical Society for kindly permitting me to base my map of Orellana's progress on their original solution; and George Naish, Esq., for agreeable and instructive hours spent in his company at the National Maritime Museum. I am more than grateful to the library staffs of the British Museum and the Hispanic Council, and to the London Library.

In conclusion I acknowledge my debt in this, as in all else, to my wife, whose command of the mellifluous Spanish language, whose interest happily combined with a talent for changing the subject, have helped me to an enjoyment of the work (if work it should be called) that will not, I fear, be matched by that of any reader.

G. M.

Cranborne, Dorset, 1954

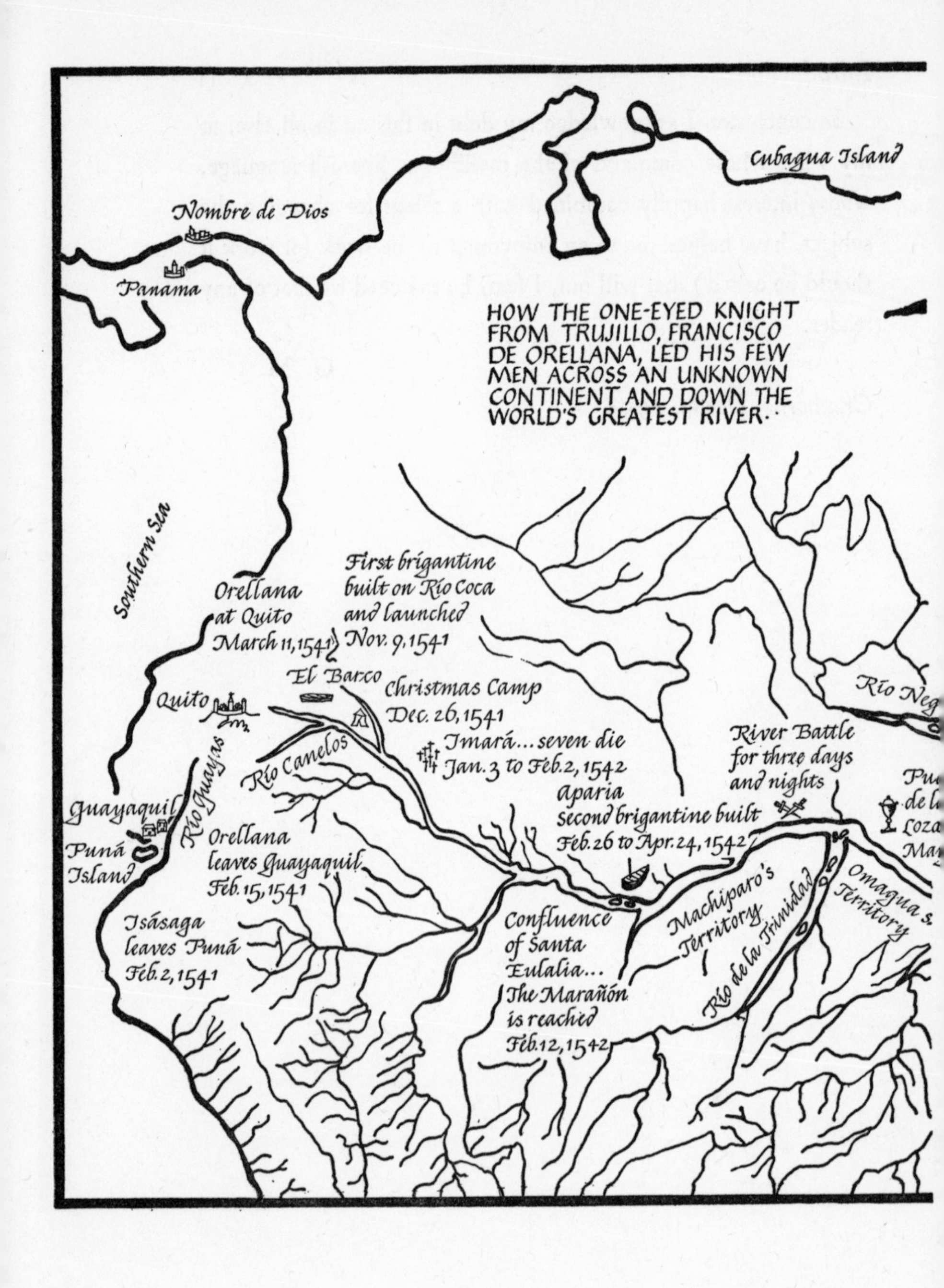
Cubagua Island
Nombre de Dios
Panama
HOW THE ONE-EYED KNIGHT FROM TRUJILLO, FRANCISCO DE ORELLANA, LED HIS FEW MEN ACROSS AN UNKNOWN CONTINENT AND DOWN THE WORLD'S GREATEST RIVER.
Southern Sea
Orellana at Quito March 11, 1541
First brigantine built on Río Coca and launched Nov. 9, 1541
El Barco
Christmas Camp Dec. 26, 1541
Quito
Imará... seven die Jan. 3 to Feb. 2, 1542
Río Canelos
Río Guayas
Río Neg
River Battle for three days and nights
Aparia second brigantine built Feb. 26 to Apr. 24, 1542
Guayaquil
Puná Island
Orellana leaves Guayaquil Feb. 15, 1541
Machiparo's Territory
Omagua Territory
Río de la Trinidad
Isásaga leaves Puná Feb. 2, 1541
Confluence of Santa Eulalia... The Marañón is reached Feb. 12, 1542

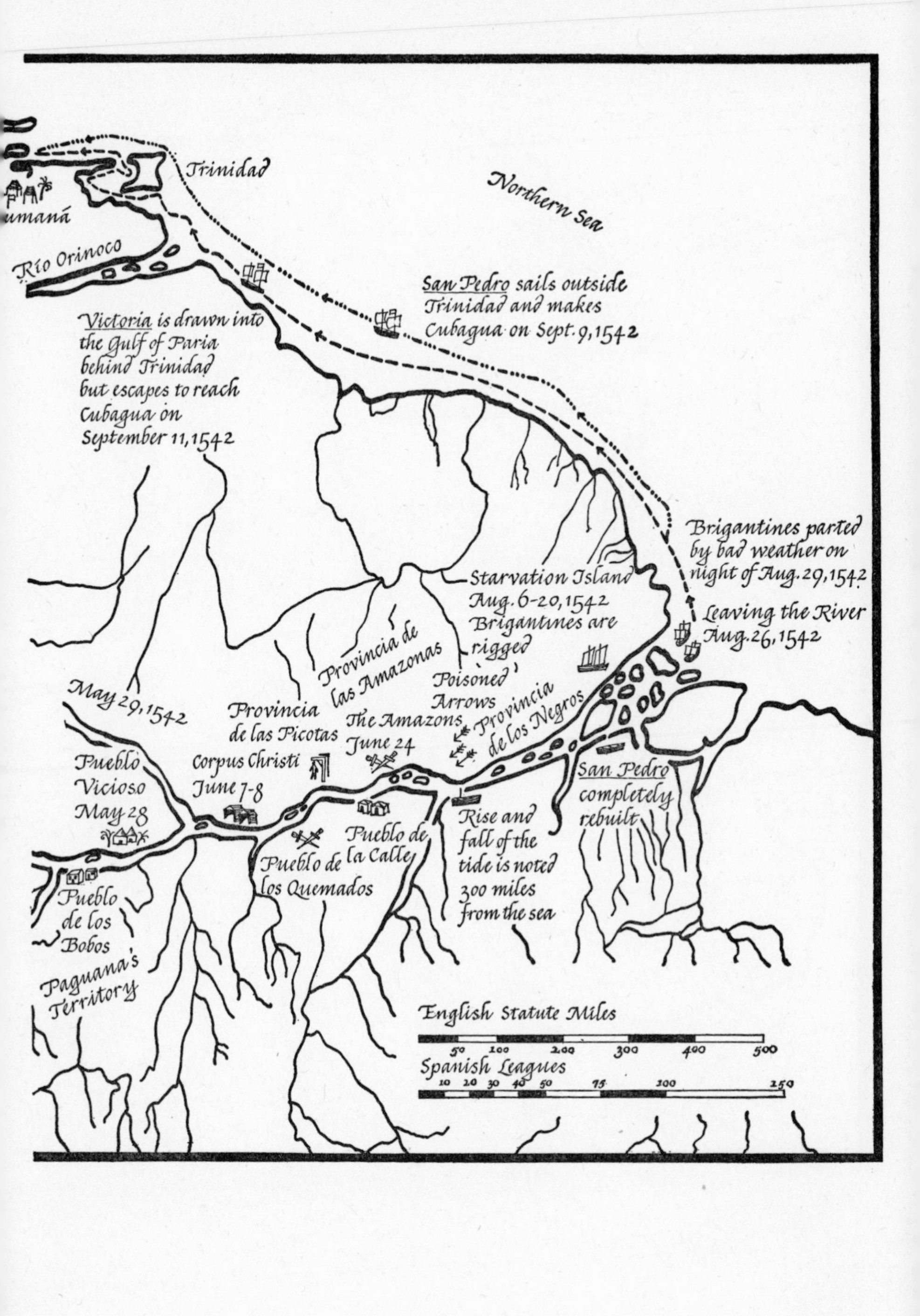

Trinidad
umaná
Northern Sea
Río Orinoco
San Pedro sails outside Trinidad and makes Cubagua on Sept. 9, 1542
Victoria is drawn into the Gulf of Paria behind Trinidad but escapes to reach Cubagua on September 11, 1542
Brigantines parted by bad weather on night of Aug. 29, 1542
Starvation Island Aug. 6-20, 1542 Brigantines are rigged
Leaving the River Aug. 26, 1542
Provincia de las Amazonas
Poisoned Arrows
May 29, 1542
Provincia de las Picotas
The Amazons June 24
Provincia de los Negros
Pueblo Vicioso May 28
Corpus Christi June 7-8
San Pedro completely rebuilt
Pueblo de la Calle
Rise and fall of the tide is noted 300 miles from the sea
Pueblo de los Quemados
Pueblo de los Bobos
Paguana's Territory
English Statute Miles
50 100 200 300 400 500
Spanish Leagues
10 20 30 40 50 75 100 150

A CROSSBOWMAN'S STORY

CHAPTER ONE

I WILL GO BACK, SEÑORES, TO THE BEGINNING OF MY JOURNEY, though I began it alone, and ended it in the best of company, watched over by the souls of the fourteen of us who perished on the way. No single man could have accomplished what we accomplished together. Nor could our leader have gone through those places without us, nor we without him.

You have done me the honour of asking me to tell my story, and I therefore say this: I shall speak nothing but the truth; and because some of the happenings which I shall try to describe are so extraordinary as to strain the bounds of reason, if any among you should come to think: "This Isásaga is a liar," let him remember that I claim to speak the truth and that I compel nobody to listen; and let him not come to me and say: "*This* cannot be," or "*That* is mere boasting," for I will not argue about my story, though I am prepared to argue for a year, if need be, and with any weapons, concerning questions of my own honour; nor am I easy of temper when my word is doubted. Further, I would remind you before I begin that there are others who can substantiate everything that I am about to tell you. Have the kindness also to remember that, as a man of some education and a graduate of the University of Salamanca, I was required to work with my pen during our expedition, and for that reason can remember its details and chronology more distinctly, and can speak of it more readily, than would an illiterate.

My journey began peacefully in the Southern Sea * on the morning of the 2nd day of February 1541, when I left the island of Puná, which island should already be known to you, as

* They called the Pacific "the Southern Sea," and the Atlantic "the Northern Sea."

it was the last stepping-stone of the Marquis, Francisco Pizarro, before he landed to conquer in the name of His Majesty the dominions of the Incas. Puná Indians are, very properly, as ready as any men to take up and use their weapons. They had fought with Pizarro, and before him they had fought continually with the Incas who governed the mainland, Peru. I mention this fact because it was in my mind when, without any premonition that my journey would take me farther than Santiago de Guayaquil at the head of the gulf, I stood by the sailing raft that was to carry me on my business. Fretted by the lightest of easterly airs, the ripples ran chuckling away from the island shore until they slid under the curtains of hot mist that cling to that coast in winter, and near at hand the Indian fishermen were walking on the water to shoot their nets. Yes, walking on the water, for each of them stood on a log of the very light wood known as balsa, and each contrived easily to keep his balance by shuffling his feet upon the turning log. None of us ever saw this without remembering the army of the Inca named Huayna Capac.

That Inca had conquered Puná, and no sooner was it done than he returned to his city of Tumbez, on the mainland. The islanders politely undertook to ferry his army back to him. They had rafts enough to carry half the squadrons, and it was agreed that the operation should be done in two stages. Beyond sight and earshot of the shore the Puná crews cut the lashings holding the big rafts together. All the Inca's soldiers were killed by drowning, or were clubbed or stabbed or strangled as they floundered in the sea. Then the islanders lashed the logs together again and slowly returned for those squadrons whom they had left feasting on their beaches. And those they killed in the same cheap and easy manner. But it was not to be easy in the end, because when he learned of this disaster the Inca naturally returned to Puná. He put thousands of the islanders to death in various ingenious ways, while their leaders were all impaled or hanged. Then he ordered songs to be made about the tragedy, that the perfidious nature of the men of Puná should be known for ever to all his subjects. But even songs could not bring back his soldiers, nor the nobles who had been their captains.

You will not, therefore, take me to be of an unduly nervous

disposition when I tell you that before I allowed my Indian crew to cast off I examined the lashings that held the nine great logs together, lashings made from lianas or tree-parasites that are common in those parts and are uncommonly useful, as you will hear later.

Damp and stiff, the sail rose on the two shears of mangrove wood forming the mast, and the Indians moved about the platform adjusting the guara boards that they push down between the logs to act as keels and rudders. One of them took his station between the aftermost pair of guaras, raising and lowering now one, now the other, to put the strange craft on its course. "Strange" did I say? Yes, but those rafts have much in their favour besides the ease in building them. They travel fast in a fair breeze, for, unlike ships, they have no swollen, half-waterlogged bodies sunk deep under the sea. Also, by making use of the guaras, they can claw up into the wind much better than most ships, if less well than the small boats of the Moors.

This raft of mine was twelve brazas long and four wide; * it carried four hundred quintals † of cargo on the sea and five or six hundred in sheltered waters. Amidships there was a hut, its roof and walls woven from waxen vijahua leaves. Before I went into the hut, I ordered an Indian to roll up the walls, for two reasons: firstly because winter is the hot season there, secondly because I intended to watch him and his companions. I lay upon the cargo I was taking with me, most of it to Captain Orellana at Guayaquil, linen of Castile, white and smooth, tools and axes from Barcelona, saddlery from Córdoba, iron from Biscay, lead for casting bullets, and sailmaker's twine from Valencia, made of the finest hemp, and the best of stuff for making crossbow strings. Those products of our great Spain, and many others that I do not mention, had been shipped to Nombre de Dios, then carried by Indians across the Isthmus to Panama, then on a ship again to Puná. Orellana had a plan to dredge a deep-water channel as far up as Guayaquil, but this had not been done at the time of which I speak, and may not have been yet, for all I know. The estuary of the River Guayas, on the western bank of which we had built

* 72 ft. long, 24-ft. beam. The braza equals our fathom.

† 2 tons 17 cwt.

the town, is shoal and shifting, and for that reason Puná was used as a trading post by the Spanish merchants sailing between Panama and the city of Los Reyes at Lima.

My Indians lay in the shadow of the sail as the raft gently moved on without needing attention. Of middle height, dark-skinned, and with thick, muscular legs, they were not ill-looking, though several of them were disfigured by the blotches and bumps that are said to be caused by eating too much fish. They wore cotton loincloths, and their necks were hung with chaquiras, their own kind of jewellery, made up of scraps of shell, and silver, and sometimes gold. Immobile as dead men they lay, save when a bowl of drink passed from hand to hand, hand to mouth.

We were sailing slowly west of south across the Jambeli Channel. The mainland, on the port bow, was blanketed in its clammy-hot mat of vapour, above which glinted the upper snowy masses of Chimborazo, one of the greatest mountains of the Cordilleras and of this, our earth. I never could feel at ease on those rafts at sea because, in addition to the creaking and groaning you will hear on any ship, there is the grinding of the soft logs and the bubbling and sighing of the water against and between them. One of the Indians made fire in an earthenware trough, and when he had a tight mass of embers he baked in them. My share was brought to me on a leaf, the haunch of a sucking pig, a few fishes, and—to take the place of bread—green bananas sliced and roasted. I carried my own horn of salt, so the meal was a good one, and to make it better I levered the bung from a wine cask. When I had swallowed only two mouthfuls I threw the rest away; it was too hot for wine-drinking, and I feared the stuff might make me sleep when sleep would be a stupidity, alone on the sea with companions so slippery, so silent, so cruel. When they had gorged, finishing every crumb, they distended themselves still more with great draughts of their kind of beer, which they call acca. Then, swollen to bursting-point, each dived neatly into the sea and, after squirming and rolling about in the water, drew himself back on the raft and at once was asleep.

In the afternoon the breeze fell, and I roused them to the paddles, fifteen on each side. Thus we came in sight of the island of Pongal, where, two years earlier, Captain Orellana, the one-eyed knight of Trujillo, had ordered a pearling station to be set up. The divers' rafts were anchored in a line about a league * off-shore. In the centre raft was the man I sought. His name was Ojeda, but he was known as El Rapalpelo.† He was pale-skinned, red-haired, and irascible, and because he hated the sun above all things he used a raft covered entirely with a shady roof of woven leaves. I saw him peering out angrily from under the low roof, and very odd he looked, for he wore a turban to keep the sweat out of his eyes. He signalled that I must keep my distance until he had got his divers up from the floor of the sea.

El Rapalpelo was a zealous worker, and the prices of divers, who were most of them Negroes bought in Jamaica or Cuba, were extortionate, and rising every month. He had twelve of them on that raft, and would have had more but he had lost a fair number to the dangerous fishes who are stirred to fury when men seek to steal from their depths the greatest prize of the ocean, namely pearls. Sharks and inkfishes eat the divers in those waters, and the still bigger mantas or quilts kill them by hugging them in their nightlike wings or by dashing them against the sea bottom. Each of El Rapalpelo's divers had gone down a weighted rope at the bottom of which there was a noose for his ankle. He put the first oyster under his left armpit, held the second in his left hand, put the third in his mouth, and, if he could stay down long enough, took a fourth in his right hand. El Rapalpelo went from rope to rope, gazing down into the water, and ready to signal by shaking the ropes should he see any approaching danger. One by one the divers came up until all were sitting, coughing and spitting, on the raft, and opening red and weary eyes at the bright shimmer on the sea.

We took El Rapalpelo's raft in tow, and he turned on his divers, ordering them to open their shells and count their catches. In a day's diving each man had to deliver to him, the overseer, a stated number of pearls. Any the diver had beyond that number were supposed to be his own property, and he was entitled by law

* The Spanish league equalled 4 Roman miles of 1,000 paces each, or 1,617 yards. The league can therefore be taken as 3⅔ statute miles.

† The Plunderer.

to sell them. But most divers preferred to keep a stock of pearls in hand, because damaged or inferior ones were not accepted by El Rapalpelo, who insisted if any man were short that he make up the required number from his credits, or, better still, from any that he had hidden away. The Negroes were skilful at hiding the pearls in their mouths, ears, hair, noses, and in other places. Yet it is doubtful if they could ever deceive El Rapalpelo. There was none sharper, and he had been a good fellow too, until the Battle of Las Salinas, in which he was wounded eight times and lost his right arm at the shoulder. From time to time Orellana had sent other Spaniards to the pearling station, but the one-armed man made himself so disagreeable to them that they never stopped longer than two days. What was more, they usually returned to Guayaquil convinced that they had been lucky to leave the pearling station alive.

It seemed that since his disfigurement by wounds the man only wanted to be alone—that is, with none round him save Negroes and Indians. He had an Indian wife whom he called La Joyuela.* His quarters were within the inner stockade of the station, which stood at the head of a shallow lagoon, very muddy at low water. There he existed with about twenty trained dogs, his wife, an indeterminate number of other women whom he described according to his mood as his cooks or his sisters-in-law, and five Guancavilcas Indians who were armed and were his men-of-responsibility. He was as ready to beat and abuse any of the five as he expected them to be with the slaves in the outer compound, yet he was said to pay them well, and they appeared to serve him loyally. His house was built of canes lashed together with lianas and roofed with leaves. The ground floor had no walls, and fires were kept going there day and night, not only for cooking, but also so that the smoke would rise and permeate the walled space above in the hope that it would discourage mosquitoes and other pests from sharing that space with the master.

We climbed the light ladder that he could raise when he wanted to be alone or if he feared treachery. Indian women were cooking below, and two of them, without any order, detached

* Jewel of Low Value.

themselves from the group and followed us up the ladder. They stood behind us in the room, moving when we moved, and fanning us all the while with feathers. An arquebus, an old one, but clean and well greased, hung on the cane wall beside the bed, which had a cotton tent over it as a protection against mosquitoes. There were stands of lances and swords, and a pair of fierce lurchers, long-coated and verminous, lay growling in one corner beside a litter of ugly pups. They were never allowed out, and it was said that they would kill anybody, save El Rapalpelo or his wife, who entered the place alone. The dogs were fat from overfeeding, which in that climate will make an animal worse-tempered than starvation—though the latter condition is the more frequent.

I handed to my host the list of things I had been told to deliver to him, powder and lead, beads and small knives and combs for the Indians, fish-hooks and a fine-meshed net, flints and candles; and I gave him a very large emerald with a flaw in it, which last was a personal gift from Orellana.

"Most kind of the Captain," El Rapalpelo said, holding up the emerald so that the flaw showed more than ever. "Most kind. I wonder what he wants of me."

I sat at the table and, since he could not read, I read parts of Orellana's letter aloud. "'. . . Kindly go first to the pearling centre at Pongal and deliver to Ojeda with my very warmest good wishes and most sincere expressions of friendship the enclosed emerald, which is a present from me to Ojeda. The colour is unusual, and it is an interesting stone. Also please deliver to him the articles separately listed, and anything else you may have with you that Ojeda may require. Then I beg you to have a talk with Ojeda about his own future, which is frequently in my thoughts and in my heart. Tell him that I feel he has been long enough, if not too long, at Pongal, isolated from men of his own race and quality. I do not of course write this in a spirit of criticism; any man who might succeed him at Pongal would have difficulty in getting half as many pearls. Give him my assurances that I miss him, and I would have him near me, so that we might see each other every day, or at least very often. If he will only accompany you now back to this town of ours he will please me vastly, and I will give him either all the action he may desire, with the possibility of great honour and riches, or if he still insists that he has done with action I will give him any reasonable position that it is within my powers to bestow. He can live here in the town and enjoy the responsibilities he has earned and knows so well how to maintain, or I will give him land and Indians, or a post of administration at the emerald mines. I trust you as my emissary to put this matter, and my wishes on it, most clearly before our friend Ojeda. I shall be very vexed if you return to Guayaquil without him. Have the goodness to ask Ojeda to deliver to me in Guayaquil my Negro slave, the small one with the cicatrice named Panama, of whom I have particular and pressing need at this moment. I ask you and Ojeda to report yourselves whenever you arrive in this town, as I have news of grave urgency that I think will please you both as it pleases me. Also kindly bring me my share of the pearls. . . .'"

El Rapalpelo made no answer or comment. When I had finished he shouted through a hole in the floor that we would eat. Then he said, while we waited: "I stay here." Indian women brought up a ragout made with oysters and the flesh of a llama kid broiled with maize. The dish was so seasoned with peppers that any newcomer to the Indies would have had his whole head aflame after three swallows. Each of us took a few drops of aguardiente in his glass to purify the cloudy drinking water and improve its flatness. While we ate, the two women fanners stood at our backs, trying to keep the mosquitoes at least out of our mouths.

He thrust his plate aside and told the women to leave us. "You will be going on to Guayaquil alone," he said. "Is that clear?"

"Can I say nothing to persuade you to come with me? You heard Orellana's promises."

"I stay here," he said again, and brushing aside the dogs with his feet, he went to an ironbound chest from which he pulled out a bag of soft leather. Slamming down the lid, he came back to me with the bag. When we had weighed it on his steelyard he poured the pearls out on the table, and we looked at them before I wrote him a receipt and scooped them into the box I had with me.

"What do you think of them?" he asked.

"They are even worse than the ones fished off Panama."

"Yet where there are small pearls there should be big ones, pearls as big as the eggs of geese, pink ones, black ones, red ones, yellow ones."

"Why will you not come to Guayaquil?"

"There, and also in Puerto Viejo, I have enemies."

"Orellana is your friend."

"Orellana is his own friend. It may be that he has need of me. Why should I go? I have gone with him before, and it cost me one third of my body. I refuse to leave this place. I stay here. Is that plain enough for you? Here I am master. Anywhere else in the Indies I shall be under orders and at a disadvantage as a weakling who has been foolish enough to have his sword arm severed at the shoulder."

"The Captain will be disappointed."

"Then it is time he was disappointed. He has a fat life. Why must he, with all his wealth, his Governorship, his Indians, his soldiers, his horses, his emeralds, his kinship with the family that rules Peru, why must he take away the best of my Negro divers? Vanity, I suppose. He wants to have a Negro prinking in front of him. He thinks his own elegance more important than that the Negro should be working for profit in these pestilential waters. And why is he always demanding his share of the pearls I find at the cost of much sweat and pain? Am I never disappointed, toiling day after long day on the rafts out there in the gulf? Have I so much? And if he wants more pearls why does he not buy me more divers, instead of robbing me of my best Negro?"

"Would you like some wine?" I asked.

"Very much indeed."

"I will give you a cask."

"You are a good fellow, Bachelor of Arts," he said, more cheerfully. "See here, I am going to make you a present, but I trust you to be discreet about it." He went again to his box, and came back with a single pearl. It was a good one, of medium size and rather dark in colour. There had been no pearl to approach it among those set aside for Orellana.

"Have you many more like this one?" I asked when I had thanked him properly.

"Not one," he answered. "Not a single one. It is the best pearl on Pongal, and it is yours. . . . But what offends me is having to give up that Negro. If only he had been sick just now, very sick and completely unfit for travel. A dead slave would be of no use to Orellana. If this Negro were sick—"

"I would still have to take him to Guayaquil," I said, "for I should not be well received if I arrived without either you or the Negro."

"Then take him and be damned to you." But he did not ask me to return his beautiful pearl, as I had expected him to do; and on thinking it over I realized that my expectations were false, because the longer El Rapalpelo lived away from the rest of us, the stronger grew his pride. Such pride, such wilful dignity, is sometimes no evil.

The Negro slave was waiting at the gateway of the stockade, and with him was another, but bigger, of his own race and station. El Rapalpelo addressed this other as Number Five, and asked him what he did there, but the Negro made no reply. Panama, Captain Orellana's Negro, after bowing to us, looked at the earth and said that he would obey the order of his master and would go with me to Guayaquil—but only if Number Five went too. The Indian women peered out through the smoke of their fires at us.

Number Five then spoke, his eyes downcast, his thick and robust voice shaking with fear and desperation. He said that if his friend went to Guayaquil he must go there with him, and added that he would be willing to pay for such a favour with all the pearls he had accumulated. He held out a small cotton bag to prove that he was ready to do as he said.

El Rapalpelo took the bag and after thrusting it into his shirt he drew his sword and began to belabour the big Negro with the flat of it, saying that there was but one cure for disobedience and disloyalty. Meanwhile I had handed the box of pearls to Panama and had drawn. With my point pricking the small of his back he marched down to the raft, his head screwed round on his shoulder, and in his dark eyes, bloodshot from much diving in the sea, there were tears as he looked back toward the friend he must leave. Behind us we heard the whack of El Rapalpelo's blade.

When a slave is obedient and does his work, it is the duty of the master to feed and protect him; if he disobeys an order or rather shows reluctance, he must be forced to obey, since the punishment for persistent disobedience is death, and slaves are very costly and therefore valuable. It will be seen, then, that sternness with any initial disobedience is in the best interests of both slave and master.

I marched him into the hut on the raft and ordered two of my Indians to tie his hands and his feet. Then they lashed him, turn over turn, to one of the thwartships beams of the floor while I stood by, my sword drooping from a hand slippery with heat. The Indians were rough with the lashings because, strange people that they are, they have less liking for the Negroes than for the white conquerors who bring Negroes in their train. At length Panama lay swaddled in liana cords. His eyes stared at me with anguish and yearning, yet without malice. Then El Rapalpelo came down to the shore to count over the things I had brought him, and I gave him a cask of wine.

"May God go with you," he said as we pushed out from the mud.

I immediately ordered the Indians to ply their paddles without sparing themselves, and told them if they had any power to do so, they should invoke a favourable breeze, because I had no intention of stopping to rest before we reached Santiago de Guayaquil, some twenty-five leagues * to the north. They were disgusted, to say the least of it, for those gentry do not relish working at night —or at any other time. Frequently I went out from the hut to urge on their languid paddling; then I would go back and sit beside the Negro, whose company, such as it was, was welcome to me. I told him that no harm would come to him, and that he was only bound to save himself from himself, reminding him that his move to Guayaquil had not been a mere order but—more serious—an order in writing. Why must he be separated from his friend? He asked that once, but did not speak again.

We paddled into the middle of a fierce rainstorm such as happens there in the winter, thunder and great javelins of lightning followed by rain in heavy drops so numerous that there was not

* Some 90 miles.

space in the sky to contain them, and they fell, one merging with its neighbours, as water rather than as rain. The whole raft streamed. It seemed that we might drown in the rain. Then it stopped, and we heard it sweeping away out to sea. The paddlers set to more energetically than before, for they love the rain, those people; and then they stopped as though an order had been given. I ran out among them. Between us and the shore was a white mark of splashing in the sea. I thought it a battle between two of the giant fishes, and told the paddlers to dip and thrust. But they answered that it was a swimmer, a man. So we waited while he approached, swimming with beating strength and with loud gasps of air. The Indians dragged him to our platform and he lay at my feet, arms outstretched, face down, his frame jerking and heaving. There was no need to see his face.

The Indians paddled on without further orders, and I told Number Five to follow me to the hut, where I lit the lantern and looked at him. A shark-knife was hitched to the cord round his waist. I drew the knife from him. He sat beside Panama, putting one massive hand on the other's hair. Still holding his knife, I asked him to explain how he had reached the raft.

He said that El Rapalpelo had bolted him into one of the cells of the divers' shed, but he had been able to communicate with a Negro, who had slid the shark-knife under the locked door to him. Noticing that the wooden wall had begun to rot near the floor, Number Five had lain flat in that narrow space, and by arching his long body had thrust on the lowest board until it snapped. After enlarging the hole with knife and hands, he had crawled out. Some of the dogs winded him, and as he rose to his feet one came slashing for his stomach and he had killed it with a lucky sideways stroke of the knife. Before he could get to the palisade he had to fight off three more dogs, and he killed one of them. With the whole station in ferment behind him, he bolted into the forest and ran through it, tearing his flesh on the prickly bushes, the sharp canes, the saw-edged lianas, until he judged it safe to force his way down to the sea. He ran along the shore, keeping our balsa in sight and building up a lead on it. Then he waded in and swam to head us. But while he swam, the storm came, and the raft was hidden from him, as was the land. He swam on desperately, not knowing where he was going. Then at last the rain moved away, he sighted us, and we waited for him. He was a lucky Negro.

When he stopped talking I thought for a little. I did not intend to return to the pearling station because, like most of us, I will go forward two thousand paces rather than go back ten. So I called to the Indians to bring us food. I gave Number Five a sodden blanket to put round his trembling shoulders. I also returned his knife and told him to cut Panama's bonds. The food was brought, smoking hot (for those Indians have a white wood that will burn like fury even when it is wet). I said I would take the pair of them to Captain Orellana and, without falsifying, would put their case before him in such a way that, with God's mercy, he would see it kindly. Then the Negroes were as happy as a moment before they had been despondent. They grinned at me and at each other, and it almost seemed that some of the warmth of their puerile happiness—can it be untrue that a man must be free to be happy?—communicated itself to me.

Then, too, our blessed Lord, or the Lady His Mother, saw fit to send over the gulf a warm air from the southward. Our sail was hoisted with a splashing of silver water from its folds and much laughter from the Indians, who got a wetting, until it solemnly wagged, grey against the night sky. The big logs began to bubble and chafe under our platform. After cautioning the Negroes that both of them must keep watch and must wake me if they saw any unusual movement among the crew or if the breeze fell, I lay down with my head on the box of Orellana's pearls. I heard the black men whispering. Then I heard nothing more, for I was asleep.

CHAPTER TWO

☼

IMAGINE ROWS OF HUTS CROWDED UPON A HUGE, SLOPING midden; people the scene with bedraggled, diseased, and nearly naked Indians; splash everything liberally with stinking mud; make it a breeding-place and a meeting-place for vicious insects and vermin of many kinds; see that the rain falls on it nearly all the time and that, despite the rain, the air is so torrid that the inhabitants breathe steam and move always through swirling vapours. . . . That is how Santiago de Guayaquil might seem in its winter state to you who, when you think of cities, think of Seville, Córdoba, Valladolid. Yet such settlements in the Indies are viewed with a certain favorable bias of the imagination—particularly by those who built them—and as the raft approached a wooden quay spattered with mud that was far from sweet, I thought how noble and splendid our Guayaquil was *going* to be, the wooden hovels grown into stone buildings with slanted roofs housing, as well as caballeros and good soldiers of the King-Emperor, a congeries of goldsmiths, lawyers, money-lenders, actors, merchants, poets, tailors, musicians, and vintners, a place of many churches and a tall cathedral cool and stately, a place spouting the wealth of northern Peru, of the mountains and Quito their city, and of the hinterland beyond Peru, across the bold and dangerous Cordilleras.

As always during the wet season, the River Guayas had fouled its nest by depositing around itself a morass of semi-liquid white clay. From the town above us to the quay on which we stood, a road had been made by laying balks of timber; but these had sunk into the slime and had become slippery and pitted with holes so that the road was less tempting than the morass on either side of it. Our cargo was unloaded into hammocks that the porters of Guayaquil carry two by two, slung from lengths of strong cane. One hammock I filled with lobsters bought from a fishing balsa that had come north from Tumbez. Fish should abound at Guayaquil, but it does not, the fishes of the river being celebrated only for their innumerable bones, their lack of taste, and the celerity with which they attain a state of putrefaction. The lobsters would please Orellana.

I settled myself, my crossbow, my pack, and the box of pearls in the best of the hammocks and was carried uphill in the rear of our long file of porters. The suction of their feet as they drew them from the clay made an almost deafening noise, while the pale slime spurted, staining their dark legs and even reaching us whom they carried. The scavenging gallinazo birds hung in a cloud over that town, where they never lacked the ordures they relish, and even descended to the feet of the porters. And now I had better explain briefly how we Spaniards came to be at Guayaquil, and why it was a great credit to us to be there, and at peace. . . .

Sebastián de Benalcázar, one of the ablest though not the most likable of all our captains, was the first to enter that province of La Culata, and choosing a site that seemed reasonable, he left some of his men there under the orders of one Diego Dasa to establish a town. Some have it that Dasa's men behaved with rapacity toward the Indians, and this is credible because the Guancavilcas Indians often wear a profusion of gold ornaments, while certain among them go so far as to encase their teeth in golden envelopes. They are a spirited race, and they fight very prettily with wands and with the redoubtable clubs known as macanas. To go on. . . . The Indians turned against this first settlement. There was a slaughter, from which Dasa escaped with only five or six of his men. He succeeded in reaching Quito, but found that Benalcázar had left that city to carry his conquest farther north. So Dasa himself raised a small force and marched back to reason with the Guancavilcas. They, however, were so little disposed to reason that they drove him off once more, taking toll of his men and horses. Francisco Pizarro heard in his headquarters at Lima of those unusual reverses, and he at once sent a more powerful expedition to the province. This force, under Captain Saera the Long-Armed, was hard at work on the stubborn Guancavilcas when Saera received orders to withdraw because Lima and Cuzco were both besieged by the Indians.

At that time I was in Puerto Viejo with Orellana, who had not long before lost one of his eyes in a skirmish and who had been ill with a fever that no amount of purging seemed to ease. Yet when news came that the Marquis was penned up in Lima and his brother, Hernando Pizarro, in Cuzco, Orellana gathered us Spaniards round him and explained that we must all make what sacrifices should be necessary in the common cause. Then he equipped eighty of us fighting men and all the horses he could buy (ten or twelve), and so we set out for Lima. And as the fighting at that time is now history and has been copiously described by others, some doing it quite well, some badly, I will say no more of that campaign, except that we made it end correctly.

But the next upheaval was civil war, Spaniard against Spaniard, arising from the determined jealousies of the two Governors, Pizarro and Don Diego de Almagro, leader of the Chile Faction. Although he had seen service under Almagro, Captain Orellana sided with the Pizarros, who were his kinsmen and had like himself been born at Trujillo in Estremadura, whose oak glades can produce nearly as many conquerors as they produce hogs. He chose the winning side, which was well for us. Orellana was Ensign General of seven hundred foot and horse sent by Francisco Pizarro from Lima to the aid of Hernando Pizarro. On April 26, 1538 we fought the bloody Battle of Las Salinas, and there was a battle! For Spaniard was fighting Spaniard, so that skill matched skill, and daring spent itself on equal daring. Like Italian carrion birds, the natives gloated on the hillsides, while down in the valley Spaniards showed them how to fight and Spaniards showed them how to die. It was a victory for our side, and it cost Don Diego his head. Eight days after the battle Orellana rode to Lima with an important message from Hernando Pizarro to his brother, and I rode with him.

You might hope that such services as ours would have been rewarded with hunting and feasting, followed by gifts of riches and positions of ease and enjoyment. Captain Orellana, who had distinguished himself, would surely at the very least of it be free to return to his comfortable property at Puerto Viejo. But the conquest always followed its own pattern, hardship begetting hardship, victory presaging a return to arms and the spilling of more blood.

Having defeated the Chile Faction, Francisco Pizarro saw many of his own captains and their soldiery gathering round Lima, and, little liking the sight, he gave them all further work to do to keep them and us quiet. Orellana's "reward" was the offer of a hard nut to crack—no less than the province of La Culata.

So he equipped an expedition (at his own expense of course), and he chartered a barque called the *San Pedro* for the sum of one thousand gold pesos.* In the spring of 1538 we shipped horses,

* Can we say what the gold peso (often called the castellano) would be worth in terms of the present day (1954)? I do not think we can, but we can get some idea of it. . . . There was no coinage at that time in the Indies; the peso there was not an actual coin, but was a weight of gold; one hundredth part of a Spanish pound, which equalled 1.014 of the British pound. Therefore a peso was about 1/6th of an ounce of gold, or about 2/5 ths of a sovereign. Today a sovereign is worth some £3, and by that reckoning a peso-de-oro, for the gold in it alone, would fetch 24/—in Bond Street [$3.36]. That, of course, is to give it far too low a value, because history shows us that money is almost continuously dropping its value. For example, a working woman in England at the time of which Isásaga speaks would be paid threepence a day, whereas now she would be paid eight times that *an hour*. To set against the high value of all coinage in the sixteenth century as compared with today —in the Indies the Spaniards had found and had taken by force vast quantities of gold and of silver. The plentifulness of lucre had set up in the Indies what we would call an inflation, a galloping inflation. This disease of plenty had not yet spread to Spain, though it was soon to do so, with catastrophic effect.

Sir Clements Markham (writing at a time when the pound sterling was worth at least double what it is today) rather boldly estimated the value of the peso-de-oro in the Indies at that time at £2.12*s*.6*d*., and in Spain at about £5 to £6. Taking this expert's judgement for our basis, we should be entitled to say that the purchasing power of the peso-de-oro at the time and in the area with which we are concerned should have been about equivalent to that of £5.10*s*. To be on the safe side—that is, to underestimate—let us put its value at a mere £3.

Then Orellana paid £3,000 for his charter. Reasonable, you may say. But we know that he frequently paid as much for a horse arms, stores, and ourselves, making a good passage north from Lima. We landed on the Point of Santa Elena north of the Guayas, and were at once engaged in fierce actions. The Indians, judging that they had always defeated such Spaniards as marched against them, had inflated ideas of their own prowess, and thought that when we came to a province we did not come to stay. They believed, in short, that we were human and could be beaten. Even if they were mistaken, their mistakenness gave them considerable strength, and their determination involved us in weary marches by day and by night over innumerable rivers, through swamps and forests, and up and down mountains. Good battles there were in plenty against this enthusiastic enemy, until at last he knew and obeyed his masters. It had not been easy; but thus it was that we came to build Santiago de Guayaquil.*

The Marquis was pleased—as well he might be—by the suc-

(the price of horses in Guayaquil and elsewhere ranged from about 500 to 1,000 pesos-de-oro).

Francisco de Xeres, writing of prices after the Inca Atahualpa had filled a room with gold to a man's height, the gold that should have been his ransom, gives the following details (and I put against each the sterling equivalent, again taking the peso to equal only £3): "A horse was sold for 2,500 pesos (£7,500) . . . a pair of high boots fetched 30 to 40 pesos (£90 to 120) . . . a sheet of paper sold for 10 pesos (£30) . . . I gave 12 pesos (£36) for half an ounce of damaged saffron. . . ." Xeres, as a horseman, was paid a small share of the Inca's ransom; it amounted to 362 marcos of silver and 5,880 gold pesos (£17,640). He writes: "If one of us owed anything to another, he paid with a lump of gold . . . remaining indifferent as to whether it represented double the amount of the debt. Those who owed money went from house to house followed by an Indian [servant] laden with gold."

The above extraordinary figures have their bearing on Isásaga's story. Spaniards have ever been overwhelmingly generous with money, but conscious of its value, which consciousness makes their generosity the more endearing. Isásaga is talking to Spaniards in Spain, and when he names a figure he does so to astonish his audience—something we all like to do.

* Guayaquil did not long stand on Orellana's site, but was moved to the place called "Ciudad Vieja" and moved again in 1693 to its present site, when the old town was connected with the new by a bridge.

cess attending our solid work, and he appointed Orellana Captain General of the province and Lieutenant Governor in Guayaquil as well as in Puerto Viejo. All very fine. But such wealth as Orellana and the rest of us had gathered in the conquest prior to the Pizarro-Almagro fighting had now been dissipated, and the return for it was merely Pizarro's authority to pacify and rule this turbulent province. We would have to begin anew if we were to recoup our expenses. So begin we did. And following on a somewhat smaller scale the example of Pizarro, Orellana sent us out to different parts of his province, making us the grants of lands we call encomiendas, where we were individually authorized to raise taxes or services or both from a stated number of Indians. At the same time Orellana got his hand again on the emerald mines near Puerto Viejo, which mines produce the finest emeralds to be seen anywhere—this is one on my finger, and it was given me by Orellana in a time of stress which I shall describe to you. He also continued to build, strengthen, and enlarge the town of Guayaquil, seeking to make the place an entrepôt of trade between the sea and the interior. He had other preoccupations, of course, and enough duties and vexations to melt a sword blade. For example, he had to proceed against certain Spaniards in Puerto Viejo who were practising the abominable crime. Two of them were burned alive, as all (except the two sodomists) considered right and proper, but a third, Bartolomé Pérez escaped from Peru to Spain.

We had had two years of this peacefulness (we called it so, and not always gratefully, for we were soldiers) at the time when this, my story, begins. The Captain, like the rest of us, frequently longed for greater scope and more glory, as became him; but I could not personally complain, for he kept me very busy, and the time passed swiftly enough. He was tied to Guayaquil and Puerto Viejo and to that mass of documents, of bumf, that clogs our Spanish system from the top to near the bottom. He used me as his trusted agent. On his behalf I went now to Puerto Viejo, now to Yaquel or Colnche, Chanduy or Chonana. Latterly, though, I had been free to spend some months on my Puná encomienda, where I had time to search—though unfortunately without rewards to match my diligence—for the gold that is known to be hidden on the island. I found certain golden ornaments by opening a large number of Indian tombs, but nothing of enough consequence to be worth mentioning. The Puná islanders were in the habit of signalling their grief at the passing of a leader by entombing with him a number of living women, as well as arms and jewellery. It was also said that they sacrificed humans to their idols. Certainly their temples were dark and hideous places, but although I saw them kill animals and birds to offer up fresh blood, there was no evidence of anything worse. The islanders converse with the devil, that I know, but I do not believe that they commit the abominable crime, as some say they do—but those there are who, on no evidence at all, are ever eager to accuse Indians and even brother Spaniards of this abhorrent and unwholesome vice.

All I know, Señores, is that Puná is a good place to be alive in. There I walked through flowering meadows and deep silent woods, and there I ate the good things of God's earth and, above all, of fruits such as star apples, guavas, alligator pears, and guayabas. Soon on Puná there will be oranges and lemons and grapes too, because cuttings were sent from Spain, and I planted some of them myself. And speaking of this happy notion of exchanging the good things of vastly different lands, I must tell you that the Puná islanders revealed to us the properties of a most remarkable herb, which we named sarsa-parilla.* It grows wild there in profusion and is no more picturesque or unusual to look at than a small-leafed bramble, but the roots have power to cure all sicknesses and fluxes. Infusions of the sarsaparilla following a violent purge will clear all vapours and ill humours from the body until the sick man not only recovers, but is twice the man he was before. We had a notion that it might be profitable to establish a commerce in the roots, sending them north to Panama, and possibly even home to Spain. But the merchants who passed that way in their rotten ships were too greedily intent on jewels and precious metals to bother about bunches of herbs, and it seems possible that sarsaparilla may never be known outside Peru, though someone told Orellana that a quantity of the roots was taken as a curiosity to Spain in the year 1530.

* *Sarsa:* bramble; *parilla:* vine.

But to go on with my story, from which I have digressed only in order to explain in what manner of place we found ourselves and what my status was—though it was, in truth, more important than I have yet had time to indicate. . . . When I had sent the lobsters to Orellana's cooks, had lodged the Negroes in the guard-room, and had got a receipt for all my goods from the quarter-master's store, I changed my clothing and combed out my beard —for it becomes a soldier to see to his appearance when approaching his Captain, and in times of peace a worn exterior is less appreciated than when there is lively work on hand. I took with me the box of pearls and various small gifts and went to pay my respects.

Orellana was thinner than I had ever seen him, though I thought little of it at first, since the winter climate of Guayaquil would melt the flesh off a thin old Moor. He asked at once if El Rapalpelo had not come with me.

"The dolt!" he said when I had explained. "There are some like that, bad luck to them, who once they are soured by wounds will have no more of their friends. When I think of the difficulty I had in coercing Ojeda into going to the pearling station, I find it ludicrous and annoying that he should be equally averse to leaving it. Also I need him at this moment. I need him badly, for I know no man so persuasive with Indian porters. . . . I must explain to you, Bachelor of Arts, that there is much to be done, and little time to do it. You will leave Guayaquil tomorrow at dawn. Listen carefully. . . ."

He told me that he had made the arduous journey from Guayaquil to Quito and back in little more than six weeks, which was enough to fatigue even a Castilian inured to extremes of climate and to the hardships of Indian wars. The reason for Orellana's swift journeying was that the Marquis had sent his younger brother, Gonzalo Pizarro, the boldest and most gallant caballero in all Peru, to be Governor of the provinces of Quito (which provinces included ours of La Culata). Orellana had held his command direct from the Marquis; now he was to be under the Marquis's brother and underling. Some might have been angered by this, but Orellana was a hidalgo who looked farther than he could see, and who always considered what might lie round the corner. So when news came that Gonzalo had reached Quito, Orellana hastened there to present his compliments and to lay at the young blade's feet the territories for which he, Orellana, was responsible.

Why, then, had Orellana returned to Guayaquil with equal, if not greater, precipitancy? Because, Señores, he had learned that Gonzalo Pizarro was equipping an expedition for a spectacular adventure; and where is the Castilian who will sit at home when great discoveries are to be made and new places are to be won?

Orellana now told me that Gonzalo's purposes were twofold: firstly to discover the city and kingdom and person of El Dorado, and secondly to exploit the cinnamon said to be plentiful in the unexplored province of La Canela, far to the east of Quito, and in the forests below the Eastern Cordillera. Orellana had eagerly begged permission to join the expedition with such soldiers and horses as he could muster, and to take his share of the expenses, the dangers, and the profits; and as the Captain was much esteemed, a veteran well versed in Indian warfare, a proven interpreter of several Indian languages, and a kinsman with a stout record of loyalty both to the King, Don Carlos, and to the Pizarro family, it would have been strange in the young Pizarro had he not accepted the offer with enthusiasm.

Now that he was back in Guayaquil, Orellana had a host of worries. He would be long away, possibly for a year or two. The responsibilities for the province and for the towns would still be his, and furthermore, as El Rapalpelo had remarked, Orellana had considerable wealth in those places, and particularly in Puerto Viejo. All his best and most active followers would insist on marching with him for El Dorado; on the other hand, he must leave behind men whom he could trust to govern the province and to take care of his possessions in his absence. Our garrisons were, in any event, so small as to make a man laugh, even a man accustomed to the standards of the conquest, when it was no rare thing for a leader to ask twenty Spaniards to face and vanquish a thousand Indian warriors. Orellana, then, whether he liked it or not—and you have my assurance that he did not—had to make up his mind to join Gonzalo's splendid array with only a small bodyguard. He had decided to make up in quality for the lack in numbers, and, unbelievable though this may seem to you gentlemen, he assured me that he was spending more than forty thousand gold pesos on equipping himself and twenty-odd soldiers. The main item in this immense expenditure was the cost of the horses, seven hundred and fifty pesos being the price of quite ordinary animals. And was this surprising? I ask you to reflect that all our horses in Peru had to be shipped out from Spain or bought from the copers of Cuba or Jamaica. These last were the best, for they were half-acclimatized to work in the heats of the Indies. A good passage from Spain takes more than two months, and the horses have to stand out on deck, enduring the tempests and, far worse, the terrible calms.* Of every two horses sent from Spain only one arrived, and he half-dead.

Obsessed as he was by the disgrace of only being able to contribute so small a force to Gonzalo Pizzaro's expedition, Orellana was not displeased when I told him I had arrived with two Negro slaves instead of one, though it is true that I contrived to phrase the thing in as soothing a manner as I could, and I omitted to mention that in making his escape the big Negro had killed two dogs. I should be misleading you were I to give the impression that Orellana was quick-tempered. Although, like most of us, he was liable to take offence wherever he might feel his honour was concerned, and he was ready to condemn and punish blasphemy or other lesser crimes, he was as a rule careful, just, and experienced. He asked if the runaway Negro had been followed closely by El Rapalpelo and his men, and if they could know that Number Five had reached my raft. On hearing that this was unlikely, he remarked that Ojeda had probably given up the Negro for dead in the forest. Panama and Number Five would be sent out of Guayaquil that same evening with a batch of horses and stores that were being rafted up the river to the starting-point for our march to Quito. Orellana said he would send to Ojeda a couple of Negroes he had bought from Gonzalo Pizarro in Quito; he added with a smile that both Pizarro's Negroes had been ill when the deal was struck, and that he had got them at a ridiculously low price.

* Hence the term "horse latitudes." When the ships' fresh water began to run out in a long calm, the horses were thrown overboard.

A few Negro slaves add distinction to any retinue, but I thought it prudent to suggest that all four should be sent to the pearling station, where they would earn money. I could not see what use Negroes would be on the high passes, for although they would eat as much as fighting men, they would not fight. Orellana answered that I must see to it that Panama and Number Five were equipped with warm clothing and quilted cotton armour, and he said that, once over the Andes, we would make our way through a hot region said to be traversed by innumerable rivers of great size and violence. The two Negroes would be useful if we needed powerful swimmers to get horses across a torrent, or to take the first ropes over for bridge-building. I still thought he was taking the Negroes out of vanity; but circumstance was later to prove him right in taking them, as I shall show.

Orellana had other preoccupations. I found him surrounded by documents, at which I had been glancing as we talked. I told him the documents were made out "*de muy buena tinta*" and asked if he had found a new scrivener (because I normally had the honour to render him such services). He hastened to explain that he had had to make out a memorandum, and that as I had been away he had employed the official scrivener of the municipality, Francisco Heres. Although Heres had been in every way satisfactory, Orellana declared that he would have used me had I been available, for there was no doubt in his mind as to where the greater talent lay. He would be most grateful, he said, watching me intently with his good eye, if I would have the patience to study the memorandum and correct any mistakes in it. So I sat at the table, and soon saw what was afoot.

"Very distinguished gentlemen:" the thing began, addressing itself to the Municipal Councillors of Guayaquil. "I, Captain Francisco de Orellana, Governor's Lieutenant in the city, etc., etc., present myself before Your Worships and state that . . ." Here were written down his past services, enumerating campaigns, remarking on wounds, and so on. But such documents resemble bananas: you must skin them before you can see the flesh, which in this case was contained in the following sentences:

"And because I would like to go (to Spain) or send to beg His Majesty, as a King and a master grateful for my past services and recognizing those I hope to give him in the future, to grant me favours which I do not choose to name until I can beg them of His Majesty." Here it was pointed out that the memorandum was drawn up in obedience to regulations which stipulated that when any among us had a favour to ask of the King, he should have it put in writing and duly certified by a competent authority. He went on, humbly enough: "Since I am of gentle birth, and a man of honour, and since in me are combined the qualities and qualifications needed for any office such as that of Governor, or any other office that His Majesty might graciously see fit to grant me, I beg Your Worships to answer, stating my personal achievements and character, and giving your opinion whether I am a person worthy to hold any office. . . . "

To which, needless to say (since they owed *their* appointments and emoluments to Orellana's patronage), the Alcalde and Regidores gave the required certificate at ponderous length, and the seven of them signed their certificate.

With interest, and some amusement, I noticed that Orellana when listing his campaigns in the Indies was careful to omit one in which he had served with distinction, namely the Guerra de las Salinas, when he had fought for the Pizarros against the Chile Faction of Diego de Almagro. Why was that? Had Orellana been irked, after all, by the new appointment of Gonzalo Pizarro? Did he suspect that in Spain, at court and in the Office of the Indies, there was growing mistrust for the Pizarros (deeply though Spain was in their debt)? Lastly, was Orellana tired of being at the beck and call of gentlemen so ruthless, so wayward, and so successful as his Pizarro cousins? . . . I dared not put such questions directly to him, and when he asked for my comments I praised the memorandum on the grounds that everything was stated twice over, as is always advisable because the dunderheaded clerks in Seville are accustomed to prolixity and like to have everything repeated to them *ad nauseam*.

He said, choosing his words, that he had thought it wise to draw up the memorandum in case things went awry while he was absent and he received no credit, in the ensuing lawsuit or fighting, for all the effort he had expended in pacifying the province and establishing towns and settlements and trade. "As for going to

Spain, Bachelor of Arts," he went on, "I am over thirty years old, and thirteen of those years have been spent in the Indies. It would be agreeable to go home and find myself a young wife there. The time has come when I should have sons, and when I should have something worth leaving to my sons. If I go to Spain it will only be to establish myself with those from whom we of the conquest derive our authority, and to whom we give our loyalty."

"The Marquis expects all our loyalty to be channelled through *him,*" I objected. "He will very soon know of this memorandum, and he is said to be extraordinarily touchy about any who think of seeking the royal favour and authority. Look at the case of Captain Benalcázar."

"Benalcázar's case is altogether different: he has conquered nearly as much territory as Pizarro has himself, and his head has swollen proportionately with Pizarro's suspicions of him. . . . My situation is this: I have always stood by the Pizarros, and am I not now laying out yet another fortune to go and serve one of them? I have a right in law to petition the King on my own behalf, and there is nothing underhand or unworthy in my memorandum."

"Do I understand that you are sending the Marquis a copy of it?" I asked jokingly. But he did not see the joke, for he frowned and dismissed me.

There are insects—would you have me call them men?—whose hiving-place in Seville is the Office of the Indies and whose delight it is to thwart the soldiers of the conquest. They maintain, those burrowers, those nest-liners, that we poor soldiers across the seas live like emperors off the sweat of docile Indians. I should like to move the Office of the Indies for the space of three winters from Seville to Guayaquil, Guayaquil where the mosquitoes are the size of small birds and can bite like snakes. And when, from December to April, the Guayas overflows its banks, inundating the swamps, myriads of comfort-seeking reptiles make their sinuous way into the habitations of man. Before you enter your bed you must clear it of vipers and scorpions, who go early to their rest. Before you lie down and despite the heat you must swaddle the whole bed in a tent of close-meshed cotton. The rich—always entitled to more and sweeter air—sleep, to be sure, under tents of linen; but the lacing of these is trying to the temper, and I am not sure that the cotton article, suffocate you though it may, is not the greater comfort. To increase the pleasures of wooing sleep, Guayaquil is alive with rats of all sizes and colours, on which the dogs gorge themselves daily, but without reducing the legions. When night comes, you hear rats on the roofs, in the roofs; they run along the ceilings, up and down the walls; they gnaw through the mosquito tents and run over the beds. And they bring with them gifts in the shape of bloodthirsty and enormous fleas.

I have perhaps said enough to explain that we who were at Guayaquil were somewhat hardened to the attacks of insects and other pests.

Yet the journey up the Guayas was an extended purgatory.

I travelled with several of the compañeros, one hundred Indians, and ten horses. We had a flotilla of six cargo rafts. If we Spaniards were mercilessly stung, even through our clothing, it may be imagined how the horses suffered. We put two Indians with fans to protect each horse by day and by night. But the Indians, though born to that country, were even worse afflicted than we by mosquitoes. They were always slapping at their bare skins, and on the Guayas they showed an expressive disgust with their situation most rare in so taciturn a people. For this reason we had constantly to watch the men who watched the horses, lest they looked to their own comfort and neglected that of the valuable animals.

At night we tied up by the bank, particularly if there were maize plantations where the horses might stretch their legs and eat; for maize was the grain we fed them always—never barley as in Spain—and they thrived on it. Rain or dry, and it was nearly always raining, we would make the Indians light many fires. Yet even coughing and weeping in the smoke we were by no means quit of the mosquitoes' attentions. Sometimes at such halts several Spaniards unable to bear the torment any longer would undress and leap into the river, standing immersed up to the chins. But the mosquitoes concentrated so densely on their faces that the sufferers, finding difficulty in breathing, came out in a hurry. It was hotter on the river than at Guayaquil because no air could penetrate the dark forest that hemmed in the sliding water; too hot for us to smother under sodden mosquito canopies, and when morning came we could scarcely bear to look at each other. Our faces and hands, stained by smoke, were blotched and swollen until we were no longer men in appearance.

The camp we were making for had been established twenty-four leagues * upriver, a distance that with favourable weather and a fast canoe could be covered in three tides even in the wet season, with much water flowing down. On big rafts, however, the progress was slow, and that part of the journey took us ten days. While the tide ran up under us, the Indians paddled, and at the turn of the tide they took the rafts into the shallows and back-eddies, propelling them with long poles.

There are such numbers of alligators in and around the River Guayas, my friends, that were it not for the cunning gallinazo birds, which follow the female alligators about and note carefully where and when eggs are laid (so that they may eat them), there would be even more alligator than there is water, and canoes would no longer be able to pass either up or down. Although those alligators would tear to pieces a wounded man who fell among them, they are cowards and recluses. They are lazy too, and delight in lying with their jaws agape until the interiors of their mouths are aswarm with insects; then they close them and consume the unworked-for offerings of nature.

The forest, so thick that the eye became lost in trying to penetrate its outer surfaces, receded only where creeks from the swollen river pushed in their sludgy way, or where the Indians had burned a patch to get space for cultivations and for building their houses. These were of canes and leaves, like that of El Rapalpelo, and although the flood had risen to swamp the lower floors, this did not worry the Indian men, women, and children, who stepped from their upper windows straight into their canoes. They were poor weaklings compared with my Puná Indians, or even with those of Guayaquil. Covered with bites, bumps, stings, and cuts, they were pallid and emaciated because of the steamy winter followed by the fevers of the summer, when the river goes down,

* 88 miles.

leaving sheets of stagnant water. But they made up for their ill looks by showing us friendliness as we were pushed and paddled up their river, breasting the islands of floating grasses, and avoiding batches of tree trunks lashed roughly together that were being floated downstream to build Guayaquil and to be shipped to Lima for a like purpose.

The canes that are so much used by the Indians for building have another interest that I might well mention: when growing, each cane or tube holds a liquid that looks and tastes like water. At the full moon the liquid fills the tube, but as the moon wanes, the liquid becomes cloudy and sinks. The clear liquid is a cure for many ailments and, taken as a copious drench night and morning, it is peculiarly beneficial to any man who comes down from the Andes severely bruised or wounded. We filled a few wineskins with the clear stuff, to carry as a potion, but it does not retain its mysterious powers, for when it was tried later it tasted vile and had nothing but bad effects. We would have done better to keep the wine, which we had drunk in too great a hurry to make way for the cane liquid.

When giving us our orders, Orellana had made this first stage of our journey to Quito sound easy and restful, yet—perhaps because we had nothing to do and hence could not overlook our personal discomforts—it was about as unpleasant as anything that lay ahead. Although we agreed that we ought to foster our strength for the long marches that were our immediate destiny, we could bring ourselves to eat little of the food we carried or found, but consumed quantities of bananas, pineapples, guavas, and little else. Fortunately for us, even if it looks more like a fluid that I dare not name before so distinguished an audience, and smells worse, the water of the Guayas is drinkable during the winter floods. In summer the same water is unhealthful, and Guayaquil then drinks water brought downstream from the skirts of the mountains and sold at so much the azumbre.*

Few journeys' ends can have been more welcome than the camp in a ravine where those who had gone ahead waited impatiently for us. Their Indians had built well-roofed cabins, but we

* Measure of volume: about 2 litres, or less than ½ gallon.

had to go to bed when the sun sank, for no sooner was a light shown than the insects gathered so thickly as to make the air unbreathable, and if the candle was not inside a lantern the swarms at once extinguished it.

Now we were occupied, for everything had to be put in order. The horses were exercised up and down the track leading from the camp, and the farrier and his helpers attended to their feet. The shoe we used was thin and flat, and to protect the soft part of the foot and the frog the heels were turned up and doubled over. We had eighteen horses, a very good number as there were to be only twenty-three of us Spaniards with Orellana. The Indians are not allowed to feed, lead, or touch horses, which they fear even more than they fear us Spaniards. For our own sakes—and for the Indians' sakes too—we cultivate their stupid fear. . . . We had some thirty dogs with us, mastiffs, hounds for tracking and hunting, and swift, cunning lurchers. Three of us were crossbowmen, and three were arquebusiers.

All our stores were separated out into equal loads for the Indian porters, each of whom, since the journey was to be a stiff and a steep one, would carry only two arrobas.* Advance parties of Indians had gone ahead to gather food and to build shelters at the halting-places. As we intended to hurry, we took with us no hogs on the hoof, but we had plentiful supplies of dried salted meat and of maize for the horses (and for our own consumption if any should be left over).

Orellana, who had stayed until the last possible moment at Guayaquil, arrived during our second night in the ravine. He had travelled up the Guayas in the greater comfort of a swift Indian canoe. His two Negro slaves had everything ready for him in one of the ranchos,† and when he had slept for three hours, he gave the order to prepare to march and sent for eight of us Spaniards to breakfast with him. We found him sitting by a blazing fire with some of the dogs round him, and he was calling out names: "Fragoso! . . . Vaquero! . . . Bocanegra! Old bitch! . . . Manchado! . . . Brabonel, brave fellow! . . ." and throwing each a piece of meat as he named it.

* 50 pounds. † Huts.

We breakfasted famously on an unexpected delicacy, a quantity of the fine trout, robalos, that are caught in the colder water higher up. Some Indians had brought these in as a special gift for the Captain, having run with them all through the night, and this brings me to a quality in Orellana that is as unusual as it was to be useful to us in the way that lay before us. What I mean is this: Orellana had an extraordinary gift for languages. As well as Castilian and Latin and French, he spoke several of the tongues of the Indies, and he was constantly learning more of them and perfecting those he already knew. That was why the trout had been brought into camp: the Indians, being able to converse with him, thought more of him than of the rest of us put together.

Before we left the camp he spoke a few words to our porters, drawn up in files three and four deep, their bundles resting on their bare feet. He did not shout, but spoke quietly in a muttering voice, neither smiling nor frowning, but seriously examining them with his one eye and fingering, as he spoke, the bleached brown beard that fell over his breastplate of black steel inlaid with gold.

Many Spaniards there were who preferred a more fiery commander, but Orellana, though outwardly calm and meditative, was no sluggard in action, as I hope will be plain when my story has been told. Let them sing the deeds of Hernán Cortés, and de Soto, of the wild, tow-headed Pedro de Alvarado, and of Gonzalo de Sandoval and his horse Motilla, and numerous other renowned and notable captains, and of how Cortés, for example, charmed the Mexicans and won great victories almost as often through his cunning speechifying and winning manners as by his military genius. I cannot believe, and I will not allow, that any of our leaders was more adroit at handling Indians than was Francisco de Orellana. And be it remarked that while Cortés had his beautiful interpreter, the Mexican princess Doña Marina, to help him, Orellana did his own talking—which I hold to be still more marvellous.

But we must be on our way, amigos, for the sun rises, and already the forest is asteam.

CHAPTER THREE

YOU WOULD HAVE FOUND OUR COLUMN AN AMUSING SIGHT —had you not been compelled to march with us. The track was a quagmire in which horses sank hock-deep, and very hot and dirty work I found it, carrying a war crossbow and quiver, and at my belt cranequin, sword, and dagger, though otherwise I travelled light. I wore a helmet, as we always did, but although I had in my baggage a steel cuirass, a throat guard, and other pieces of plate for serious fighting, I preferred to travel in an escaupile, which is a vest of stuffed and quilted cotton that offers protection against Indian weapons. I had leg guards of the same padded material, and on my feet light shoes made from the greased leather of the wild llama of Peru, the huanacu. The disadvantage of this leather is that the Indians do not know how to tan it, and it will soon harden when it gets a wetting. But it softens again if boiled in fat or oil. We made use of it for reins and girths, and the sinews of the huanacu were good for fixing the steel bow of a crossbow in its wooden stock.

Our track soon twisted out of the ravine, crossed several savannas, and so came to the bank of the River Ojibar, up which we travelled for the rest of that day, February 18, fording the river nine times in the march. When we of the advance guard had made the wide crossing, we would halt, as was proper, to guard the bank until the leading files of the main body were across. Toiling behind them would come the long line of Indian porters, three by three, each Indian carrying his bundle by means of a thong passed under it and tied in a loop to his forehead. They walked stooping, a long stick in each hand to take the weight, or some of it.

In the middle of the Indian files Orellana rode with most of the horsemen and the led horses. He sat his favourite black stallion, which was called El Trompetero because of his habit of neighing and screaming to all mares in the vicinity, an animal short-legged for strength, long-pasterned for comfort, well ribbed-up and wiry for endurance, a sure-footed animal, speedy on both turns, and very ardent in battle. He was above the average height, standing six and two-thirds palmos * to his withers, and although he was well up to the weight of nine arrobas † that all such chargers must carry with a rider wearing plate and fully armed, he was fleet enough for killing deer with the lance, and in head, shoulder, coat, and carriage he was full of quality, showing the exquisite blood of the Córdoba strain founded by the Moors, who brought sires from the Yemen or the Hejaz and put them to the best of our local mares. If his mouth was of silk and his manners were those of a lady, his heart was a great ball of fire, and he contrived to look magnificent even on such a march, when the horses' coats were clogged with sweat, mud, and living and dead flies. They took to the water willingly that day, and had to be prevented from drinking too much.

Then we of the advance guard would move on, relieved that our wait was at an end, for though most of us had grown soft through lack of campaigning and were very tired, the mosquitoes seemed worse when we stood still. And that night was spent at a place to which fantastically imaginative travellers had given a name: Puerto de Mosquitos.

Rain in torrents all the next day as we worked our way up the Ojibar's broken banks, crossing the river four times with difficulties and delay, for although it was narrowing all the while, it was becoming more treacherous, the pools deeper, the rocks bigger. Just before dark we came to our camp. The Indians sent ahead by Orellana had done their work reasonably well, building ranchos for all of us and for the horses. Some of the roofs had been broken in by the day's waterspouts, but our own Indians, collecting armfuls of leaves, soon made every rancho fairly comfortable. For, behold, even in the wildest places, if man but knows how and where to look, he will find that our Lord has provided blessings, and the means to greater comfort. The strange thing is that the In-

* 15 hands. † 225 pounds.

dians, who are heretics, seem better at looking for the blessings than are we Christians. Speaking of comforts, the mosquitoes were already smaller, weaker, and less numerous than lower down. We lit fires in all the ranchos to dry our wet clothing. A number of Indians had clumsily fallen in the river, and their bundles had to be sorted and dried.

On February 20 we passed Mamarumi, which means Mother of Stone (I shall have more to say later about the Indians' use of the word "mama"), where the river launches itself from the lip of a precipice and falls in a spout that is smooth and whispering until it strikes the lower level, when the whisper turns to thunder and the smoothness to curtains of cool spray and beds of groaning foam. Above that place we crossed two gorges on Indian bridges that swayed under a footsoldier and still more under a horse. The strength of each bridge lay in six stout liana cables made fast to trees on either bank. Two of the cables served as rails, and the other four supported the wooden platform. The contraptions were cunningly lashed, for although the Indians are often careless (and their carelessness in such matters may not be accidental), they are unmatchable at their own skills.

That evening we halted at the third of Orellana's temporary camps. Fifty of his Indians had been hunting on our behalf, and had killed a good supply of monkeys and other game. They had also built two long barracks for us. We dined well, but unfortunately for us Spaniards the Captain decided that night to double the guards. Indians from the low countries hate climbing into the mountains, and he feared that ours might decamp. So we watched and patrolled all night with the fiercest of the dogs. The Captain made the rounds several times to see that his sentries were alert, and he was challenged, some three hours before dawn, by Marquez the Silent, who was with me. The Captain asked how we did. I said I was cold, which was the truth. At that he laughed, and told me that when he had last descended from Quito he had passed a night at the same place and had felt so *hot* that in the morning he had taken off his clothes and bathed himself for a long time in the boisterous mountain stream, finding that warm too. Yet now, climbing out of the thick heat below us on the brink of the Southern Sea, he felt the chill by contrast as keenly as I did.

He asked me if I had forgotten the mosquitoes down there, and I admitted that I had, but said that, as he brought them to mind, I was glad to be quit of them and could the better tolerate cold nights.

"This is the lesson of life, Bachelor of Arts," he then said. "The future is always good; the present we judge by the past; and the past always seems better than it was." With that he left us and the dogs to our watch.

We next had to climb a mountain they called San Antonio. The track often dived into a gulley, only to climb yet higher on the other side. Many times we had to halt to allow a party of Indians to cut out steps. Now the horsemen all walked, leading their animals. The track had, it is true, been cleared and made for us in advance, but a few hours of the rain that fell continuously were enough to wash away such steps as had been cut and such ledges as the advance party had troubled to sink into dangerous bends on the hillside. Sometimes the leading man or the first of the horses would disappear into a hole full of mud. Then Indians would be called forward with their wooden shovels to fill in the hole. Our progress was one of annoyances, continual falls, bruises and cuts, wetness and mud from head to foot. Added to fatigue and discomfort was the depressing effect of the stupendous landscape swathed in restless clouds of rain. Now we travelled on the greasy rim of a precipice so awful that few dared glance into the gulf below; now the track would lead to an abyss into which we must slither and out of whose darknesses we must hoist ourselves. When the inclines were very steep and slippery the horses had to advance up the Indians' steps, bound by bound. But on the downward slopes, even where the track twisted and had a precipice on the outer edge, it was judged wiser to make the horses slide. The best-schooled of them would obediently push forward both forefeet, close together, crouch with their hocks tucked under them, and without much urging would thus launch themselves and slide down at speed, steering themselves by balance and inclining inwards on each corner.

During one of those almost miraculous slides we lost a bay mare that Orellana had bought for nine hundred pesos from Pedro de Gibraleón, one of the Regidores of Guayaquil. She lost her footing at a corner, flew out over the edge shrieking, and fell for a long time until those of us who had steady hands and strong stomachs saw her roll out dead and with all her legs broken, far below. Four condors, the vast and beautiful birds that float, gossamer giants, about the snowy regions of the Andes, came silently down past us into that horrible place. They settled near the mare's body to await putrefaction, which would beckon them to the feast. So much for nine hundred pesos; she had been a willing beast, though a shade touched in the wind. But in my preoccupation with the horse I had nearly forgotten the rider, Andrés Durán, a rather pompous and elderly person who had been Alcalde at Puerto Viejo. He had not been on her back, of course, but he had stationed himself at that corner, and seeing her lose her balance he had courageously grabbed at her bridle to steady her and had himself been pulled to the edge. By the mercy of God his very long spurs dug themselves into the clay and held, while he lay on his rump, shoulders and head out over space. He denied it later, but as we pulled him to safety we heard him rattling out prayers and promises like a shower of old dried peas falling into a bucket.

After this accident all the remaining horses were more nervous of the sliding ordeal. Each would stand snorting and quivering at the top, while men below tried to entice them, and men above drove them forward with encouragements, insults, and blows, and the Indians, clinging to trees, rocks, and bushes overhanging the path, whooped and whistled.

The track sometimes went into grooves so deep and narrow that the horses got stuck, and several of them were hurt in such places, which had been formed by the action of water, and not the passage of travellers. Many trees had fallen across the track, their roots washed clean by the rain, and these had to be cut or dragged clear.

After two days of that kind of journeying we saw above us a narrow pass in the ridge, and the Captain ordered the advance guard to hurry forward to it. When we were through the pass without any sign of Indians, hostile or otherwise, we saw below us a green valley, more sightly at such a moment than the most velvety of emeralds or women. At the town of Guaranda, in the valley, we were hospitably lodged and entertained by Spanish encomenderos of that province, the name of which is Chimbo. As we had not a single horse who was not injured in this way or that, Orellana most reluctantly decided that we must rest in Guaranda for a day or two, and there, as he had foreseen, we had trouble with our Indians, who gave themselves up to drunkenness, their vice, their pastime, and their passion.

Three days earlier, as we climbed up through thick forest, I had a shot at a big black ape. The war bolt lodged in its shoulder and it fell from the high tree it was in, but picking itself up, ran off on hands and feet. Two of our Indian hunters followed the ape. They caught it, tore the bolt from its shoulder, and plastered the wound with clay. Then they led it along like a dog, at the end of a rope with a slip knot. As we were not short of food, and the ape therefore looked too hairy and ugly to eat, the Indians were allowed to bring it along with them. They said it would soon be tame, and would make the kindest and most amusing of pets. Each day showed a softening in its behaviour toward men, for all Indians of those lands have an extraordinary faculty for understanding animals and pacifying them, and that is one reason why we have to watch them jealously to see that they make no overtures of friendship to either our dogs or our horses. I could recount some interesting facts about the Indians' methods of training animals, but firstly they would hardly be credited, and secondly I have not the time to lay them before you. The two hunters were certainly more enamoured of the hairy ape than they ever had been of their wives, their parents, or their children. Yet they had not been in Guaranda an hour before, weeping, they sold the creature, sold it for a sufficient quantity of maize wine to stupefy themselves.

When we left Guaranda we could muster less than one in three of the three hundred and seventy Indians we had brought from the Guayas. Many had slunk off. Others had drunk so sottishly that they would not be able to work for a week. The encomenderos of Guaranda declared that they had too few—and not too many—Indians; we could not even ask them for porters, let alone take any, without seeming ungrateful for their hospitality. It was March 2 when we left, climbing above the level of vegetation, and timing our progress so that early on the following morning we entered the Pass of the Arenal,* so called because of the pale yellow sand and gravel with which the rock is spread in a thick, flat carpet. We knew it was wise to travel there in the morning because in the afternoon there is often a wind so fierce and so cold that Spaniards have been frozen to death by it in a few minutes. The upper part of the mountain called Chimborazo reared above us, and the snow lay at times close on either hand. Most, though not all, of us suffered from headaches, nausea, and sometimes vomiting. Although the road was smooth, the horsemen had to get down and walk in order to keep feet and legs from freezing. Nevertheless, we were most fortunate in our weather and did not have to crouch in shelter that afternoon. As daylight began to fail, some animals looking like hares, but with bushy tails, came out from holes among the rocks. The dogs would not hunt a step in such high places, but we crossbowmen had good sport, enlivening the otherwise dreary ultimate half-hour of the march, and collecting many of the beasts for dinner. Then we came to some caves. Before this, Orellana had considered stopping at a former palace of the Incas, or fortress, I do not know which. It was a gloomy place. The Indians said it was haunted, and they told Orellana he could put them to death in any way that took his fancy, but they would never enter that building alive. In truth, with the harsh wind moaning on its sloping walls and in its deep black doorways, it looked fit only to house the souls of patricides.

The Captain had providently loaded a score of Indians with faggots. We wrapped our blankets round us and gathered by the two fires, all of us, horses, dogs, and Indians, in one big cave. We put our camp kettles on to boil and, skinning the small animals we had shot, flung them in among the meat and bananas and peppers. Although the mess boiled readily, it took a long time to cook because boiling water has no strength in it on those passes, the air being so hungry for heat that it steals it away as soon as the water begins to bubble. The horses were enticed to lie down among us, and were watered and fed with maize from the saddlebags. To prevent Indian escapes we Spaniards lay nearest the

* 14,000 feet.

mouth of the cave and took it in turns to keep awake, challenging any man who moved. After living in the hot country we were sadly incommoded by the cold. We seemed to lie in a cave of ice. The wind snuffled at the entrance and probed its slimy-cold fingers over and into us. We told each other, and it was the truth, that we were lucky to be lying in there. We reminded each other of worse nights spent out in the open before or after battles.

To that cave of cold and non-life we had climbed on our feet, which is the most astonishing way to travel, since the traveller feels and recognizes the changes in condition wrought by each movement of his own thighs. We had climbed through the humid lowlands with their bananas and palms, and choking forests where the most prosperous tree is the matapalo, the vampire tree that kills its neighbours and devours their sap; then thinner woods with beautiful tree ferns; then bushes already dewed with the mists of the heights; then the last trees, a species resembling, most touchingly, our olive trees at home, but with bark more like that of the birch; then small shrubs and geraniums and myrtles; then an area where only lichens grew; and lastly this place of non-life, of sand, rock, snow, and frost, the playground of the wind.

At dawn (six o'clock) ice had formed everywhere, on our eyelashes and our beards, in our kettles. From the entrance to the cave, frost so thickly covered the ground that we could not see where the deep snows began. The Indians were already afoot, eating maize and peppers and drinking their pestilential acca. All of them shook with cold, and they had not the spirit to resist their misery. We also would have risen, but Orellana ordered us to stay in our blankets, since it would be stupid to take the road before the sun was well up. While we lay there, joking to engender warmth, or at least some forgetfulness of the cold, I asked the crossbowmen to look to their weapons, stripping out the triggers to take any rust from them and their pins, greasing the metal parts, and rubbing beeswax into the cords. The Captain said nothing either in praise or blame, but after a few minutes he remarked to the arquebusiers that their curious noise-machines were doubtless in greater need of attention than the equally indispensable crossbows, and what were they waiting for? (I would have had him say "far more indispensable crossbows" myself, and that is what

Orellana should have said, the crossbow being, as all know, the favoured shooting weapon of any true caballero—but Orellana had regard for the feelings of the least of his men, and whatever opinion one may hold of their noisy, dirty, and uncertain weapon, arquebusiers are men like the rest of us.) As we had found it difficult to cook meat the evening before, a great mess of banana porridge was made with an azumbre of aguardiente in it. This porridge is windier fare than a wagonload of radishes, but it is not unappetizing, and it fills the whole body with heat.

We marched all that day in cold more keen than the day before, and we slept in five stone huts with very thick walls and thicker roofs of Peruvian thatch skilfully made from layer upon layer of grasses. This part of the track being dangerous when the snow drifted, it had been marked in the days of the Incas by great stakes driven deep into the gravel. The Indians were told to dig out a number of the stakes, that we might burn them and keep warm. They obeyed, though with an unusual show of reluctance because under the Incas it had been an offence punishable with death to destroy such stakes or indeed any part of the road. We noticed that the Indians made no fire for themselves, and in the morning four of them were dead, though whether from the cold or from the agues that attack them when they climb to the heights, we did not know; and the dead men's companions would not say. To tell the truth they could scarcely speak at all, for the skin round their mouths had been flayed by the wind and laid open, raw, by the cold. Our own faces, better protected by hair, were almost as sore. Our feet were swollen, and our fingers were bursting open with chilblains.

On March 5, eighteen Indians collapsed and were left on the road. We were traveling on the side of Carguairaso, the mountain that is also called Chimborazo's Wife. It is a most unhappy mountain and one to avoid, because the earth often trembles and opens in fissures that could engulf a whole village—were there any villages. The Indians were all by this time so weak and spiritless that we Spaniards had to take over the Indian tasks when we negotiated several icy torrents, also some horrible chasms, during the day's march. After another day of hard conditions in which we twice had to swim the horses across rivers because the liana bridges were too flimsy to carry them, we arrived at Latacunga, where there stands a building that was once a palace. The Indians had to be driven inside. They squatted, coughing, in the echoing emptiness that once, with the shimmer of gold and silver sheathing, the soft colours of feathers, and the warmest of vicuña carpets, had housed their regal masters. No luxury remained, alas, and we camped in severe discomfort, though in shelter. We asked each other where the dancing girls were, and the singers, and we cursed those who had stripped such places for their own profit. A few of the more energetic among us explored the different chambers, tapping at the massive walls, made without mortar, but with each stone fitting to its neighbours so exactly that the joints were all but invisible. It is said that a treasure lies hidden in those walls, but even cannon would not open them up, and he will be a clever one who finds it.

Four more days of uneventful and easier marching took us to the plain of Tiopullo, where some of us were housed by Alonso Gomez, an acquaintance of mine, for he had come, like me, from Santander to test his luck in the Indies. He had lost a leg and the use of one hand when fighting under Benalcázar for the conquest of Quito, but he had been lucky with his encomienda, and he was a good man on the land, so he was doing well. He ordered several llamas to be killed and cooked with peppers and a kind of grain they have there which is like rice, but not so good.* The seed is sometimes white, sometimes red, and the plant grows to a man's height. The Indians make a potent drink from the seed, and good soup from the leaves. The wounded Gomez was married to an Indian woman of great beauty. This woman had six sisters, all of whom lived there too, and Gomez had eighteen children, or so he claimed. So far as food, and particularly fruit, was concerned that one-legged veteran envied nobody, for the twin valleys of Quito are gardens, and they will be richer still when the depredations of the wars are forgotten and they return to the prosperity they enjoyed under the rule we defeated. So we slept that

* Quinua. Markham writes: "An insipid and not very nutritious grain . . . probably the hardiest cereal in the world." Garcilaso says he sent some of the seed to Spain in 1590, but that it did not take.

night sleekly, as we had not done for a long time, and unpunished by insects except for a good many friendly little fleas, whose attentiveness seemed little more than a sentimental joke.

We marched before dawn, and had not long been on the road when Orellana with Alonso de Robles, Arévalo the Horseman, Alonso de Cabrera, and two others cantered past, saying that they would arrange good quarters for us in Quito. We answered that in being so punctilious about our comfort they must not neglect their own. . . . There are times when every man longs for a horse. By hurrying on our lagging Indians we managed to stumble into Quito that night, only to be told, though we had nearly worn our feet off, that we had been much too slow.

It was now March 11, and Gonzalo Pizarro, with the noblest array ever seen in northern Peru, had ridden out of Quito in the last days of February. Gonzalo, indeed, had neither waited for us, nor sent a messenger down the road to Guayaquil to find us, nor left a letter of apologies and explanations for Orellana in Quito. I did not see the Captain that night; nor did I seek him out, for I guessed what his mood must be.

CHAPTER FOUR

SAINT AND JAILBIRD, MISER AND GAMBLER, WITHERED VETeran and beardless apprentice, all true Castilians in Quito had marched with Gonzalo Pizarro; those males (I would not call them men) who remained came buzzing round us, telling of the splendour of Gonzalo's force. And since it is ever the nature of inferior beings to sneer at those better than themselves, the stay-at-homes made merry at our expense, saying that we should go back to Guayaquil, that we should have galloped all the way to be in time to go with the young Pizarro, and that we could not hope to follow in Pizarro's path, particularly since it was the wet season and the country to the east would be impassable without the assistance of hordes of Indian attendants. They assured us that the native warriors beyond the Eastern Cordillera would ask nothing better than the sight of so puny a force as ours, that they would slaughter us, impale our bearded heads on poles in front of their houses, braid girdles for their women with our hair, and piece together necklaces with our fingers and toes, teeth and ears.

If anyone listened to such chatter, Orellana did not. He coolly told us that we were going east, and that he intended to find Gonzalo Pizarro and take his full part in the expedition. He assumed that we felt in the matter as he did, and that our resolve to do our duty and gain honour would only have been strengthened, as his had been, firstly by the failure of Pizarro to wait for us or even leave a message for us, and secondly by the yappings of those soft creatures who had preferred their comforts in Quito to the excitements, the glory, and the risks of such an expedition. Having made it clear that no personal feelings were going to keep him, out of pique, from going after Pizarro, he said that his distinguished young kinsman had treated us infamously, and had shown a boorishness that presaged ill for Gonzalo Pizarro's future in Peru. Had he, Orellana, not hastened out of politeness to report to Gonzalo when the latter took up his appointment at Quito? Had Gonzalo not then given him the firmest of assurances that he wished to have him as his Lieutenant on the expedition to El Dorado? Orellana said he would discuss these matters very fully with Pizarro when we found him, and the sooner we found him the better.

He said he hoped that the expedition, encumbered by a huge supply train, would have travelled very slowly. He was informed that Pizarro had with him 220 Spaniards, of whom about half were mounted, and 2,000 trained dogs; he had 4,000 Indian men and women acting as porters, servants, and drovers, and these last had in their charge a great herd of hogs and another of llamas. Some estimated the number of hogs at 2,000, others at 6,000.*

When some of us exclaimed in wonder at these figures, Orellana angrily interrupted, saying that in his opinion the expedition was too cumbersome for the work at hand. It was easier, as we all knew, he said, to maintain a small and compact force in good fighting order, especially when a way had to be cut slowly through forests where food was hard to find. He assured us that, although he had never been there, he knew a good deal about the country we would have to cross to reach Pizarro. It was a difficult country, but would be less than normally so for us, as we would follow in the tracks of the expedition and would, our Lord aiding and protecting us, find the bridges still standing and the way cut through the forests. We were going among unpacified Indians who, like the valiant warriors of Popayán, had ever resisted the rule of the Incas. Nor would they have had much opportunity as yet to learn the respect due to Spaniards and Spanish arms. Such enemies would have been brushed aside by the army ahead of us,

* Cieza de León puts the number of Spaniards at 220, Oviedo at 230, Ortiguera at 280, Garcilaso at 340, and Prescott (citing Herrera, Zárate, Gomara, Garcilaso, and Montesinos) at 350. Cieza de León would seem to be the most reliable, and he is borne out by Gonzalo Pizarro himself, who, in his letter to Charles V, states that there were "more than 200" Spaniards. There is surprising agreement on the figure of 4,000 Indians. The dog estimates vary from 1,000 to 2,000, and the hog estimates from 2,000 to 6,000, but in any event there was, as Prescott remarks, "a goodly supply of bacon."

but, as was their way, they would be hanging about the flanks and the rear. They would assuredly fall upon us from time to time. He knew that he could trust us to give any number of hostile Indians the lessons they might require. It behoved us to be in a fit state for such energetic pastimes, and with this in mind he gave us orders.

First, as was right, he spoke of crossbows,* telling me, as leading crossbowman, to see that each of my men carried a good supply of bolts that were polished, oiled, and feathered. Similar bolts, to the number I might think necessary, were to be made up in small bundles, and one such bundle was to be put in the pack of each Indian porter. I was also to be responsible that each crossbowman carried two spare strings and a bastard string † as well as two spare nuts. The Captain declared that he would take it as no excuse if in action a crossbowman said he could not fire because he had no bolts, or his string was broken, or his nut had

* There is a twentieth-century tang or taint to the history of the crossbow (as to so much else in history). In its day people made as much fuss about it as we do about the Atomic Bomb. The sword, the lance, the arrow, all tended to cut clean wounds. But the squat, relatively heavy, rather blunt crossbow bolt was more like a bullet. It punched a ragged wound, and carried into it fragments of clothing and armour. The wounds had a tendency to fester, and as those were days of more wounds but fewer casualties that was a serious matter. But there was another aspect of the crossbow: it was a class weapon. For the first time in history it gave the lowly footsoldier a weapon with which he could smite the aristocratic knight in armour, who, for centuries, had enjoyed the chivalric butchery of the battlefield. The knights thought the crossbow most ungentlemanly, a bad thing, a device that might ruin the character of war. Small wonder, then, that in 1139 the use of the crossbow—except against infidels—was banned by the Second Lateran Council as a weapon hateful to God and unfit for the use of Christians. The prohibition was repeated in somewhat stronger terms by Pope Innocent III at the end of that (twelfth) century. Prohibition had no effect whatsoever. . . . Weapons once they are put into the hands of men write their own laws.

† The bastard is a short string that can be clamped to the steel bow, and cranked sufficiently to allow the string proper to be changed or taken off. The nut is an important part of the trigger mechanism (see diagram on page 340).

been lost. He asked me to take the others to the town butts to test their shooting as well as the accuracy and powers of carry of their crossbows. And he gave me other instructions with which I will not weary you. Indeed, I have only detailed those few to show that Orellana knew what he was about as an officer, and moreover was himself something of a crossbowman, which, as everyone knows, or should know, is a sign of quality; for to describe a man as a crossbowman * in our Castilian is a great compliment, as you know, since in our race if every sportsman is not a gentleman (which is arguable), every true gentleman is a sportsman—from which fact undoubtedly springs much of our success in arms.

Having dealt with the crossbows, the Captain then gave orders to the arquebusiers, the horsemen, the sword-and-shield men, and those responsible for the dogs. When all had been settled, he left us, biting at his beard, for he was in no mood for the company of any man, or woman either, and besides he had other business to attend to. No sooner was he gone than the rest of us began to discuss the details of Gonzalo Pizarro's array. For you will understand that in the Indies, vast though they are and numerous as the fishes of the seas their inhabitants, one hundred Spaniards constituted an army, even a great army. I will give you but two famous examples in proof of what I say: Francisco Pizarro sailed from Panama in 1531 on his third expedition to Peru—the one that was to result in the conquest—with 180 Spaniards and 27 horses; and twelve years earlier Cortés had conquered Mexico, a kingdom bursting with wealth, pride, and power, conquered it with 553 soldiers (of whom 32 were crossbowmen and 13 arquebusiers), 110 sailors, and about 200 Indians.†

Many of the Indians whom we had brought to Quito were in the grip already of the obstinate and fiery plague that attacks such lowlanders when they climb to that city on the heights. The sick ones would all die, and those of their companions who had the luck, the will, and the strength to survive would be of little use to us. That day, accordingly, Orellana visited Pedro de Puelles,

* *Un ballestero.*

† Figures of Bernal Díaz. Cortés himself, in his letter from Vera Cruz, speaks of "400 soldiers."

whom Gonzalo Pizarro had left in Quito as his deputy with the rank of Lieutenant Governor. Puelles, an astute person with a reputation for carefulness in money matters, said that Pizarro had denuded the province of its Indians to find the four thousand he had taken with him, whom he had kept securely in chains that were only struck off on the morning of his departure. The Lieutenant Governor assured Orellana that all that could be done to help us would most willingly be done; but there was nothing more hopeful from him than assurances, until Orellana offered to pay so many castellanos a head for each Indian up to the number of one hundred and fifty. Then Puelles became more cheerful and said that if Orellana would deposit the money with him then and there, he thought he could buy the Indians that evening, and would have them delivered to Orellana the following day. Orellana paid, but there was no scrivener present and no legal record was made of the transaction, and since Puelles was of good family, Orellana did not like to suggest such a thing. Returning to us, Orellana ordered that our own sick Indians be removed from their stronger companions and sent on their way home to Guayaquil, a road that those of them who could walk were only too anxious to follow, though it is doubtful if any of them reached the end of it.

While we crossbowmen were shooting at the butts beneath the wall of Quito that evening, and our arquebusiers were doing likewise—except that the dogs retrieved our bolts,* but could not retrieve their bullets—we fell in with a certain pimply Portuguese by name of Antonio Hernández, who was well known to us as an arquebusier of mediocre skill and very persistent ill luck. This man had seen service with most of us under Benalcázar, and we also remembered him in the Guerra de las Salinas, when he claimed to have rendered Orellana some trifling service. He told us now that he had not marched with Gonzalo Pizarro because he had been persuaded against his will to remain in Quito with Pedro de Puelles and teach some of the youth of the town how to fire an arquebus. We knew how much weight to attach to such an explanation and suspected him of living with some woman in the

* The Spaniards trained their dogs to do this without damaging the feathers of the bolts.

upper part of the town, but we did not prevent him from returning with us to pay his respects to Captain Orellana.

Orellana brightened at the sight of the uncomely Portuguese, and made as much of him as though he had been a duke or a great swordsman. He even declared, again and again, that Hernández must march east with him, a declaration that found little favour with the rest of us.

Next morning Orellana again went to Pedro de Puelles, and again got promises, but nothing more. Puelles swore that he had sent out twenty horsemen to buy in two hundred Indians from the country to the north. He could not imagine why they had failed to return, but return they surely would, and with the Indians, either that night or the following morning. On leaving the Governor, not at all satisfied with the way things were going, Orellana fell in with the Portuguese arquebusier, who, far from attempting to soothe the Captain, said that it was a disgrace, and the Governor ought to be ashamed of himself. Hernández swore that Puelles was extremely rich in Indians, whom he had hidden carefully away while Pizarro's men were scouring the province. According to the Portuguese, Puelles could have supplied one hundred and fifty porters the moment he took Orellana's money, but he was keeping his Indians hidden away so that, as soon as we were gone, he could set them to work on a silver mine in the slopes of Pichincha, the boiling mountain that stands over the city. Orellana paid close attention to all that Hernández said, and he asked the arquebusier to find out exactly where Puelles was keeping the Indians, how many of them there were, the state of their health, and how they were guarded.

Everything being ready save the Indians, Orellana let us have most of that day to our own devices. The morning was crisp and beautiful and the time passed agreeably save that at two in the afternoon, as often happens in Quito, clouds came swiftly up from the east and accumulated over the town and its valleys until, in a tempest of warm wind, thunder, and lightning, and with Pichincha roaring its approval of the storm, rain fell in such a deluge that the sloping streets became violent watercourses and it seemed that the buildings, though they are low and strong and clamped like molluscs to that volatile rock, might be swept away.

Only a year before, Pichincha had erupted, doing much damage to the town and its people.

Before sundown our storm had blown to the west and all was fresh, the streets having been washed clean—a very pleasant state of affairs. And as those were to be our last hours in a proper town for many long months, I will tell you a little about Quito, a very remarkable place. Even its setting (apart from the fact that it is the highest town on God's earth) is unusual, for two valleys contract like an hourglass, and at their junction, between two mountains, Pichincha and its less boisterous sister Antisana, stands Quito. The females of Quito are not numerous, but they are already justly celebrated for their beauty, and they are easier to know, though no less correct, than the ladies of Spain. If women flourish there, so do many growing things, and the climate has much to do with that. The temperature of Quito is the same as that of Castile, which is not extraordinary when it is noted that Quito, though sited far to the south of you, stands at such a height as you in Spain cannot conceive of, and is constantly swept by healthy winds and drenched by such storms as the one I have mentioned. For every hour that it rains in Castile (which indeed could do very well with a little more moisture) it rains ten hours in Quito (which could do with less). However, Quito soon dries out in the good sun that warms it every morning. In winter there may be more rain than in summer, but there is no other change, and the two happy valleys and the town between them in truth have only one season, spring. Consequently the earth is thickly covered everywhere with wild flowers where it is not in use for maize and other necessary crops, which give forth abundantly. Among the many vegetables under cultivation there is an earth nut which is afflicted with the name po-ta-to.* This potato grows underground, as does a truffle, and it throws out a pretty flowering plant. Its skin is soft and thin, and the flesh when boiled is tender as that of a chestnut, but very insipid. It would not seem to be a vegetable that would ever interest you in Spain.

Where was such beauty and sweetness ever seen as in the baskets of fruit that Indian women sold in the plaza? Where such

* *Patata* in Spanish.

mounds of chirimoyas, the best of all fruits, of aguacates, granadillas, pineapples, guayabas, and Peruvian strawberries? Those were sights and smells and tastes I was long to remember, amigos, and often with the anguish of hunger that can engrave such simple sights and sensations on the memory.

Before Francisco Pizarro led us into Peru and sent Benalcázar marching north to Quito, the town was the northern capital of the Incas, and a prosperous one. Its prosperity had waned, for although we Spaniards had taken benefits to Peru, and will take more, there are those among us who say that it will never be so good a country as it was under its own rulers; for it is hard to conceive that there ever was a more fortunate country than this Peru—until we arrived. . . . The Inca held himself responsible for everyone in his realms, down to the humblest. No man went hungry or ill-clothed; wrongdoing was sternly punished and virtue, being the common state, went unnoticed. When our conquest began, Peru, though in civil war owing to a quarrel about the succession to the Inca's throne, was more prosperous than any country we had ever heard of. Water was disciplined, and was distributed in countless rivers, canals, aqueducts, and ditches, until even the desert flourished. The hills were covered with flocks of llamas and pacas, while the valleys almost sank under their weight of grain. The Incas' roads were finer by far than the best of the Roman roads in Spain, for they had hostels built every few leagues offering food and shelter to all travellers, and depots, stores, and forts along the way for the use of the army.

The day before, in order to test the fighting powers of our crossbows, we had gone down the road that runs south from Quito. I had stepped out three hundred and fifty paces and when the road was clear we had all shot down it to beyond the mark.*

* If elevated to some forty-five degrees, crossbows such as those used by Isásaga and his friends might well carry 400 yards. The late Sir Ralph Payne-Gallwey, Bt., wrote: "In the autumn of 1901 I shot several bolts [with an old heavy crossbow from Nuremberg] across the Menai Straits from the battery of Fort Belan to Abermenai Point; this was done in the presence of a number of sporting friends. The distance achieved by the bolts (3 ozs. in weight and 14 ins. in length) according to Ordnance Survey was between 440 and 450 yards."

But what a road!—smooth-cemented, with a stout wall on either hand, and wide enough, though the Peruvians had no horses, for six horsemen to ride abreast. The surface of the road was shaded by trees, many of them fruit trees, in the branches of which the small birds played and sang. Road, walls, trees, appeared to run on into the infinite, but we who had marched it league upon league knew that sometimes it crossed deserts where the sand drifted so high that the way had to be marked by great beams (of the kind I mentioned earlier) that were driven in as posts and joined by ropes. To those on the roads—before we went to Peru—every place was helpful, because the Inca's discipline extended over all his roads, and spread over the fields on either side, and over the houses of the cultivators. If any man crossed the walls to take what was not his, the punishment was death; and that was good law, since it meant that those living on any road regarded all travellers as their brothers. When we went first to Peru, although it was a land of unimaginable wealth in gold and silver, there was no theft. The rich man left his house empty without fear, and only put a small stick across the doorway when he left home, and this not to keep people out, but merely to show that he was away. We put locks on doors, and we padlocked our coffers; so with fear of evil, evil came. . . . Truly, those of us who did our duty in that strange land would wonder from time to time why the Lord our God had ordained that Peru should change so swiftly through our coming. Soon the cloud-like flocks that had given meat and wool in abundance were slaughtered or dispersed; the roads were cracking; the crops sprang no more because the watercourses had dried up, none caring to keep them clean; and poverty without humility had appeared where before there had been honourable humility without any poverty.

The decay was not all of our doing, of course. Indeed, the most of it was done by the people of Peru, partly because they lost heart after our victories, partly because they hoped to starve us out of their country. We Spaniards are known for our loyalty and our courage, and neither of these qualities is surprising in us because for seven centuries we have been forging our race in the fighting to rid Spain of the Moorish invader. Among us of the conquest, as among all peoples, there were the good, the bad, and the majority who were now good, now bad, according to mood and circumstance. We knew it was our duty to bring the lands we came to under the dominion of His Majesty, Don Carlos; we knew it was our duty to bring the Indians into the shelter of the true faith, and thus to offer them the hope and blessing of life after death. . . . I would only say, without disloyalty, to have done with this sad subject, that it was puzzling to see suffering and decay follow in the wake of purposes so good.

Some I said were good, some bad: Quito had fallen to one of the most ruthless among us, for Sebastián de Benalcázar was as ruthless as his iron cannon. He was born the son of peasants on the borders of Estremadura and Andalusia, and he left home when still a boy because he had killed his father's donkey in a fit of rage, or so the story goes. He walked to Seville—this happened in 1514—and took service as a sword-and-shield man in the fleet of Pedrarias, bound for the Isthmus of Darien. Few could have guessed that this starveling was to be a captain among conquerors. He knew that his name was Sebastián, and that the name of his village was Benalcázar; his surname he did not know. But he was an exceptional soldier from the start. Pedrarias thought much of him and sent him with the expedition to Nicaragua, where he helped to establish the town of León. He later followed Francisco Pizarro to Peru, and it was in 1533 that Pizarro sent him north as a captain over one hundred and forty good men. The battles for Quito were fought out bitterly on the plains of Riobamba. For long the issue was in some doubt, but at the last, science, exploited by Benalcázar's tenacity and ability, prevailed, and he flew the standard of Castile over that high city. (I say city, but the royal title of "city" had not been granted it when we were there in 1541.) In 1538 Benalcázar was still forging his way north, ambitious to carve out generous territories for himself, because his promotion had been too rapid and his character was too turbulent for him to remain the henchman of the Pizarros. After fighting many battles, and bloody ones, to win Popayán and Pasto, he marched always north into New Granada.* From there he went down a very great river † to the

* Colombia. † The Magdalena.

Northern Sea and took ship for Spain, intending to ask the King to grant him the northern provinces that he had conquered. This was thought by most of us in Peru to be the chief reason why the Marquis had sent north his forceful and brilliant young brother to govern Quito; it presumably meant that no matter how many rights and favours Benalcázar might be granted at court, the Pizarros would fight him for them if he chose to set foot again in the section of the Indies that they regarded as their own property (under the authority of His Majesty, of course). In short, Benalcázar had done what it was in Orellana's mind to do, given the opportunity, though it must be admitted that the achievements of Orellana, considerable though they had been at the time of which I speak, were in no way comparable with those of Benalcázar. But Francisco de Orellana was soon to stake his claim to present fortune and future immortality—and we with him.

I must tell you something of the country round Quito, for it is a crossbowman's paradise. Deer, rabbits, partridges, pigeons, and sweet-fleshed doves abound. Dogs will work well enough in the valleys, but are useless if you take them above the town, which is a great pity because of the huanacus, the wild llamas. These brutes, of a washy chestnut colour, are game and swift, and it is almost impossible to get near them for a shot. The Incas had their own way of hunting the huanacus and other game and, in keeping with the rest of their stupendously organized system, it was, if not sportsmanship, fantastic enough in all conscience.

They hunted once every four years. Apart from this there was no hunting, which we in Spain would hold to be a palsied state of affairs, for there are those of us who would like to be at it all day every day, and they are by no means the worst of us, nor the lowest born, nor the least learned. . . . When a hunt was proclaimed, many thousands of beaters assembled, enough to throw a cordon round several square leagues. Every wild animal that failed to pierce the cordon was driven to the centre, where the beaters joined hands and the game was corralled in a human fence. Very often, we were told—and this not counting the deer and the other four-footed game—there would be as many as forty thousand huanacus and the smaller vicuñas caught in one such hunt; of these the majority of the females and some of the males were set free after being sheared. The coarse wool of the huanacus went to the populace—that is, into the communal stores and depots—while that of the vicuñas, much finer stuff, was at the disposal of the Inca. The meat was smoke-cured, and was in such quantity as to feed that district until the next hunt. And now I come to perhaps the most extraordinary feature of this hunting: an exact record of the numbers killed, sheared, set free, was kept. How, you may ask, could this be, since the Peruvians did not have writing either in picture form like the Mexicans, or with letters and figures as in our own miraculous system? The Peruvians had knotted cords of varying length into which were twisted pieces of wool or thread of different colours. With this device they recorded their game tallies and everything else too, registers of taxes and benefits, lists of workers, old people, invalids, births, marriages, forms of army enrolment, invoices of stores, weapons, and pay. With those quipus, as they were called, they also made histories, romances, songs, and verses. I speak in the past, because all that is dead, or nearly so, and the quipus are no longer seen save as curiosities, at any rate by us Spaniards, and they will soon be indecipherable even to the descendants of the Indians who took such pains with them. I think it ill that such things should fade away, since it took many centuries and much genius to bring them forth and develop them. . . .

To turn once again to the Peruvian hunts, and then I will have done with them: were they not perhaps in some measure an explanation of our conquest of Peru? I think they were, since they showed the Peruvians to be docile (and we are not docile), patient (as we are hasty), and tamed (which we, though disciplined when need arises, can never be). Theirs was not hunting, but a kind of farming. Which man among you would farm when he might hunt? And if His Majesty, good luck to him, decreed that there were only to be mass hunts every four years, would you and I not steal out of an evening with our hunting crossbows, so silent and precise, and our very best dogs to the cool, secret woods, where the wild boar may come delicately sniffing, or the pheasant may sit heavily on a branch outlined against the moon, and to the chuckling meres where swans and wild duck may be floating? But to go on. . . .

That second evening in Quito, Orellana's two Negro slaves, who were our cooks, had a surprise for us, and one that greatly pleased. Some of the dishes were flavoured with cinnamon, and after eating we drank a warm cordial made with the same delicious spice, which had been sold to Orellana by two Indian traders arrived that afternoon from Canelos. Better still, Orellana was able to tell us that he had induced those same two Indians to agree to leave Quito as guides for our small party; and to be certain that they would keep their word—as all men ought to do—the Captain had had the pair of them locked away with such of our Indians from Guayaquil as remained with us. Number Five said that he had first stewed the cinnamon in the ordinary way, but this had quickly lost all its taste, so what we ate had been pounded into a fine powder and sprinkled on the cooked food. Having tasted it (somehow it is easier to prove anything by taste, smell, or sight than by words), none of us doubted that in Canelos there would be profitable encomiendas for many Spaniards. Even the Indians prized the cinnamon, using it as a valuable article of barter; how much more would it be welcomed in Spain, where the whole populace will never cease to cry out for spices! * We

* The European demand for spices was probably as great in the sixteenth century as that for tobacco is today. Why? . . . Since beasts could not be fed after November, they were slaughtered in that month and the meat salted down. There was no fresh meat in winter. There were (outside Peru) no potatoes. Vegetables were few and indifferent. Fruit was not, in Europe, what it is today, and little of it was preserved for the winter. Coffee, tea, chocolate, were yet unknown. Wine was but a sour shadow of its present self as developed by the genius of France, while the few wines that we might consider drinkable were drunk by the nobility. Sugar existed, and was craved; it was inordinately expensive. Hence the desire for spices—to make dull food less dull. (Today the worse a man eats, the more is he addicted to pickles, bottled sauces, vinegar, mustard, etc.) Further, medicine, then even more in its unpromising infancy than it is today, used spices for its potions and its ointments and as "protection" against plagues. When Rome declined (as all great powers must), the spice trade from the East enriched Constantinople. Then Venice took Constantinople's place. Then the magnificent seamen of Portugal, by opening a passage from their country to India, made Lisbon the centre of the spice trade and the richest port in the world. In her American conquests Spain saw Portugal as her most formid-

asked Orellana how far it would be to Canelos, and he answered that a friend of his, Captain Gonzalo Díaz de Pineda, some three years earlier had led a Spanish force beyond the Eastern Cordillera and had driven a path deep into the province known as Quijos. There, on the rough forested slopes, they fought a battle with the local Indians, who gave an excellent account of themselves, killing a number of Spaniards, including a good friar. Before he marched back to Quito, Díaz de Pineda learned from his prisoners that he had all but reached Canelos, the cinnamon country, and he had also learned that farther on, beyond the forests, there lay fertile plains inhabited by Indians who decked themselves out with gold. This Díaz de Pineda, Orellana told us, was one of the hidalgos (and one of the best of them) who had ridden out of Quito with Gonzalo Pizarro.

Yet to all of us the cinnamon was at best but a commercial excuse for Gonzalo's expedition; the true goal was, of course, El Dorado. And where would El Dorado be found, Orellana said when we fell to talking about it, if not in those vast low-lying plains known to exist east of the Eastern Cordillera? No Christian had yet reached those plains, and Peru, as he pointed out, is but a strip of mountainous country running north up the shores of the Southern Sea. Was it likely that riches such as those of the Incas should exist on the fringe of the land mass, and none in the mass itself? Surely not, he argued, because the Old World showed that riches, like nature's coverings, like the birds, were distributed in Spain and France, England and the Low Countries, while in the parched Orient, as the traders of Venice had proved, they abounded yet more copiously.

In discussing El Dorado we trod perhaps the most worn track of conversation when one Spaniard met another Spaniard in Peru. The Indians, knowing our interest in gold, had at first attempted to keep the existence of El Hombre Dorado * secret from us. But the secret was too big to be kept. It first slipped out at Tacunga,

---

able rival, and one that must be bested in trade. The Spanish adventurers were therefore almost as eager for sandalwood, cinnamon, pepper, mace, cloves, camphor, nutmeg, and ginger as they were for gold, silver, slaves, and honour.

* The gilded man.

not far from Quito, in 1535, when Luis Daza and a few of his friends had it from a Chibcha messenger who was on his way from New Granada to the Inca Atahualpa. They heard from the Chibcha of a king who was smeared with aromatic oils and then sheathed all over with gold dust. Gold was his everyday raiment, and thus sheathed in gold he descended daily to bathe in the lake that washed his city walls. At night, attendants brushed or scraped the gold dust from his skin so that the floor of his sleeping chamber was thick with it, but they thought no more of it than we would of straw or rushes. Since Daza had heard the story, it had been confirmed all over Peru and New Granada, and the only strange thing about it was that no Indian could, or would, say where El Dorado was to be found.

Orellana said that Gonzalo Díaz de Pineda had described the climate of the approaches to the cinnamon country as one of almost unendurable heat; and it seemed likely that farther down, on the open plains, it would be hotter still—a hopeful thought, because no man, let alone a king, would bathe every day in his lake unless it were set in a torrid climate.

Then we went to our beds to dream of El Dorado. But not for long. Soon after midnight we were roused by Orellana himself and by the Portuguese arquebusier Hernández, both fully dressed, armed, and ready for the road.

When we had left him, Orellana had gone once more to ask Pedro de Puelles for the Indians who had been paid for, but who so far had only appeared in promises. Puelles had impudently replied that Captain Orellana must be patient and that he would have his Indians "tomorrow or the next day or the day after." Orellana said nothing to Puelles about it, but he already knew from the Portuguese that the Lieutenant Governor had two hundred able-bodied Indians hidden at a farm not much more than a league out of Quito, to the north.

Orellana therefore ordered us to collect our Guayaquil Indians and to double-load them. All the remaining gear was to be carried on the horses and by us Spaniards, though only as far as the farm of Puelles. The dogs and horses were wakened and fed, and the latter were saddled and loaded. At last all seemed ready, and we went into the silent streets, making our way to the northern gate. Orellana halted us and asked for the two Negro slaves. Now, a Negro is difficult to see in darkness, but it was impossible to see those two, because they were not there; so tall Arévalo the Horseman was sent back to find them. We were standing in against the houses and, knowing that something a little unorthodox was in the Captain's mind, we were all alert and ready for trouble, when we were startled by an immense uproar behind us. But all was well, for it was only the Negroes yelling, and Arévalo soon silenced them. He had found Panama and Number Five snoring in some deep straw in the wash house, and because he was happy at being awake himself at that hour, Arévalo woke them by flinging a tub filled with soapy water and dirty shirts over them. So they had wakened imagining that they were being attacked by white mantas in the seas off Guayaquil.

Orellana called out the watch, accounted for our numbers, and explained that we were marching out to join Gonzalo Pizarro. Thus we left that town, and in different fashion from Gonzalo and his men, who had paraded out very pleased with themselves, their numbers, their accoutrements, and their prospects.

Hernández guided us to the farm of Puelles, and when we got there Orellana, after whispering to us that we were to behave openly and without any hint of subterfuge or—worse still—amusement, ordered Hernández to beat upon the great doors, announce his own name, and call out loudly that they were to be opened in the name of the Lieutenant Governor. We were kept waiting so long that Orellana became abrupt with those inside and said that as we were come on lawful business and by the authority of their master, if they kept us waiting much longer we would know how to punish them for their lack of manners and sense. So at last they opened and Orellana strode in with Hernández and about ten of the rest of us. There were only four Spaniards there and a few women. When they saw what manner of visitors they had, the Spaniards put aside their swords. They knew Hernández, who explained to them that Captain Orellana had bought one hundred and fifty Indians from Pedro de Puelles, and indicated that that number of healthy Indians, preferably males, must be handed over with provisions of their sort for a long journey, within thirty minutes. Orellana spared no pains to see that these instructions were properly carried out, and in the stipulated time we had marshalled the new Indians, loaded them, and Orellana had written out a receipt for them. As an afterthought he told Puelles's servants that they must be ready to receive more Indians because the Lieutenant Governor had obtained two hundred new ones, who would arrive "that morning."

It was after three o'clock in the morning when we took to the road, urging the Indians forward at their best speed. Puelles's ones were much glossier and stronger than our Indians from Guayaquil. The Portuguese arquebusier marched beside Orellana, and was as full of himself as though he had won great honour in battle instead of having swindled and deserted his former master, which was the way I looked on his behaviour. He even declared that the arquebus he carried was (or had been) the property of the Lieutenant Governor, and this seemed to please Orellana, though to my mind it was nothing more or less than stealing; and if a man does not own the weapon he carries, what does he own? At any rate, we were all glad to be moving, and to have our belongings and stores carried for us. Only the Indians were glum, for they saw which way we were marching. They had no chance of escape; our dogs were on the watch, and Orellana had detailed an unusually strong rear guard, with which he rode himself. At dawn we were already some leagues from Quito.

CHAPTER FIVE

DURING THAT FIRST DAY'S MARCH FROM QUITO A PAIN IN my groin became so bad that when the Captain at last ordered a halt, I fell to the ground and could not move. Vayón the Pike, a queer old fellow, for he was as gentle in some ways as he was rough and cruel in others, noticed my plight and told Orellana, who came at once to my side and explained my symptoms to one of the Indian guides from Canelos. This Indian took off my boots and set to work upon my toes with a jagged piece of quartz, conversing in Quechuan meanwhile with Orellana. Sweat bubbled from my head and ran into my eyes. I begged Orellana to withdraw, lest I should disgrace myself before him, but he answered that he would stay with me, and that I might do anything short of blaspheming and he would think none the less of me. Then that caballero, my Captain, although he was wet and tired and hungry and had many other important preoccupations, sat down beside me and to pass the time told me that he held me in great affection and esteem and would never hear of marching on without me because with my crossbow I was worth three experienced soldiers of ordinary skill, and my pen would doubtless serve us almost equally well before our expedition was ended. He called to the Negroes to bring a skin of aguardiente, and he bade me drink all I could swallow, which was not much.

When I asked if the Indian knew what he was about, because he seemed to be trying to saw off my toes, Orellana explained that I had been attacked by insects somewhat resembling fleas that exist in the dust of Quito. Those pests burrow under the skin of a man's feet to lay their eggs, which ordinarily cause nothing more than a fierce itch. But when they lodge under the toenails their poisons go up the leg, and the Indian said that the small eggs must be cut out with some nicety because if they burst in my toes they would cost me leg or life. I carried in my belt a

Barcelona dagger, its steel prettily clouded with milkiness and well engraved too. Its edge was keen because I was in the habit of sharpening it with some white wood that grows in the Indies and is useful for that purpose. I gave the Indian the dagger and begged Orellana to persuade him to use its point instead of his lump of quartz. Then the surgeon made more progress, until at last, and not too soon, he announced that all should be well. The pain had been drawn down to my foot, which they dressed with salt and wrapped in a cloth.

Orellana sat me at his side and tried to persuade me to eat and drink, saying that the Great Captain, Gonsalvo de Córdoba, had declared that any soldier, to be a soldier, should swallow two hearty meals each day. None of us could agree that this dictum, even if it emanated from such an authority, held good in the Indies, where we fought at least as stoutly as our soldiers had done in Italy, though we often held ourselves lucky to get one meal in twenty-four hours, and a poor one at that, for we were more accustomed to wounds than to meat. Yet the Great Captain himself would not have disparaged our performances. And it is true that many of our methods—particularly at close quarters with the short, straight sword and the pike, and also in the way the light cavalry operated, stinging the enemy from all directions and keeping him guessing—derived from the lessons applied by his genius in the Italian campaigns.

I could not walk the following day, and the Captain arranged to mount me on one of the most comfortable of the horses, a bay bobtail called La Rabona. I handed over my crossbow to the mare's owner, young Alonso de Cabrera from Cazalla. When I call him young, he was not unduly so in years—for at that time he was twenty-four—but he was fair-haired and had little beard. This man was, by general esteem, a hidalgo, and he loaned his good animal to me cheerfully, trudging that abominable road on his feet.

We climbed. Though I had bound my legs with cloths and wore cotton armour of the thickest kind—the kind at which people poke fun, calling soldiers so dressed Pack Saddles *—I nearly

* *Las Albardas.*

froze. The mare was warm enough because she was well protected with cotton armour fringed with hawks' bells, but none of her warmth got to me. We climbed toward the mountain called Antisana, and at times to our right we saw another and greater peak, that of Cotopaxi, its white surfaces glinting like a host of swords drawn when the sun is pale, clear, and low in the sky. There were traces of Pizarro's march up the same road—skeletons, rubbish, and ashes. Some of the skeletons were human. Our Indians regarded the clean-picked bones and perhaps, in their ignorance of the hell to which heathen are doomed, they envied their kinsmen who were already dead. We began to feel the effects of the high places, headache and sickness. The Guayaquil Indians could not walk properly and were most pitiable sights, but the ones we had taken from Pedro de Puelles seemed stronger, and the strongest were the ones who chewed most keenly at coca leaves. From morning until morning they have this stuff in their mouths, working away at it, though they never swallow it. They say that when they chew coca they feel no hunger, and that it gives them more energy than would the best meat or grains. And this appears to be the truth, though probably it is a benefit granted only to Indians, and then only after long use and interminable miserable hours of chewing.

They cultivate the coca trees as carefully as though they brought forth babies. When they have harvested the leaves and laid them out to dry in the sun, they pack them by ramming them tightly into cotton bags, and thus carry them on journeys. The chewing habit seems to accord well with their general character and appearance, for they are an unrewarding people.

Because of their lethargic marching we did not reach the pass that night and had to bivouac in a place without shelter. We had a few small tents, but most of them blew down upon the occupants, who were too stiff with cold to do anything more to alleviate their own discomfort. A wild wind gusted down from the snows above us, and sometimes it gusted, twisting in spirals, so that it seemed to come from every side at once. Guard duties were taken by the horsemen that night because we could not allow the beasts to stand still in the cold. Alonso de Cabrera, though he had walked all day, insisted on taking my turn on guard. The pain in my wounded foot helped me to forget the cold.

It was a miserable awakening. The Indians huddled in circles round fires whose heat was snatched by the wind. They were eating a little maize, some dwarf red peppers, and salt. Provided there be enough of it, this is their favourite eating; they scoop salt onto their tongues, then bite at the pepper pods, and lastly swallow some maize. As they had had more than enough to carry without bringing their own kinds of intoxicating drink by which they set such store, Orellana said that each Indian was to be given a tot of aguardiente. The Negroes reported that some of the Indians would not drink, and Orellana commented that they must be dying.

When we began to move on, the Indians were so sluggish that Orellana left a horseman, Andrés Durán, in charge of them with the two Asturians, Alonso and Francisco de Tapia (who were friends, but not brothers), and twenty of the best dogs, while the rest of us hastened on for the pass, a place of most evil repute.

The pass treated us kindly to begin with, for though the wind was bitter the sky was blue, and had I been able to dismount and walk I would have been happy enough. Juan Gutiérrez Vayón, noted expert with the long pike and a veteran of Italy, gave us a song, to show that he had more than enough wind and spirit for such a climb. This is what he sang:

Pase el agua, ma Julieta,
Dama, pase el agua;
Venite vous a moy.

Ju men anay en un vergel,
Tres rosetas fuy culler;
Ma Julioleta,
Dama, pase el agua;
Venite vous a moy.

Vastly pleased with the song, Orellana complimented the singer on his knowledge of foreign tongues, which delighted Vayón the Pike and amused the rest of us—for this was a man who was uncouth in his native Castilian, and who could scarcely bring out seven words but one of them was a crudity or an abortion. Then he sang another song, but in that case I will not give the words, firstly because it was longer than the other, and secondly because it would debase any lofty sentiments to which I may put my tongue from time to time. Yet I must say that in those high and awful places, so far removed from the things of which Vayón the Pike so fruitily sang, the song was irresistibly ridiculous, and we laughed until the wind blew tears from our eyes.

The track through the pass was of the roughest, and at places was dangerous. Ahead and above us we saw Alonso de Robles's advance guard winding their way, no bigger than mice, between great boulders and crags. Then the air darkened and there came such a roaring about us that we thought the earth about to open and make one of its biggest swallows. But instead we were enveloped in frozen snow flying so fast that it rattled like shot against helmet and armour. Horses blenched and turned their quarters to the blast, their tails curling miserably between their hocks. Before I could stop La Rabona (did I mention that I am no great horseman?) she was off downhill at a pace that would have alarmed a centaur. At last I managed to pull the mare round under the lee of a towering rock and, overwhelmed with shame, I was doing my best to spur her back into the flying snow when the rest of the horsemen joined me, and the whole party took refuge where I had stopped. We had seen nothing of the advance guard, but they must surely be sheltering like ourselves, and it was certain that no man, either on foot or mounted, could force his way onwards and upwards into the blizzard. Orellana, shouting to make himself heard as we huddled together, asked if any of us had opinions as to what should be done. But "*unos dicen cestas, y otros ballestas,*" * some thinking that we should at once withdraw from the pass, others that we should stay where we were. So without delay he made known his decision: we would shelter there until it was evident that we were freezing to death, or until the blizzard had continued so long that there was no alternative to withdrawal. He then sent Baltasar Osorio, Vayón

* Literally: "Some said baskets, and others crossbows."

the Pike, and Juan de Mangas back to help the three compañeros who were guarding our Indians; and he ordered them to keep so close to each other that they were always touching.

When the three had gone, blown away down the pass, the Captain set us to digging a shallow pit in the lee of the rock. We put the horses in the best corner, giving them maize from the saddlebags, and we packed in beside them, lying down and taking all the dogs under our blankets. How the wind bellowed and whistled! What power there was in it! Sometimes it shook the immense rock above us. Snow piled up behind us until our pit was four times as deep as we had dug it. There was horror in the thought that the weather thus treated us when a few days' march to the east the forests were suffocating in clammy heat. When darkness approached we rolled dice to determine which of us should crawl out to feed the horses and see to the halters. The losers were Hernández the Unlucky and Cristóbal de Palacios, from Ayamonte. Orellana rose when they did and tried to look up and down the pass. But he could see nothing. So we lay and shivered and slept and woke until the sudden dawn, when the wind eased and the snow stopped.

Although he was greatly worried about the safety of the party in our rear, Orellana decided to take advantage of the weather's improvement, which might well be temporary, to get our main body through the pass. As there were six well-armed Spaniards and plenty of trained dogs guarding the Indians, he sent no more of us back.

When the sun came through, it glinted on the armour of Robles, standing on a small summit two crossbow-shots above us. He vanished, and soon we saw the advance guard climbing on rapidly up the pass. When we came to the place where they had been we saw that they had had the luck to be near a small cave when the storm caught them; but they had been less fortunate after all, because a little farther up we found the snow blood-stained round the remains of a horse. While hastening to the cave, the animal had come down and broken a leg, and in the morning Robles had watched for our approach while the others stripped the carcass of most of its meat. We saw from the chestnut hide that we had lost La Bandera, a strong mare with a peculiarly gallant manner of flaunting her tail, and the Captain was much put out, though some of us reflected that if all went well, from then on we would have fresh meat for supper.

So it came about. When we issued from the pass, it was afternoon. We saw for scores of leagues to the east, with the land dropping away in green vastnesses flecked here and there with silver that we took to be water. A league below the pass we came to some huts strongly built with timbers that must have been hauled there, and with big stones piled high to protect the walls. Here some of the advance guard had halted to await our coming and had already roasted the horsemeat. Robles and his two horsemen had very properly ridden forward to watch from a position on the ridge below us, and Orellana asked for three horsemen to go and take over the outpost duty. My foot pained me sufficiently to make sleep impossible, so I asked for this duty. Rodrigo de Arévalo, the Horseman, as we called him, and Juan de Elena having also volunteered, the three of us negotiated a steep track with rock steps down which the horses jumped or slid until we came out on a paramo * and, riding across it, found the three watchers, who, nothing loath to be relieved, cantered back to the camp.

As our position afforded a wide view over open ground, there was no call for the three of us to be awake, and I asked Arévalo and Elena to let me take the first watch. When they had loosed their girths, they each filled a bag with sand and tied it to the halter. They wrapped themselves in their blankets and lay down, each on his sandbag, which he had partly buried in the ground. This is a good method of tethering in wide spaces without trees where both rider and horse must be ready for emergencies. It has several advantages, not least that the senses of the horse are more acute than those of man, and if the horse is startled he will pull on his halter and so waken his rider. No sooner had they lain down than they were asleep.

Lance in hand, I sat with all that vastness around and over me, and the mare under me dozing on her feet. The sun was below the other side of the Andes, toward Guayaquil and Puná.

* *Paramos:* barren desert plains on the high Andes.

There was a mellow flood of light until he must have plunged below the rim of the Southern Sea, whereupon the clouds, lying like the angels in their multicoloured robes upon the summits of the Cordillera, rose up and vanished. Far to my right the peak of Cotopaxi reflected, as though its snows were red-hot, the last of the departing light. Fingers of purple and violet showed in the reddened summit until there was a last flash, then darkness. It seemed black dark to me until I looked above and saw the flocks of stars pasturing in the vault of heaven. Which was the more awesome, I asked, the tumultuous and monstrous sea of snowy ridges and peaks that lay behind me, or the smooth, steaming forests that flowed away in front, dropping, dropping?

I could not sleep at all, and when I insisted, Arévalo allowed me to stand guard the night through, while Elena, who must have been very tired, never stirred in his sleep, even when his horse lay down beside him.

The main body came forward with bad news: not a single Indian remained save the two guides from Canelos. Caught at the very mouth of the pass by the blizzard, the porters had instantly dropped their loads and scattered like so many crows. Andrés Durán and the two Tapias had managed to stop a few of them, and these had lain down on the snow, asking to be killed. During that terrible night these ones too had slunk off. Most of the blame for this misfortune could be put on the dogs, which at more normal heights would have chased every flying Indian and brought him down.

This meant we were in some danger of starvation. We could have saved our skins by returning at once through the pass and to Quito, but there was no talk about that, for all said that our best hope lay in a rapid advance, uncomfortable though it would be without porters. The six Spaniards who had been in the rear had rejoined the main body after marching all night, and each of them had brought in as much from the Indians' bundles as he could carry, while Durán had turned his charger into a pack animal loaded from his nostrils to his crupper. They had thus brought, among less vital supplies, a fair number of the many crossbow bolts that I had been at such pains to prepare.

I saw Arévalo talking with Orellana and the pair of them looking at me. Then the Captain came and asked to see my leg. I admitted that it was hot and full of air, though less painful than before the Indian had opened the toes. He dismounted, holding his rein over his arm, and took off my boot and the cloths under it. After he had examined the toes he told me to put my bare foot in the bronze stirrup, pushing down on it with all my strength, and to sink both hands in La Rabona's bleached mane, gripping tightly. He took a pair of shoeing pincers from his saddlebags, and with the pincers he tore off first one toenail and then another. There was much bleeding, and he said he thought I would heal. He dressed the toes with salt and with some thick grease he carried in a pomade pot. Then he bound each toe separately with strips of cloth and put my boot on for me.

When we were riding after the others, we noticed the tracks of rabbits, and Orellana ordered the crossbowmen and the dogs to the flanks. Young Cabrera, using my crossbow, shot three rabbits before either of the others (even Márquez the Silent, who was a marksman) had shot one. I envied him, for my day was proving most uncomfortable. The track was steep and sometimes broken. I could not dismount like the other riders at the bad places. We came upon the skeletons of more of Pizarro's hogs, llamas, and Indians, lying among the droppings of his hundred horses. Here we saw an old boot of cracked leather, there a broken lance from which the metal head had been cut. After the steep places we came out upon another paramo, where we made camp and cooked the crossbowmen's rabbits. When the Canelos Indians saw us throwing the entrails to our dogs, they snatched them from the hungry animals' jaws and devoured them, saying that they were the only parts of a rabbit worth eating.

The throbbing had lessened in my foot; nevertheless, the Captain changed the cloths, which were dripping blood.

Next morning we moved on empty stomachs. There was no food except maize, which was reserved for the horses, and some smoked horsemeat that the Captain said must not be eaten before midday, as there might then be nothing else. Soon the monotony of eventless marching was broken when Cristóbal de Palacios trotted back from the advance guard to say that numbers of Indians were gathering ahead of us in the fringe of trees at the lower edge of the paramo. He was told to return to the advance guard and bid them halt and rest their horses till we reached them.

On the paramo grew rushes, a few small shrubs, some creeping plants with blue flowers, and nothing else. The trees mentioned were the outliers of the forests, and were of the type resembling olive trees, fairly widely spaced. Moving among the trunks were the Indians, swarming busily, seeming to number several hundreds. The sight of us to them was like rotten beef to maggots. They buzzed.

Although we had the incline with us, and the ground offered excellent scope to cavalry, our position was unfavourable in that it displayed to the savages the miserable size of our force. Orellana formed up the footsoldiers so that the crossbowmen and arquebusiers were in some measure shielded. He ordered the Negroes to watch the two Indian guides and to hold the four reserve horses. He divided the twelve horsemen into threes, and knowing me to be green at such work, he took me in his own group, the third member being Andrés Durán, who was somewhat portly and whom that situation found inclined to bluster and wrath.

It might have seemed that as we were but twenty-three fighting men, two Negroes, and two Indians, and we had sixteen good horses, some could have mounted pillion while we cantered off to outflank the Indians. But such behaviour would have been extraordinary, it being our way, no matter how great the Indians' superiority in numbers, to meet them squarely and give them a drubbing whenever that was what they asked for. The slightest sign of apparent wavering on our part would always bring them screeching on, disdaining wounds or death. I have seen such tactics used to lure them against a strong position, but on this occasion we should have been swamped by their numbers, and it was plainly the thing to probe at them for a while until they learned to fear us.

The Indians crowded forward from the shade of the trees, moving slowly in a mass, but each individual wasting energy by dancing about, whistling and chattering. They waved their weapons in the air, darts, javelins, slings, and clubs made from black palm-wood edged with sharp bits of obsidian; to these last they give the name of macanas, and they are in general very nimble and expert with them. Orellana, bidding me and Durán follow and the rest to halt, cantered forward until we were very near the Indians, when he pulled El Trompetero back on his hocks, and, my bobtail stopping with equal suddenness, I was all but pitched over her ears, which would have been an undignified disaster. Haranguing them in Quechuan, he said we came in peace and only intended to overtake our friends who were ahead of us. If they were wise, he told them, they would allow us to pass. If, on the other hand, they molested us we would cut each of them to ribbons. It seemed to Durán and myself that our arms would drop off from weariness before we had killed a tenth of them. When Orellana had finished, the answer came with a shower of stones from the leather slings and a javelin or two. So we wheeled and trotted back to our own people, where he calmly gave his final orders. The marksmen were not to fire until the enemy was within eighty paces, and then, unless a volley was ordered, they were to fire by half-and-half. (Since it takes time to reload either crossbow or arquebus, this time can be cut by one lot firing while the other is reloading, and so it goes on.*) The horsemen were to operate in their threes on

* For the first shot the arquebusier had to get out flint and steel, light his match, or mêche, a length of cord saturated in saltpetre solution, and blow it to a glowing stump. Then he primed his piece. There was no uniform calibre, every piece being supplied with its own mould, in which the user cast his lead bullets. At this period the hand cannon had developed to the arquebus, the barrel lengthening, the bore diminishing; but the mechanism was still wonderfully simple. In the rear of the muzzle-loaded barrel was pivoted a curved lever, a serpentine; the short upper arm held the match poised, and the long lower (or trigger) arm by its weight kept the match at "safe" until the trigger was pressed up to the stock, when the serpentine descended and the match entered the powder pan, causing the discharge (all being well). An arquebusier carried as his basic equipment: a long length of match; a powder flask; a ramrod and cleaning rod; an armourer's tool; a combined powder-tester, powder-measure, and match-cutter, engraved with the measures of different charges; lead bullets; spare lead; and his mould. It will be appreciated, then, that if his weapon was simpler than our rifles, its usage called for a higher degree of skill and nerve and a geat deal of luck; and its paraphernalia were more complicated.

our well-proven system, charging, breaking, charging again; but on the cry "Orellana!" all were to rally to him for a concerted charge. He reminded those on foot to close their ranks and stab for the bowels, and to lock steady if the enemy charged. Lastly he told us that we were Spaniards who feared nothing and nobody, and that the Lord our God fought with us while our blessed Santiago * would himself lead and inspire us.

Then the Captain had time to give me a few quiet words of advice. He told me to hold my lance shorter, and to aim for the face or the throat because those Indians are remarkably tenacious of life and even when mortally wounded they may find strength to seize the lance. In such a case I must wedge the lance between arm and body and hope that the speed of the mare and the leverage thus obtained would wrench the weapon free. He told me to hold the rein higher with my left hand, and not to interfere at all with the mare's mouth, but to neck-rein her on the turns. In this connection he warned me to remember in any emergency that La Rabona turned better to the near side than to the off. And when we charged I was to let her feel the spur eight strides before the impact and again if need be.

Seeing that the Indians were already a crossbow-shot and a half out from the trees, the Captain raised his voice and said that we must not let them think we respected them. He ordered a steady advance, with the horsemen in the rear of the foot. So we rode slowly on in our threes until Orellana raised his lance point on high and shouted: *"Señores, Santiago!"* Down the slope we galloped, fanning out into four separate groups, sand and gravel spurting from the hoofs, the hawks' bells on the harness madly jingling, each rider crouched forward, his knees high,† his head

* Saint James, patron saint of Spanish arms.

† "They learned to ride from the Moor. . . . There were two styles in Spain at the time of the conquest . . . à la brida was the ancient style . . . erect with long leathers. . . . The other school, à la gineta, was like the present-day forward seat . . . almost kneeling on the horse's back in the high Moorish saddle, the lower leg drawn well back, the heel well down, lower than the toe. They also used the powerful Moorish bit, and rode with a high hand and a single rein on the curb. The horses were trained to neck-rein, and a good rider put no pressure on their mouths except for a sudden

low, his beard blown hard over his chest, the point of his lance glinting blackly. As we neared them we saw them blench. The spur! Our speed increased. Through them we tore in furrows of madness.

I regret to admit that I failed to spear a single Indian while we were there in the thick of so many, though doubtless the two caballeros made up for this. To speak the truth—which is the only thing worth speaking except between lovers or lawyers—it was all I could do to go with the mare, for she, brave beast, was bounding and kicking as she galloped. Then at the last I saw an Indian with raised macana and I caught him with my point near the shoulder. He span and fell. I felt neither shock nor anxiety, but only elation and lack of breath. We were through them. El Trompetero fell back on his hocks, twisted round, and my mare followed him. The Captain led us off at an angle, then into the rear of the enemy. So we went through them again, and I felt blood hot on my face without knowing whose it was or how it came there.

As soon as we were through, Orellana turned again to charge across their front at a group that had been separated from the rest. As we charged them, three horsemen came galloping in from another angle, passed close behind us, and entered the enemy's ranks with the crash of the felled oak among saplings. This group of Indians would not face us, but threw their javelins and turned to fly. I found myself ahead of Orellana and Durán, who had slowed their pace in order to kill more Indians. I fixed one on my lance, splitting him in the back of the neck, and while I was holding the mare and wrenching at the lance, another Indian turned and struck me. The macana slid from my helmet and gashed my cotton armour. Then La Rabona, rearing as the Mameluke bit hurt her mouth, struck our enemy down with an

---

stop or rein-back. The bit had a high port, and often a long branch. The raising of the hand pressed the port into the horse's palate without pulling at the sides of his mouth."—R. B. Cunninghame-Graham: *The Horses of the Conquest*.

"My country was won *à la gineta*."—Inca Garcilaso: *Comentarios reales de los Incas*.

iron forefoot. The three of us circled clear and rode back to our own people on loose reins, the horses' heads low. We stood on one flank to breathe them. Their coats were lathered. Their thin flank heaved, glittering with sweat and blood. I was as winded as they. The crossbowmen and arquebusiers began to shoot.

"Santiago, y a ellos!" *

While the shock of the firing was still firm, we charged them, each trio from a different direction, and each returning at them where and when least expected. We had them in a maze of bewilderment, yet they were many, and still they whistled and jumped and fought, although here and there we found soft patches of cowards who would wince and fly from us. Some of these I speared without difficulty, but one whom I took for killed turned and smote so truly that had it not been for my good barbote † of proof he would have separated my head from my shoulders. The shock on my throat numbed me. I stayed in the saddle until we were clear of them, but when the mare, following the other two, turned sharply, I lost all sense of balance and fell. Durán, who had seen me fall, caught La Rabona's rein. Back he came pounding to me, and Orellana after him. Then, while Durán stayed beside me, Orellana alone charged, and turned, and charged again those Indians who ran to cut me down. It is one thing to mount when the leathers are long, and quite another when they are shortened to ride à la gineta, but somehow I got my foot there, and somehow I heaved myself into the dancing saddle. As we cleared their flank a heavy javelin flew across my nose and made Orellana's corselet ring. He led us back to the others, shouting to Number Five to bring me another lance, for I had stupidly left mine lying where I fell.

When the marksmen had all fired we advanced. One section of horse guarded each flank of the infantry—if I may call such a handful infantry—forcing the enemy to fight on a narrow front, while the other two sections harassed him and picked off stragglers. Soon our sword-and-shield men and the pikemen were giving him a taste of our bitterest Spanish medicine, while from be-

* "Santiago, and at them!"

† Steel throat guard.

neath the line of swords and pikes our gallant dogs leaped out low, to tear at the Indians' vitals. By constant exertion and superior skill we were able to move slowly on downhill, doing much damage, but we were so few that there was no rest for any of us. Nor had we eaten a bite that day.

At length those on foot had to halt from lack of breath, and while the marksmen loaded, we horsemen cleared a space, strewn with dead and writhing Indians. The rest took to throwing their javelins in showers. By this means they wounded several of us, and but for our armour, proof, cotton, or mail, or more often a mixture of all three, we should have come badly out of it.

Orellana now decided that when the marksmen had fired a volley, all of us horsemen would charge frontally, and our task was to cut through to the Indian captain, a tall one with many feathers about his person, and wearing what looked like a woollen cap. Orellana had seen that this fellow kept the others at the work, exhorting them by word and example in the most admirable manner. Nor could any of our crossbowmen or arquebusiers lay him low, for when it was seen that they were about to fire he was shielded by those around him.

So we charged, Señores, with all the will and the strength that we and our horses could muster by that time, and we cut a swath through them, but they fought so stoutly as we neared the centre that we had to turn among them and come out by the way we had gone in, and this with difficulty, for the Indians were keeping low and striking at our horses' legs. At the second charge, which immediately followed the next volley, we went deeper in, and Arévalo the Horseman, with a graceful backhanded sword-cut, nearly separated the Indian's head, woollen cap and all, from his body. To offset this good work, as we withdrew, Arévalo's section remained surrounded. Though Arévalo himself managed to cut his way clear, Cristóbal de Palacios was down among the Indians, and his horse too, while Juan de Elena, his lance broken but his sword whirling and darting, rode close pirouettes round them to keep the Indians off. We galloped in at once from all directions, and Arévalo was the first to get there, when even worse befell. An Indian who had dropped to one knee, holding the hilt of Palacios's lance on the ground, transfixed Arévalo's good horse under his armour and through the heart. He instantly crumpled, and I was glad I was not on him, for he was stretched at full gallop when this happened. Arévalo, however, landed lightly on his feet, his sword still in his hand. When we had cleared a space amid great confusion and shouting, Orellana took Arévalo up behind him, and Elena, who had done well, took Palacios. We withdrew without further damage, and Orellana shouted to the Negroes to bring two more horses and lances.

Clamorous with delight at having killed two of the fearsome beasts, the Indians were dismayed to see the twelve of us bearing down on them again as though nothing had happened, and as though we were ready to go on charging them thus all that day, all night, and all the next day (which was far from being the case). And without the voice of their good captain to stiffen them, they broke and fled, first one part, then another, then all of them. So we, whistling up the dogs, who were now in their element, being ravenously hungry, cantered among the flying enemy to the edge of the trees, and even in and out among them, killing many. Orellana did not call us off until we had turned them into a rabble, until the last of the rabble had vanished, until not a living enemy was to be found. In the course of this pursuit we came upon four Indian pigs,* slightly smaller than our Spanish hogs, and each with a stinking gland on its back that must be cut out carefully or it will taint the meat. The pigs were still warm, and the Indian hunters had evidently killed them and then laid them aside, thinking to kill us too before eating. We carried this food thankfully back to our friends.

A battered party were we, but none of us was dead though none was unwounded. Orellana told us to kneel, and he gave hearty thanks to the Lord God, to Blessed Mary, the Holy Mother of our Lord Jesus Christ, and to the saints, and most particularly Santiago, who watches so patiently and cleverly over us on such occasions. Then, bidding us rise, he said: "Crossbowmen, arquebusiers, swordsmen, and caballeros, you have this day one and all fought like men and Castilians to save your lives and do your duty." Then he clapped his hand to El Trompetero's sweaty

* Peccaries.

neck and cried joyfully: "*Amigo mio,* you are *a horse!* Today you have been as good as Motilla." *

This, then, was the first fighting for us of that expedition; and the victory to us. Thank God for it. Amen!

* "As good as Motilla" was the highest compliment they could pay a horse. Motilla, a dark bay with a white star and a white sock on his near fore, was the horse of Gonzalo de Sandoval, without question the best of the captains of Cortés, and perhaps the finest and steadiest Castilian officer in the Indies.

CHAPTER SIX

☼

DIZZY FROM EXHAUSTION, OUR WOUNDS STIFFENING, WE trudged down through the trees, leading our brave horses, to whom we owed so much. Even the two Negroes, though they had done no fighting, had been hit many times by stones from the enemy's slings, and one of the Indian guides was sick with a javelin wound in the chest. At last we came to a small stream, and when we had watered the horses and washed their wounds, we did likewise for ourselves while the Indian pigs were roasting for our dinner. As I had stood guard all the previous night and also my throat was so swollen that I could not speak, I was excused duties, and I slept like the dead, for my wounds and bruises had taken from me all remembrance of the toes that had been plaguing me.

In the morning we were a sad party. Four horses had died during the night, and three others, one of them La Rabona, would not eat. Although Orellana did his best to be cheerful and said several times that "one cannot catch trout without wetting one's feet," he must have thought a good deal about the forty thousand gold pesos he had spent on equipping himself and us. Most of that sum had gone on the eighteen horses, and now we had only ten of them left. This loss did not all weigh directly on the Captain because some of the hidalgos, for example Robles, Arévalo, and Cabrera, owned their horses, though in certain cases (I will not go into details) Orellana had had to pay their debts in Guayaquil or Puerto Viejo before they could set out with him.

That was an awkward time for me. I do not refer to my wounds, but to something more serious: Alonso de Cabrera was demented at seeing his valuable mare like to die, and the devil of it was that I, knowing myself to be no horseman—though none could best me with a crossbow—felt in some measure responsible, and I kept telling him so frankly. Cabrera would not answer me, or even look at me. We had used up all the oil and salt in doctoring the horses' wounds and our own the night before. I frequently went to the stream to wash out cloths, and with these, clean and cold, I tended the mare. Cabrera did likewise, and he appeared to ignore my presence until at last he said to me: "Bachelor of Arts, have the goodness to go away, far away from me; otherwise I fear that I may kill you." So I left him. La Rabona had a bleeding contusion on the temple, a deep graze in one flank running round to the belly, and a slashed fetlock, which was perhaps the worst of her injuries, because air had got inside the leg.

Lacking neither meat nor good water, we stayed there that day and the next, and by the following day I was ready once more to march, carrying my crossbow. We had passed the time of our rest in fleshing the horses that had died, cutting up the meat, and smoke-curing it. Without that meat I do not know how we could have continued, for there was nothing else to eat, Gonzalo Pizarro's force having stripped all the country around and scared away the game.

That morning we entered an ambush in a swamp whose rushes met high over our heads, a place where no horse could operate. The Indians attacked keenly, but we fought them off, killing seven or eight, and took two unwounded prisoners who told the Captain that Pizarro's men had laid waste their villages, so they had moved deeper into the forest, fearing that from then on they were to see nothing but "the hairy men" and those who were their slaves. As a matter of policy, Orellana gave the prisoners beads and told them he would be glad to trade in a friendly manner with their tribe, and would pay well for any food they might offer us. We left them staring at their green and yellow beads, but we had not gone far when an Indian drum with a stuttering beat sounded behind us, and soon this appeared to be answered by others, higher in tone, ahead. Our success in the ambush, which had been easily won, had put us in good heart, and we were inclined to joke about our serenaders, though I heard some say that Orellana should have killed the two prisoners instead of freeing them to carry tales, and that he should at least have taken the precaution of slitting their tongues. It is our way, as well you know who are Castilians, to speak out our thoughts; and Orellana had to listen to such criticism, though he did not bother to answer them.

He still had time to worry about my foot, and he made me ride for several leagues on El Trompetero, while he walked at the stallion's black shoulder. It was a comfortable ride, for arching his neck, the animal walked beside his master like a dog, and I did not even have to look where he was going or to touch the rein. Orellana talked little, but once he remarked to me that at least we had lost no *men*. I commented that horses in the Indies were more valuable than men, which was the truth. But he reminded me that there was no priest with us, that if any of us Spaniards died on the way to join Pizarro we must die unshriven, and that the blame for this, and the eventual punishment, which would undoubtedly be severe, would be attributed to him as Captain. He said there were too many priests in Guayaquil, where there was too little for them to do. The same could be said of Quito. Yet in both places he had hesitated to encumber his small party with a man who would eat but could not work or fight. "I will never do such a thing again," Orellana said. "No other expedition of mine will march without its friar or friars. I tell you, Bachelor of Arts, that my responsibility in this matter lies very heavy on me. I cannot take any pleasure in the fighting for worrying about whether any of you is being killed."

Lower and lower we went, yet often we had to climb steep slopes, because many hundreds of rivers run from the sides of Antisana and her sister and brother mountains of the Cordillera, and *all* those rivers seemed to make a point of crossing our route. Their size, depth, and rate of flow varied astonishingly from day to day, from hour to hour, even from minute to minute. Some that Pizarro and his army had waded, with water no higher than the knee, we had to swim or bridge, and sometimes the joke worked the other way and we walked almost dryfoot across a river bed beside a bridge that must have taken Pizarro's Indians twenty hours to build. Where a river was contained in a gorge, those ahead of us had spanned it with a bridge of the native kind, but such bridges were seldom stout enough to carry horses, and they would have to be led upstream until a place was found where the banks afforded foothold and they could be swum across.

At one such crossing La Rabona was lost. The mare did not have the strength to breast the current. She was swept under the bridge and among sharp rocks that gored and maimed her. Then she floated out of sight, her shoes sometimes gleaming above the flood. Young Cabrera had been in the water with his mare and had felt her stroke falter and die as he clung swimming to her stumpy tail. Only the skill and water-courage of the two Negroes saved Cabrera himself from drowning. I wanted to go to him as he lay vomiting on the bank, but Orellana wisely held me back. The mare had been a wife to Cabrera. He had bought her as a filly on the island of Jamaica, had broken her himself and trained her to war. And she was only six when she thus perished.

At another crossing we had to fell four big trees across a gorge and lever their trunks together so that men and horses could cross on them. At another we made a big raft, and the Negroes swam with a rope so that we could all ferry ourselves over with the horses, hauling the raft to and fro on the rope.

On the evening of our first day's march we passed through two Indian villages, or what Pizarro had left of them. Both were deserted, and many of the frail huts were burned. We hoped that Orellana might consent to halt at the second village, but it was big, spread out, and badly set for defence. He elected instead to sleep in the dripping forest. The two Canelos Indians quickly made a long, narrow shelter that kept much of the rain off us, but the ground under us exuded moisture like the lips of an infant. The dogs and ourselves ate horsemeat; there was no grain for the horses as they stood steaming in the warm rain. The forest was so dark and matted and sodden, so teeming with vegetable vigour, that we thought animal life might be completely suppressed. The guides declared, however, that there were jaguars and bears and pumas, and they recommended that the sentries should carry pikes. They had no need (unfortunately) to inform us that we were again among mosquitoes. During the night we heard no drums, but there were intermittent roaring and booming sounds, and these were loud enough to keep us awake and were most abysmally depressing The Indians explained that all the noise came from one mountain, called Sangay, that is in continual agitation, flinging up to the sky ashes, mud, and water, as well as flames. They insisted that we were as far as eighteen or nineteen leagues * from Sangay, but we would not believe them.

Next day we were often marching down the banks of the River Quijos, which gives its name to the insalubrious province. Antisana still rose behind us, and that sight was in some measure reassuring, if only because we knew that Quito lay on the far side of the mountain, and that the infernal forest thicknesses ended before it.

At one place the advance guard had halted, and when we came in sight they hurried on, but we saw what they had been at. They had killed a most immense snake by cutting off its head with a sword or an axe. We had already seen snakes of all sizes and colours, and were to see many more, but we knew better than to fear them, no matter how repellent their appearance, and for the following good reason:

Know then, Señores, that in the reign of the Inca Yupanqui one of his armies made its way into the forest region where we found ourselves, and nearly all the Peruvian soldiers were killed by snakes. Accordingly the Inca sent a sorceress to the place where most of his men had died, and this aged female, by the use of certain charms and incantations, changed the disposition of the snakes. They became gentle and timid where men are concerned, and so they remain to this day. If any of us had been inclined to disbelieve the Indian story, which is part of Indian history, experience showed us that it was the truth, and that snakes seek to avoid man, not to destroy him.

The Captain bade me go forward to overtake the advance guard and tell them that they were to waste no more time on playing games with snakes, but were rather to concentrate on smelling out hostile Indians. While I was telling them this with certain interesting embellishments of my own devising, we saw a bear among the trees. The ugly and unlucky Hernández at once got out his flint and steel and, in spite of the rain, after several attempts lit his match. He stole forward, priming his piece and hold-

* 66 to 70 miles.

ing his muddy fist over the pan to keep it dry. He was all atremble with excitement, but I, knowing it would be a miracle if he managed to fire, followed him silently. He pressed his trigger. The serpentine came down with its glowing match. The damp priming sizzled. The Portuguese groaned. The bear stood looking at us amiably (for, as we later knew, he had been gorging himself on honey). I shot a war bolt into his heart and he dropped clutching at his chest. I had fired from only forty paces, and I had great difficulty in hacking and wrenching the bolt from between his ribs.

It had been one thing to kill a useless snake; it was quite another to kill a bear. When the main body came up, everyone was delighted, and I received much praise, which must have depressed Hernández, though I admit that he concealed his chagrin remarkably well. We skinned the animal, taking all the meat and grease we could get from it, and giving the bones and scraps to the dogs. Seeing that we scorned the offal, the two Canelos Indians began to eat it until they visibly swole. Instead of cutting off small pieces of meat as we do, they put a whole slab in the mouth, and then slice free the surplus on a level with the lips. The spectacle soon palls. Their faces, low-browed, were painted with horizontal red and white stripes. To make the scene still more unusual, many scores of brilliant butterflies, some as big as pigeons, came at once and fluttered round the Indians and the mess, attracted (despite their beauty) by the smell of meat and blood.

The Captain questioned Hernández on the failure of his arquebus, but the truth was that the place was unsuitable for such chancy weapons, with everything dripping wet, and our clothes and boots and belts all covered with green mould and slime. I was glad and proud to think that I could rely on my steel warbow from Mondragón so long as I kept the string free from the damp by rubbing beeswax well into the small fissures between the threads. When I expressed these simple reflections—most mildly, for I had no wish to seem superior to the Portuguese, whatever others might, and did, feel about our respective merits—Orellana ordered me with sudden and unwarranted sternness to go on ahead with the advance guard since my shooting was, according to myself, so marvellous, and to desist from holding up our march with my "boastfulness." The Captain was under strain at that time, and I readily overlooked his rudeness because he was sharp with all of us—if inclined for some inexplicable reason to be soft with Hernández the Unlucky. I may say that the Captain's foolish partiality had no connection with Hernández's nationality, because we had another Portuguese with us, the most excellent Hernán Gonçalez, who had made a name for himself with sword and shield in Peru, in Popayán, and in the battles to found Guayaquil; yet Orellana never fussed over *him*. It would have irritated me less had I seen anything to like in Hernández; but as I have said, he was ugly, pimply, and above all unlucky. But to go on . . .

The two Indians, seeing that we were in no mood to delay because *they* were dining, hastily chopped off the bear's feet so that they could at their leisure remove the claws, which they value as personal adornments and as scratching implements, they being people who continually suffer from this itch or that.

During that day we heard Indian drums, but neither so often nor so loud as the day before. It was a day of negotiating rivers and building bridges, but in the evening we came to a torrent that seemed likely to defeat us. It was an astounding sight. Water, tree trunks, stones, went crashing past, and standing near the edge we listened to the growl of stone upon stone as the water force carried all before it on the bottom. The sight of the foam-streaked lumps of water, of the great trunks leaping clear and smashing against each other, of boulders bouncing like children's play balls, made the hottest blood run chill indeed.

Alonso Márquez, whom we called Márquez the Silent, though occasionally he could say too much, came back to Orellana with the news that Pizarro and his men and horses had crossed the river farther up. There at some narrows where, confined between vertical cliffs of rock, it ran with increased fury, we saw among the spinning clouds of watersmoke the remains of a bridge that had been hung on liana cables of great strength. It had been wide enough for horses to pass over almost in comfort, and it had had guys hauled out at angles to steady it. But now the guys were cut through and so were half of the cables forming the bridge; the wooden platform had dropped into the torrent, though here and there a solitary log hung forlorn over it.

Once again Orellana cursed Pizarro, his first thought being that the bridge had been cut behind them by its builders, to prevent other Spaniards from joining in their adventures. Soon, though, the Captain's attention was given to our Indian guides, who ran hither and thither looking at the sodden ground and examining the bushes; and to make the matter still plainer, our dogs growled and bristled and, putting down their noses, sniffed their way into the forest tangle where only animals and Indians could move. One by one the dogs returned to us, so we judged that there were no Indians hidden near us, at any rate on that side of the river. Orellana stood at the edge, outlined against the spray, glancing at the remains of the bridge and then examining them more carefully. He called the Canelos Indians and talked with them. Then he came back to us.

He said that we had all seen the river and knew that neither man nor horse nor dog could live in it. Yet we must quickly make our way across it because the Indians who had cut the bridge would return at dawn, if not earlier, and in strength. Orellana judged that all of us were men enough to cross on the two cables, one below the other, still remaining. The only way to get the horses and dogs over would be to sling them in a tarabita, and that would have to be made, for although we had carried tarabita gear with us when we left Quito, it had had to be left behind when we lost our porters on the high Cordillera. The first thing, he said, was to send six men over, two of them crossbowmen and one an arquebusier, to guard the far side of the broken bridge. He gave Alonso de Robles command of this small party, and Robles chose Márquez and myself to be his crossbowmen.

Robles was a shrewd and accomplished officer, good in all situations, a graceful horseman, a clever swordsman, and an outstanding arquebusier. Since he hailed from Don Benito, in Estremadura, he was a countryman of Orellana's. Robles did not at first give an impression of strength, for he was small and slight, with hands and feet like those of a woman. Yet he had the determination, the nervous energy, that one often finds in persons of meagre proportions, and added to his vigour he had in him a deep well of calmness and fortitude, for the greater the emergency, the calmer would he become and the more dependable. Best of all, nobody could accuse him of being all things to all men, yet he seemed to be no man's enemy and every man's friend, and although he would give orders as they should be given, with an absolute and unwavering decision, he was not like some who would haughtily say: "You *will* do this." Robles's way, and it was better, was rather to say: "Amigo, *you* are the man who can do this."

He now wished to lead the way across, but Orellana forbade it. Then I stepped forward to the cables, but the Captain told me to wait, because I was a crossbowman. So Diego Bermúdez jumped catlike onto them and easily made his way over, finding them to be sound all the way across. When it was my turn I clasped the upper cable to my chest and shuffled my feet sideways along the lower one. From end to end was some twenty paces, a distance that seemed ten times greater when a man was blinded with spray, swinging over the jumping torrent, and with its roaring in his ears. On the other side Orellana's party had lit two fires in order to have light to work in, but it was his wish that we should stand guard on our side in darkness, so that any hostile Indians would not know that we Spaniards were already astride the river.

Robles set us in the pattering rain to slashing a space in the undergrowth so that we would be able to land the horses and immediately lead them to a safe corner. Over on the far side they were shaping a hardwood clew to slide along the upper cable with a horse suspended under it. They were also making belly bands and girths to hold the necks and all four legs. Meanwhile others had set up a lighter clew to which a leather bag was attached. In this we drew over stores and gear, saddles, packs, and also about twenty of the dogs, who had first been muzzled lest they should bite their way out of the bag and thus commit suicide.

By the best of good fortune, as you will agree, Diego Bermúdez asked permission to do some work on the cables, and knowing his skill in such matters, Robles quickly asked him to continue, and to ask for any help he might need. Bermúdez first cut free two cables that dangled in the cauldron and spliced the best lengths of them together to form a new, strong cable. This done, he made one end fast to the big tree that supported the existing cables on our side, and the next time the bag came across with a dog in it he made the free end of his new cable fast to the bag, bidding those on the other side haul away. Hanging to the clew, Bermúdez travelled over at the same time, and there he strained the new cable taut with levers and lashed it. Three cables now spanned the river, the bottom pair hanging side by side and touching throughout their lengths. Taking twenty short lengths of liana round his neck, Bermúdez seated himself astride the two lower ones and moved toward us, lashing the cables together at short intervals until he was again with us. I wish I could describe the celerity and neatness with which this was all done, but I will only say that Diego Bermúdez was a seaman of Palos, and add that his father and his uncle had sailed with Columbus. He looked a seaman; he was clean in his person, and if his legs were short, his trunk was long, thick, and loosely muscular, with apelike arms. Contrary to our custom in the Indies, he wore his hair and his beard trimmed short, and made a fetish of cutting them himself almost once a week. There was a small gold ring in his left ear, and he preferred to the Spanish sword a thing like a billhook with a spike on the back of the blade, and this weapon he wielded two-handed.

The result of Bermúdez's work was that men could now cross more quickly and safely because the foothold was twice as wide and as solid as before. Robles asked the seaman what our friends were taking so long about on the other side. The answer was that they were burning out a groove in the clew; this groove had to be deep and smooth, and sloped up at each end, or in pulling the horses over we would soon chafe through the cable.

It is a fine thing, and most heartening, to have fierce, well-disciplined dogs with you on guard at night. Nevertheless the minutes passed like hours as we stood listening, slapping the mosquitoes on our cheeks, and staring through the rain into blackness that moved the more we stared. We judged that our wait was nearing an end when Orellana sent eight more dogs across to us, keeping only four of the best on his own side. The dogs were followed by eight Spaniards with another rope, the two Negroes, and the two Indian guides. On noticing that the Indians had shed their cotton clothing and looked as though they intended to slink off, Robles at once had the pair of them shackled to a heavy chain.

We then saw those on the other side lead forward a horse and we knew it to be El Trompetero because he neighed once as they girthed him. Being, like his master, a veteran of the Indian wars and schooled in all martial doings, he submitted peacefully to the girthing. They were shown up against the fires as they worked hastily round the stallion, and we could see Orellana soothing him with voice and hand, though nothing could be heard above the voice of the river. Then they signalled to us and launched the horse over the gully. Down he swooped until his feet were only one braza * above the raging water. "Lay on!" Robles cried, and seven of us heaved on each rope. At another shout from Robles we all turned, and fixing the ropes over our shoulders, we walked into the alley we had cut in the edge of the forest. We soon had El Trompetero out of the harness, and when he had given himself a shake he went off quietly to be tied to a tree.

While they were girthing up the next horse, Bermúdez went out along the cables, and he came back shaking his head. The passage of the Captain's charger—and he had come quietly—had caused much chafe. It was a pity, Bermúdez said, that we had neither a proper tarabita clew with a small wheel set in it nor enough grease to smear the length of the cable. In the intervals of heaving over more horses Bermúdez prepared another cable, so that it might be set up quickly if needed, and by using all the grease we had got from my bear we managed to keep the clew slippery and thus drew five horses across. But the cable was then so badly worn in the middle, at the point of greatest sag, that half the strands were frayed out. Bermúdez was told to make haste and set up his other cable. He did so, saying that it was stronger than the original, having more strands. Here, however, was a disadvantage, because the groove in the clew had to be enlarged to fit the new cable, which wasted much time.

It chanced that the first horse to be put on the tarabita after the delay was afraid of the contraption. He fought against being

* Six feet.

girthed and was down several times, biting and kicking. When at last they launched him he came over screaming and flinging himself about so that the whole tarabita danced and creaked. He was half-mad when we landed him, and it took a long time to ungirth him. Although the eyes of the remaining four horses had been bandaged to prevent them witnessing this exhibition of nerves, they had heard enough to upset them, and also the best-schooled of the horses were those that had been sent over first. While they were launching the next animal the dogs on that side became excited. He began his journey kicking and jumping as wildly as his predecessor, but when he reached us he was dead, hit by javelins in many places, and one had entered his head by way of his eye. An Indian trumpet was sounding continuously close at hand. Our companions on the far side had formed up facing the trees, adjusting their armour and freeing their weapons. They had stationed the three horses they still had with them on the edge of the gorge, while they stood in a fringe protecting the horses against the yet unseen enemy. The Indians were using no arrows, but only javelins and throwing-spears that flighted slowly. If our people kept their eyes open and their shields ready they were able to avoid damage.

When this bother began, as there seemed to be none of it on our side of the river (for which we were heartily thankful), I chose a natural trench under a bush and lay in it with my crossbow wound and armed. I soon saw an Indian creeping up toward Orellana's party, and I killed him easily. A few unaimed javelins came my way. I killed another. Truly, the crossbow is a superb weapon in such cases. Although they could neither see nor hear me, they felt me, and to their marrows. Lying a few paces to my left, Márquez the Silent was doing similar good work, while behind me, standing in the shelter of a tree trunk, Hernández the Unlucky fretted and fumed because as soon as he saw a target, his arquebus refused to fire, and small wonder after three days and three nights of continuous rain.

Our people across the river took to making sudden dashes with their four dogs at the edge of the forest, and we would see a swirling in the greenery, and them hard at it with their swords. The day was now established, and with the rain still falling and the pig of an Indian trumpeter continuing to draw wailing notes from his wooden conch, it was not the most inspiring of dawns. Robles on our side ordered us to stay where we were, for he had no doubt but that Orellana, being so badly placed, with no room to fight, would soon have to cross to us. Now and again, even above the noise of the river, we would hear a drum rumble and the warriors stamping their calloused feet as buck rabbits will stamp when hiding among brambles, half-frightened, half-angry. Still our people continued to hold sternly, and one of the arquebusiers on that side, a fine operator whom we called Biscayan Perucho (his real name was Pedro de Acaray), got his firespout going. This infuriated my neighbour Hernández all the more, but I paid little heed to the fool because it was easy and interesting shooting so far as I was concerned, and like Márquez I kept as silent and as still as my work would allow, knowing that sharp eyes were searching for me from the other side of the river.

Things turned against Orellana from the moment that the Indians, flighting their javelins higher, began to wound the three horses on that side. They galloped forward through our people, who could do nothing to stop them. One horse bounded into the trees, where he was speared to death. The others kicked and bucked about the small space until one went over the edge into the torrent. In the midst of this scene Orellana must have ordered a withdrawal. Rodrigo de Arévalo took to the cables with one of the dogs slung round his neck, and the others followed at intervals. We gave them all the help we could, but each man was struck several times, and Perucho had seven javelins hanging from his escaupile when he got across and, taking cover, prepared his arquebus once more. The Indians had appeared in the clearing, and we had much successful shooting, for as fast as we could fire we knocked them over. The single horse that still rampaged about was El Gordo, a common animal, hairy about the legs and nothing to look at, but very strong. He did much unwittingly to hold the Indians back until all our friends were across. Orellana came last in a thick shower of javelins and spears. He wore Milan plate and survived his ordeal with nothing worse than a nick out of one ankle (because he had bared his feet to get a better feel of the cables).

When the Indians had butchered El Gordo they were so avid to be on terms with us that they flew at the cables and came across in a continuous file. With three arquebusiers (the others had begged dry powder from Biscayan Perucho) and three crossbowmen firing, you would have thought no Indian could live to our bank, but a number did, and they were instantly cut down by Robles, who stood at our end of the tarabita, allowing nobody else to have a share of the swordplay. It was in all our minds that if this continued much longer we would not have a bolt or a bullet left for more work of the same nature. Accordingly the Captain ordered that the cables be hacked through, and this was done so quickly that many Indians fell into the cauldron, whence their bodies could be seen emerging as limp as dolls that had lost all their sawdust. We then withdrew to the six horses that had remained safely under cover, thanks to the forethought of Alonso de Robles.

I think it can be claimed that we had done well in this dangerous affair of the tarabita, and also that we had been fortunate.

Had we followed from the tarabita the track cleared by Gonzalo Pizarro's Indians, we should have been exposed on our right flank to the Indian javelins. A party of six *macheteros* was drawn up, and six others to relieve them when their arms stiffened. So we hacked our way through virgin forest until it was prudent once more to join Pizarro's way. Then Orellana sent forward as advance guard Robles, myself, Juan de Aguilar of Valladolid, Baltasar Osorio, and five dogs. Then too, with many polite apologies, the Captain had the two Indian guides freed from their chain, and he made much of them, pretending that they had been shackled contrary to his orders, and that he would never have allowed it had he noticed what Robles was doing. The truth was that he noticed everything and he had approved Robles's precaution. Orellana had lost some blood from his ankle wound, though it was nothing, and he was very tired from the night's exertions over the tarabita. While we of the advance guard were moving on we heard him tell Arévalo the Horseman to wait behind with a strong rear guard.

I walked in the lead of all our force, except that ahead of me walked Brabonel, the lurcher. This dog was a good worker, but no Casanova. He was long-coated, had many white hairs, and was minus his tail. He picked dry places to walk on when he could, which was rare. Sometimes he had to swim, the track was so waterlogged, and when that was necessary he would turn a cold and critical eye on me as much as to say: "It is all very well for you two-legged storks, but how would you like to be me?" From time to time I fed him with scraps of putrefying bear, which he liked better than the half-raw smoked horsemeat on which I regaled myself.

We had been working all night, marching all the day before, and there we were with another long day's march ahead of us. Nor were our surroundings such as to raise our spirits. The forest abundantly lived, yet it was also dead, a forest without sappy spring or seared autumn. Myriads of growths from the smallest tuber to the mightiest tree flourished though half-choked and distorted by equal numbers of dead and rotting neighbours. Mist hung in the treetops, and great blankets of moss, pale, dripping, spongy, descended from them so weightily that many high branches were thus brought down. Some had fallen across the track, and Robles gaily put his horse at these. We laughed a little, reminding each other of Hernando de Soto.

That officer, as you may know, was one of those who disagreed with Francisco Pizarro when he had the Inca Atahualpa put to death. Therefore Pizarro sent de Soto away at the head of an expedition to the Sierra de Vilcaza. To express his satisfaction at the prospect of honourable fighting, de Soto jumped his horse over all the wide ditches that crossed the road; and the watching Indians marvelled, declaring (such simpletons are often surprisingly near the mark) that the Spanish officer and his mount were one and indivisible. There can have been few finer horsemen than de Soto, for I have often heard men who knew him say that he had spurs in his rump, meaning that any inferior horse would go better for him than the very best for anyone else, and without apparent urging. The detractors of de Soto (particularly here in Spain, where it is sometimes, I fear, the fashion to speak ill of those who do not stay at home but risk their necks to increase the realm) say that he was too partial to the Montería Infernal, the bloodthirsty sport of hunting Indians with dogs and horses. But there—we must not be hard on him, for he was a horseman and willing to hunt anything that could run. And to go on. . . .

The foliage made of the track a dark tunnel. Gloomy were the skeletons of dead trees held as upright as in life by the tangle of parasites that had strangled them after sucking away most of their life. The lianas, those same that so usefully can replace ropes, mounted in coils round the trunks to a great height, from which they threw out their tendrils. These descended, caught root, mounted in their turn, their endless turn. Or some of them swung down diagonally to other trees and sprouted up again without touching ground. When the tree died and went to dust, it left where it had mounted in all its strength a great spiralling skeleton of the creepers that had killed it. Loud, loud squelched our boots as we slid and splashed on, vainly peering about us for a monkey or a bird to kill or a wild fruit to devour.

Brabonel growled, the hairs rising from his head to where his tail should have been. I unslung my crossbow and drew it with the cranequin. Robles trotted up behind me, asking if I saw anything suspicious. Before I could answer, horse and rider vanished into the mud with a loud crackling. Indians leaped from the thicknesses around us. In order to protect Robles the three of us and our dogs gathered round the pit, each facing outward. When I had shot one Indian I drew my sword, for they closed at once on us. Brabonel, crouching by my feet, sprang at an Indian, knocked the wind out of him, and cleverly killed him with two great bites in the soft of the stomach. I called the dog back, but he went into the thick of them and I had not time to see his end or if he did more damage. Those Indians carried spears and also weapons shaped like swords but made of black wood hardened in slow fires and sharpened. They pressed us vigorously.

Robles came crawling from the hole, a man of mud. His horse in falling had impaled himself on the sharp stakes the Indians had planted at the bottom of their pit, and Robles had had one of his feet crushed in spite of the bronze stirrup and his steel boot. Once the little man had taken his stand among us, we moved from the edges of the pit and closed shoulder to shoulder, with the four dogs protecting our legs. The savages were all naked, and their spears were too short to pierce our guard; nor did they throw them, because, in their ignorance, they thought to take Spaniards alive. In a close space and with stout compañeros, four men trained to the science of weapons and footwork can feel comfortable enough against a crowd of courageous botchers, and when they felt the sharp edges of our swords, they began to consider the sweetness of life.

Orellana, who had heard our shouts to each other and the barking of the dogs, came cantering up the track, jumping fallen timber as Robles had done. He was followed by his four horsemen. All smeared with mud they were. The Indians withdrew under cover, and I took up my crossbow again. I heard Robles ask Aguilar to go down into the pit and kill his horse. The animal was thrashing in his agony, and Robles had no heart to kill him. Somebody said it would be foolish not to take the meat. And Robles agreed that this was only good sense, though when he came to stand beside me at some distance from the accursed pit, and with his back to it, I saw that he several times took hold of the foot of his beard and wiped his cheeks and eyes with it. Occasionally an Indian would jump out on the track ahead of us and let fly with an estorica, and Robles would cleverly shield me while I tried to take a shot before my target skipped back into the trees. The Indian estoricas are not much to look at, but they are such a cheap weapon, and so useful in skilled hands, that I often wonder we do not use them in Spain, Italy, France, and any other country where men must from time to time amuse themselves and honour the customs of their ancestors by indulging in a little bloodletting. The Indians of whom I now speak could, with these simple flat pieces of wood, each with a clip, or spring, of bone at the end farthest from the hand, hurl a short spear some distance, and more accurately than you would imagine. As the end of the throwing implement comes forward, the spear leaves it and flies hissing, low over the ground.

When the compañeros had done with their fleshing and had cut the meat into transportable pieces, we moved on in one compact group until we came out once more on the bank of the Quijos. There the Indians were rash enough to come at us in the open, and we welcomed them so heartily that they fled, and bothered us no more. Their estoricas had done us considerable damage. One of twelve that we killed there was a fat one, a real plump beauty. Him we slit open, and we doctored our wounds with his grease, having neither oil nor salt.

A league or two on, we came to their village, which was surrounded by a stockade with a heavy gate. As we approached, a few Indian children fled into the forest. We entered, closed the gate, and, after posting sentries, searched every hut and corner. The place was deserted. The hearths were all but cold. We picked up just enough roots of I know not what species to be worth boiling for our company, and buried in one hut we found maize and also a big jar holding an evil-looking and worse-smelling paste. We gave all the maize, and little enough there was of it, to the five remaining horses, and the paste delighted the Indian guides, who put a handful of it in a gourd, added water, stirred the slimy mess with their dirty fingers, and drank again and again, passing the gourd to and fro with signs and noises of brutish satisfaction. The drink was red. Orellana tried it from another gourd and then advised us all to do likewise. Our Indians said that it was one of the many forms of chicha, and that it had been made by roasting bananas, pounding them to jelly, and adding red powder taken from some tree. The powder evidently helped the sweet paste to work up strength and also gave it the colour of blood. The Indians insisted that it was chicha of the best quality, meaning that it was of exceptional potency. For with those men, and their women too, drinking to excess is an institution and an evil. They imagine, of course, that in drink they become brilliant and fascinating, while the truth is that, like drunkards in other lands, they merely make idiots of themselves, and since they are uncouth sober, drunk they are unspeakably so. Yet drink is a blessing, properly used, and there are occasions when too much of it will do any man good. We Spaniards, I have no need to tell you, are rather abstemious than otherwise, but in that village we were glad of the banana chicha.

Although we scarcely noticed that it was still raining, for rain had become part of us, of the air, of the earth, we recalled the droughts of Spain with voluptuous intensity, seeking to remember the feel and the smell of earth so dry that it is hot dust. We joked about the sodden clothing rotting on our backs, and remarked that to travel in the province of Quijos a caballero should carry clean, dry linen underclothing to put on for the evenings' restful comforts. Very ugly was the rust that coated such plate as we wore, and our swords, crossbows, and arquebuses were thick with it, and horrible to the touch. I rubbed my bow over with fat from the horsemeat, and while we waited for the stew to cook, we crossbowmen laid out all the bolts that remained, examining the feathering, and dividing them equally among the three of us. I cannot remember how many there were, except that there were too few, for we had lost a great number by shooting across the gorge and then into the forest, where it would be about as easy to find a crossbow bolt as it is to single out a woman of Moorish blood in Granada or, for that matter, a bachelor of arts in Salamanca.

Then good it was to sit round the communal blaze, the dogs making much of us, and each with a gourd holding his few boiled roots and some lumps of horsemeat. Most of us would have given a finger for some salt, but all the same it was, or seemed to be, among the best of dinners. Orellana was put out by the death of Brabonel, an old warrior and one of his best-trained dogs, while Alonso de Robles was unusually cheerless, thinking of the sorrel that had seen so much of the conquest under him. But Robles ate his meat like the good soldier he was.

When they had done with eating (that is to say when they had finished all we gave them), the two Canelos Indians picked lice from their bodies and ate them. Andrés Durán said he had been told that under the Incas this habit of eating lice had not been discouraged, being considered the best remedy for sore eyes and some other ills.

As there were still, praise be to God, twenty-three of us Spaniards, we divided the night into four watches, while the Negroes and the two Indians were detailed to swish the horses and protect them from mosquitoes. The Captain carried a timepiece, but it had long since stopped, owing to the weather we had been enduring, and it never went again. He ordered each watch to count the minutes by their pacing, and the commander to be responsible for his term of three hours. Orellana chose to command the modorra, the drowsy watch before the dawn, which generally proves to be the longest and the most important because Indians are not usually night fighters. As luck had it, I was to be one of his watch. We lay down round the fire, in the hut where we had eaten, sleeping with the harness on our backs and our hands on our swords. But how we slept! I remember thinking it stupendously odd, when they woke me to go on guard at three in the morning, that when I had been busy with studies, brawls, and love-making at the university, I had often found sleep elusive, yet had not cared at all, because, for all my learning, I had not known sleep to be so wonderful.

CHAPTER SEVEN

☼

MORNING'S LIGHT REVEALED ANOTHER TRIAL, AND THE one that in those forests we most feared—namely, trial by hunger.

It had seemed to some of us during the night that we heard a continual munching, as though rats were gnawing at the framework of the hut in which we all slept. This noise had been made by a host of big ants (each was about half the length of my trigger finger). Working in a column, they had eaten their way through the wall of leaves and marched across to our store of smoked horsemeat. Every piece of meat had been stolen, because even if it was inside our packs the voracious insects had bitten a passage to it, carved it into cubes as big as themselves, and carried it off into the forest. Their traffic to and from our hut had been so dense that they had worn a deep path in the herbage inside the stockade. As for the stockade itself, they walked over it, moving vertically as easily as they did on the level ground. When we discovered our loss, the ant column was still entering the hut, though only a few dusty crumbs remained to be taken. If we picked up our packs, their determination did not stop short at robbing us, for they bit us most savagely, and they were not easy to kill. We spread a line of burning embers across their march. The column first sought to outflank the fire. Finding this to be impossible, the leading file marched stoically into it, and although they and their followers and their followers' followers were burned, the column marched on until it began to pass over the smoking bodies. Seeing this, we marvelled, and admiration was added to our anger with those raiders.

Orellana chose an advance guard of two crossbowmen, myself and Alonso Martín de Noguel, two sword-and-shield men, Mateo de Rebolloso and Baltasar Osorio, six dogs, and the Indian guide who, although he was still suffering from his javelin wound, seemed to be the better scout and tracker of the pair.

It will not hurt the strong steel of a war crossbow to be bent for an hour on end, though the neat little hunting crossbows that some of our Sevillian ladies handle so prettily would be ruined if kept in tension for fifteen minutes. Alonso and I therefore took turns at marching ready to fire. We had all the dogs working in front, then the Indian, then the crossbowman on duty. By watching the dogs and the Indian we were able to detect in time several pit-traps of the kind that had cost Alonso de Robles his sorrel. But about midday we were attacked all along our column, from the foremost dog of the advance guard to the last soldier of the rear guard. Obeying our training, we of the advance guard stood firm save for the Indian, who threw himself into the mud, pretending to be dead. The compañeros whom we could not see were steadily fighting their way forward to us. It is a maxim that a soldier must always stand and carry himself boldly, no matter how thick the air with an enemy's weapons, and our guide soon paid for his cowardice when the Quijos Indians, thrusting us back a little with the weight of their onrush, overran and killed him. When we were all united in one solid column, Orellana ordered an advance in the hope that we might come to a clear space where we would have room to fight and use footwork. The enemy pursued us, and the rear files were very hard put to it, the horses of Andrés Durán and Juan de Elena being killed under them by estoricas. To check the estorica men, Orellana sent all three of us crossbowmen, each protected by a sword-and-shield man, to be rear guard. So we went on, moving ten, twenty, or one hundred paces, then standing to fire. Always the enemy used his estoricas, and some of us were wounded, though I was fortunate, partly because of the thoroughness with which I had protected myself since Quito with plate on throat, arms, head, and thighs, and the extra thick padding of my escaupile, partly because of my surpassing skill with the crossbow (which so many have praised in unmeasured terms that I do not account it vanity to mention it), and lastly because my shieldsman, Mateo de Rebolloso, had a quick eye and concentrated coolly on his task. It was the first time that I had had the services of that slender Valencian, and I swore that it would not be the last if I could help it, and as we worked I loudly praised and encouraged him.

Rebolloso was elderly, being somewhere in the late forties, and he was attacked by a sickness that made him cough, often to the point of spitting blood. Yet what he lacked in strength he made up for in skill. I heard by his croaking breath that he was tired, and suffering from the heat, but he never missed the flight of a spear, and his shield, though it seldom interfered with my marksmanship, was always in the right place, and always held at the nicest angle of deflection. This was most needful, and was hard work because the spears were short and heavy and were launched with astonishing force. There was much grace in Rebolloso, I had good opportunity to notice. And I thanked God for it. Although his movements were as quick as was necessary, they never seemed hurried, but rather were accomplished with an almost languid certainty—and that is the truest characteristic of the expert fighting man. . . . All the same, I did not appear to have my usual success against the Indians, who guarded themselves with long shields made from hardwood rendered still harder by charring.

Feeling that they were bundling us on, they became bolder and bolder, until Orellana lost all patience—as indeed was only proper in a Castilian—with this continued rear-guard action, and little but wounds on our own side for the tally. He, Robles, and Arévalo came up behind us and suddenly charged the Indians crowding the track. As we stood aside to let them spur to the gallop, we smiled at their set faces and the rust and mud that covered their harness. Three abreast they struck the wall of wooden shields and galloped on, scattering the warriors and disregarding thrusts and throws. Needless to say, we ran after the horses and slew a number of Indians, which was a tonic to us, since we had long been suffering from their attentions and wondering whether in the end they would eat us, until suddenly the horses had turned their confidence into fear. As, however, in this account of our journeyings through new country I would above all seek the blessing that only truth can give, I had better say at once that we had no reason to suppose that those savages *would* eat us if they caught or killed us. Nor did we worry about that, Señores, for once the human envelope is dead, the immortal soul quits it, and what matter if one's corpse be enjoyed by men or dogs, fishes or crocodiles? To think of an Indian wench who is well shaped and who smiles benignly as she gnaws at my haunch, nicely browned over a slow fire, occasions me no suffering, except that the poor girl will surely go to hell for her *gourmandise*. What does make me sweat is the fear that firstly I might through some hasty stupidity offend our Lord and lose this life and the next through my own lack of tact, or secondly that, there being no priest at hand, I might go to my death unfittingly introduced to those supreme caballeros who await on high all who have been marksmen in the Indies.

When the melee was over, the Negro Panama asked me to go with him to his friend Number Five, who was lying on his back and, hardly knowing what he did, was pulling at the estorica spear buried in his own shoulder. Bidding him lie still, I put my foot on his huge chest and pulled the spear out. I gave Panama my dagger and asked him, if he valued the other's life, to cut a suitable wedge of flesh from one of the still-warm Indians. With this I sealed Number Five's wound, and we bound the place with a pad of cotton and strips that Panama tore from his own clothing. We soon moved on, and as there seemed to be nobody else to do it, I helped Panama to support the wounded slave. We could not have marched long like that, but we came to an open space where Orellana called a halt, saying that he wished to speak to us all. The rain had stopped for a little, and the throbbing sun that replaced it made our sodden clothing smoke and our heads ache.

The Captain said that the surviving Canelos Indian believed that Pizarro would be encamped at Zumaco, which was several long marches distant; he also believed that from that place on we should be in less danger of Indian attacks, and that if attacks came the work might be easier because we should in the main be on open ground on the banks of rivers. Between us and Zumaco, according to the guide, there still lay two wide rivers and many smaller ones. Taking all that into account, and particularly that we were without supplies of any kind, the Captain had (regretfully I know, because his own pride and his injured dignity were concerned) decided that our only hope lay in sending forward three caballeros on the three remaining horses. They must press on day and night until they reached Pizarro and informed him of our situation and, above all, of our need for food. He himself,

Orellana hastened to add, would stay with the rest of us, nor would anything or anybody persuade him to leave us who fought so well and who endured so many hardships and annoyances without disgruntlement, whimpering, or complaint. As the ride promised to be arduous, and the horses were in poor condition and half-starved, he proposed to ask the three best horsemen to go, and these were, in his opinion, Alonso de Robles, Rodrigo de Arévalo, and Alonso de Cabrera.

The Captain's plan found favour with everybody. I held the horse for Cabrera, and as he swung himself up I wished him well most warmly and sincerely. He brushed my shoulder with one iron gauntlet as though to say that he had forgiven me the loss of his mare. The three, after saluting with their lances, trotted away. We marched on in their tracks.

Our wounded Negro was raving in some tongue that neither Panama nor Orellana could understand. Orellana several times inquired of Panama if Number Five was a Christian, but he could get no satisfaction out of the Negro, who in his distress at his friend's condition did not seem to have any clear notion what a Christian was, or whether Number Five was one. Christians or no, those Negroes have remarkable constitutions, and Number Five's legs carried him along that day, with the smaller Panama supporting him and at the same time pinning his arms to his sides lest he should tear off the bandages. During the night, which we spent in the rain because, being unfed, we had no strength to make ranchos, the Negro became worse.

Next day we forded the River Quijos by walking through in single file with the Indian in the lead and each man holding on to his neighbours. The water was violent and in places was neck-high. Hernández, last of the line, was holding his arquebus above his head and his powder horn in his teeth, but he lost his footing, went under with all his belongings, and was nearly drowned. The list of the man's misfortunes would have been laughable had Orellana not continued, despite them all, to show him increasing favour, and had it not been important to us in those circumstances to have arquebusiers who would be more likely to loose off bullets than harmless curses whenever a target appeared. Many of us said—openly of course—that Hernández, though well-meaning, was not fit to carry an arquebus. That the Portuguese met such criticisms with unfailing good humour did not make us change our tune.

A few leagues on from the Quijos we came to another big river, the Cosanga, which was in spate. According to our guide both rivers united lower down to form an important stream called the Coca, and when I say important, I mean that it was big and also that it was to play an important role in our journey, as you will hear. But we are still on the wrong bank of the Cosanga. . . . What we did was to make use of a small island that had no great air of permanence, being composed of mud and reeds, in which the current raised a hissing sound. We attached a light rope to Panama, and at his third attempt he managed to swim to the island, having left our bank far upstream. The rope was then fixed from bank to island, and most of us were able to cross by holding on to it. But a few, including Number Five (normally the best swimmer among us, after Panama), had to be attached singly to the smaller tarabita clew and hauled through the water. They arrived in a very saturated condition. Three of the dogs were unfortunately drowned as they tried to swim unaided. The others we pulled over, attaching a cord from the clew to the collar or round the dog's neck. From the island to the far bank the same tactics were successful. Still the rain fell all the time, and it was our misfortune, since it was evident that Pizarro's people had forded there without difficulty.

To increase the weary effort of marching, from then on the big Negro was unable to walk. We made a litter and all took turns in carrying three corners of it, the fourth being held continuously by Panama, who was in a painful state of alarm that his companion was dying. Many officers would not have taken so much trouble over a wounded slave, but Orellana was firm about it, saying that the Negro was a good servant and that, for all any of us knew, he might have embraced the Christian faith. Had we been in a hurry we might not have been free to waste time and strength on the litter; but we were only advancing steadily, and if we had abandoned Number Five to die, we should have lost Panama too, because he would never have consented to leave his friend, being as headstrong, if not as brave, as any man among us.

Still lame from his insignificant ankle wound, Orellana constantly moved up and down our column when he was not taking his turn at the litter. He urged all of us to look diligently for anything edible in the way of fruit, game, or roots. The Canelos Indian said scornfully that we would never see game because we made too much noise. We should walk barefoot, he said, carrying only our weapons. Had we followed his well-meant advice our appearance would not have been much worsened, for the clothes hung from us in tatters through which the muddy skin showed. Most of us were young and sinewy men, yet so exhausted were we, so weakened by sweating combined with hunger, to say nothing of our wounds and aches, that we shambled along like a pack of octogenarian beggars. Lianas had already grown across parts of the track cut by Pizarro's Indians, as though nature intended to hold our two parties asunder, and if we had to cut a path, our arms had little strength in them. When Orellana permitted a halt we grubbed for roots, and the Indian showed us where to cut greenstuff from palms, a kind of cabbage.

Some of us, seeing no game, suggested that it would be wise to kill and cook a few of the dogs before they and we dropped from hunger. Orellana answered that although we saw no traces left by the horsemen who had ridden on ahead, he was sure help would not delay in coming, but that if the same question were put to him on the following day, he would consider it on its merits. He pointed out that the dogs were good ones, and good soldiers of the conquest, also that their term of usefulness would not be ended when we had joined Gonzalo Pizarro. One of our best bitches, a bellicosa called Isabeluca Rinzón, chose this dubious moment to give birth to a single puppy of her own sex. So Orellana gave orders that bitch and puppy were to be carried with the slave in the litter, and this was done.

That day we found some villages, but all deserted and with no food to be seen. We joked about it, saying it was plain that many Spaniards had passed that way, but the jokes were a trifle sour. We stopped for the night in a village where twenty Indians had been tied to stakes and burned. Orellana shook his head, and said that Gonzalo Pizarro's expedition had not begun well, and he hoped it would end better. The Captain had a profound admiration for the conqueror of Mexico, and he was inclined to ask in difficult times: "What would Cortés do now?" As we rested there, and we were at least sheltered from the rain, Orellana reminded those of us who lay near him that when Cortés had left the coast to begin his apparently foolhardly march into the heart of Mexico, a great and hostile country, he planned that his base should remain friendly and secure, and took pains to convince the natives of the coastal towns that he was their loyal friend and would free them from the taxes and the oppressions of the Mexicans in their water capital far away. But then Cortés was of another type from the Pizarros; he was a lawyer (of sorts) and a ladies' darling before he was a commander, and he had much skill in making men, even Indians, love him. "The duty of every Castilian in the Indies is to extend the occupation and to found settlements," Orellana said to us, looking out through the drips from the roof at the deserted huts and the wet, charred bodies. "Wherever we go we should remember that it is easier to be friendly with the Indians than to fight them, and we should endeavour to bring them under the cover and the promise of the Holy Church. If fighting is asked for, fight we must and will. But by God, gentlemen, fighting is no end in itself; and we cannot pacify all the Indians by burning some of them. . . ."

I think that few paid attention to the Captain's words, which, being random observations, were spoken in a low and sad voice. He said more, and I listened, but I cannot remember it.

When we set out in the morning, the same men pressed him to allow them to kill at least two dogs. He had to give in to them, for hunger makes men fierce, but he said that the killing must be postponed until evening, when he would halt earlier than usual since the dogs would need a great deal of cooking, being tough.

That afternoon Biscayan Perucho brought down a sloth with a shot that awoke the forest and caused much scuffling of unseen monkeys in the treetops. Soon after, as we were about to ford a river at a place where it ran smoothly, the Indian pointed, and we distinguished an iguana high in a tree on the far bank. I confess that the sight of the green reptile made my heart so unruly that its beating shook my whole body, while my stomach rose into my chest. Few strangers to the Indies could imagine why we should covet so unwholesome-looking a creature, but we knew from experience that the flesh of the iguana is succulent and of good flavour, some comparing it favourably with rabbit, others with veal, though I would put it somewhere between the two. We saw that the iguana in question was sucking the eggs in a heron's nest. The tree hung somewhat over the river, and iguanas are at their ease in water, and very quick to seek safety in it. Although had there been fighting to do I would have been the first to volunteer, I was extremely nervous, knowing too well what grief would be aroused among my friends should the iguana escape. But as leading crossbowman and a celebrated marksman they called on me to kill it, and to choose another crossbowman to shoot with me.

While the others lay down under trees watching us, Márquez the Silent and I looked to our crossbows, wound them, and each chose a good bolt. Lowering ourselves quietly into the water, we moved out, keeping only our faces and our crossbows above the surface. There was a rapid current, and we had to avoid floating trees and weed-masses. Márquez had agreed that we would keep level with each other, and about ten paces apart. Halfway across we found firm footing, or so it seemed, on a bed of small stones, and we halted, glancing at each other. We took the bolts from between our teeth and set them in their grooves. We brought up the tillers until we could sight the iguana over the knuckles of our thumbs. I fired first, because I do not believe in prolonged aiming, which renders the hands unsteady. It chanced, though since I was immersed nobody but myself knew of it, that as I pressed the trigger my hinder foot slid on a round pebble, and this was enough to throw my aim high and to the right. But whereas my bolt merely buried its head in the tree, that of Márquez went through the centre of the iguana's body and impaled it. The groan from those behind us, who supposed that if I missed, the other had small hope of success, was changed to a yell of joy, and all but the wounded Negro and his companion and the arquebusiers (who always must think of their temperamental gunpowder) took to the water with a splash.

After he had congratulated Márquez on his fine shot and had listened to my explanation, Orellana said we would make camp there on the bank, and that there would be no more talk of killing good dogs for food. In a short time the Canelos Indian had found wood that burned even when saturated with water, and two fires were lit. The sloth was skinned, and the dogs, unaware that the deaths of that animal and the iguana had saved two of their number from death, made merry with the skin, swallowing it down to the last shaggy green hair and then quarreling over the sharp claws. When Márquez held up the iguana with its tail touching the ground, its nose was on a level with his own. Even in death, its eyes hooded, it looked venomous, with its crested back, its puckered and bowed legs, and the hanging pouch under its jaws. We were in luck because it was a female, and these are better to eat than the males.

We roasted it scales and all, fearing that if we skinned it some of the white flesh would be wasted. When Vayón the Pike, who looked to the cooking, announced that all was ready, Orellana stepped forward to divide the meat. The sloth was cut up into twenty-one pieces (the Indian asked for the intestines, and Number Five was too ill to eat at all). It was lean and exceedingly tough, and if we had had with us even the meagre comfort of a camp kettle we would have stewed it. The pieces were set out on hot stones to keep warm. Then came the turn of the iguana, which was found to contain a good number of oblong eggs. These are a delicacy, oily and sustaining. As he carved, Orellana said that Perucho, Márquez, and myself would each get as our share an egg and also a piece of the tail (which is the next best part after the eggs).

Some of the compañeros were ill-mannered enough to complain at this. They declared that I had missed the iguana by nearly its own length, and that it would therefore be more fitting to give me the head than the tail, some scales than an egg. I kept silent until one of them, García de Soria, went altogether too far; he said he supposed I would blame my poor shooting on alti-bajo.* At this I waved my crossbow under his nose, asking him and the others to name any mark and I would shoot against them one by

* When the steel bow was not set and held with absolute nicety in its wooden stock, with exactly the same length and strength of arm on either side, the bolt would not fly truly, and this fault was known as alti-bajo.

one, our meat being the stakes, until I had the meat of ten men and none of them had any. And I would swallow their meat in front of them, where they could scent it, and would not leave enough to satisfy a sparrow. Being Spaniards, they at once agreed, but Orellana intervened and forbade it, saying it was a form of wager, and we all knew well enough, surely, that wagering on active service was an offence. At the same time he had the kindness to say that *he* believed me when I claimed I had slipped at the moment of shooting. How else, he asked, could he credit my miss, when never once at the butts had he seen me fail when shooting at half the shell of an oyster? Then he handed me an egg, part of the tail, and a generous piece of sloth into the bargain.

We were eating when the Indian and the dogs warned us that we were in danger. So we took up our arms and closed our ranks. It was a party of mounted Spaniards commanded by Captain Sancho de Carvajal, and with them was Alonso de Robles on a strange horse. Good Robles was so delighted and relieved to see us all alive that the tears ran down his face as he told Orellana that all three of our horses, and Arévalo and Cabrera too, had arrived safely at Gonzalo Pizarro's camp, which had been set up in the valley of Zumaco, as the Canelos Indian had guessed. Orellana took Robles aside and questioned him as to what kind of reception the three of them had got, and Robles answered that Pizarro had treated them like brothers as soon as he knew that they came from his cousin Orellana, and that within an hour this party had left to go to meet us with all manner of gifts in the most welcome shapes of food and wine. Orellana thereupon begged Carvajal to be good enough to stay with us there beside the river that night because we were in sore need of rest. Carvajal replied that he had enough horses for all of us to ride from that place on, and that he and his men asked nothing better than to comply in every way with the wishes of men who had accomplished so much.

Pizarro had sent with Carvajal and Robles his personal surgeon, whose name I cannot recall, but none of us would admit that we had any need of his saws, knives, and purges, and he was disappointed to find that his only victim was a wounded Negro, whom, incidentally, he did not manage to kill.

As our journey from then on was comfortable and safe, I will not weary you with a description of it. On the second day we were approaching the valley of Zumaco when we saw a party of caballeros cantering out to meet us. Orellana had been unusually silent during the whole ride, and I saw him frown and play with his beard as he watched those who came so gaily and confidently toward us.

Gonzalo Pizarro spurred his small horse forward from the rest and, wheeling it alongside that of Orellana, put his arm around the shoulders of the knight from Trujillo and told him he had been sorely vexed on his account, and had never in his life been so glad to see anybody. Orellana may have felt inclined to answer tersely, but he was polite, if a little unbending. Then Gonzalo made a short speech, congratulating all of us and particularly our leader on accomplishing so arduous a march. He said he was delighted to have such men with him, and he promised to use our talents and our powers of endurance to the full. Introducing to us collectively his Quartermaster, Don Antonio de Rivera, and his Ensign General, Juan de Acosta, he asked those two to see that we were comfortable in the camp quarters assigned to us and that we were issued with new clothing and anything else we might desire. Finally, he announced to all of us who were there that he intended to appoint Captain Francisco de Orellana to be Lieutenant General and second-in-command of the whole expeditionary force, and that he would have the necessary documents drawn up by a scrivener the moment that we reached his camp. This appeared to most of us to be making handsome amends for any previous remissness on the young Pizarro's part. But Orellana looked wan and listless, and when he thanked Pizarro he asked forgiveness for his uncolourful words and appearance, pleading extreme fatigue—which may or may not have been feigned.

CHAPTER EIGHT

THE INDIANS OF ZUMACO WENT NAKED, WHILE THEIR women wore nothing but small clouts over their private parts, and this may have been immodest, Señores, but I assure you that those Indians showed more sense in the matter of dress (or the lack of it) than they did in anything else, for if you can mention to me the name and characteristics of a hotter, wetter, more pestiferous place than that valley of Zumaco, I shall listen politely, I shall give my earnest attention to your opinions, but I shall *never* believe you. The damp heat at Zumaco would rot the finest new clothing in a week, and what did not rot would be consumed by insects and vermin. As for steel, burnish it, grease it how you would, in the morning it was rust. Men seemed to fare little better. There was sickness among the Spaniards and death among the Indian servants, who could not breathe cleanly in that miasmal swamp, where mud was as inescapable as were mosquitoes. The camp, made up of leafy huts set in ordered lines, was no worse organized than the many I can call to mind, but was by far the most squalid, and, strange though this may seem, neither I nor any of Orellana's party were distressed to find it so. I will give you the reason for this, if you have not guessed it: a soldier's pride is as important to him as the state of his feet, and humility in a soldier is as reprehensible as a cluster of blisters. We arrived in rags. We had lost all but three of our horses. We only had one miserable Indian, a skinny wretch from Canelos, one Indian and two Negro slaves.

Thus we joined the dazzling expeditionary force of whose glories we had been told so much in Quito; and when we found Pizarro's men to be ill-housed, discontented, and glad of our arrival because they relished any change in the monotony of the day's round, it became easier for us to take our places among them.

Also the warmth of Gonzalo's welcome and his immediate appointment of Orellana to be his chief lieutenant made their impression throughout the camp, where there was much speculation as to the reasons for it. Was Pizarro so fond of his kinsman from Trujillo? And if so, why had he marched from Quito without him? Was the appointment made because Pizarro regretted his rudeness? Or was he impressed by the successful efforts Orellana had made to join them? On the day following our arrival Orellana was officially installed in his new rank, with all the numerous documents that must be drawn up on such occasions and with oaths subscribed to and witnessed by a score of hidalgos, the scrivener, the friars, and Gonzalo himself. Afterwards Gonzalo withdrew with Orellana and the other officers for a conference, and when that was over, Orellana did me the honour of sending for me and telling me what had been decided.

We talked in his hut, which was small but comfortable, with a bed, a table, a chair, and a carpet in it. He lay on the bed and asked me to draw the chair to his side, for he had been dosing himself with camomile because he had no appetite and feared he might be sickening, though it seemed likely that he was only feeling the anticlimax of our arrival after the strains of our journey. He explained that he had sent for me, firstly, because I appeared to be the only footsoldier of our small company from Guayaquil who was strong enough to face another immediate trial of endurance, and secondly because I was a man of education and one in whose discretion and whose loyalty he had full confidence.

I assured him that his confidence was not misplaced, which was the truth.

He then told me that Gonzalo Pizarro had sent out several strong patrols from Zumaco, but these had found only rivers and forests. The work of supporting so large a body of men and horses at Zumaco was constant, since the local Indians were wild and were seldom to be found in villages. They preferred to live in hovels widely scattered and inaccessibly sited. Nevertheless, the patrols had found no base as satisfactory within a distance of twenty leagues.* Until our arrival Gonzalo had been wondering, since there had already sprung up factions and rivalries among his

* 73 miles.

officers, whom he could leave in command at Zumaco while he himself led on a picked force of eighty footsoldiers.

In view of the exhausted condition in which our party had reached Zumaco, Pizarro had decided to take none of us. But Orellana had talked to him of my proficiency with the crossbow and my steadfastness on any march, and thus had had little difficulty in persuading him to number me among the eighty.

The Captain said he had no need to remind me of my duty to Gonzalo Pizarro as our commanding officer and as an inspiring leader with only successes to his name. But he wished me above all to regard myself as his (Orellana's) representative with Pizarro. He asked me to keep my eyes and my ears open, and when I deemed it advisable I was to make notes that other men would not be able to decipher, but with whose aid I could give him the fullest account when next we met of all that we had done, including the distances and directions of our marches. He asked me to note particularly the possibilities of the cinnamon forests, to bring him back samples, and to pick out any places there where I thought towns might be founded. I was to form my own opinions as to what lay beyond the cinnamon country, and as to the likely whereabouts of El Dorado.

Orellana then gave me two rings, the first cunningly fashioned in the shape of a gold serpent, and the second this square emerald I am wearing, a flawless stone, as you can see. He also gave me a note in his own hand to the Quartermaster, Don Antonio, so that I might draw any stores I might need for the march.

I did not keep the rings on the fingers where he had placed them. Instead I opened my shirt before him and put his gifts in a small bag of doeskin that hung on a hair chain from my neck. After further mutual assurances I left him and hurried to the Quartermaster's store to profit from Orellana's note.

Next morning, after we had all heard Mass, we marched eastward, and although several of the officers who were to remain at Zumaco and a great many of the men marched with us on the first short stage, Orellana was not there, nor any of our party from Guayaquil. As for me, I was ready to outmarch any of the fresh soldiers with me, and to do my duty at least as well as they.

I do not intend to describe at length this march with Gonzalo

Pizarro, since my object is rather to tell of my association with Francisco de Orellana, and of the deeds we accomplished together. In order to make plain some later events, however, I must draw the outline of what now took place.

Our march led us through country so rough that an advance of one league seemed more like an advance of ten, so far as the effort required was concerned. There was nothing that could truly be called fighting to enliven this march or make it pass quicker. Rather it consisted in cutting open a way through the matted forest, in searching for food and for Indians who might have food or know where some was to be had. We suffered from rains that seldom stopped, from heat, from the attacks of insects, and from hunger and fever. It was a march that demanded fortitude, endurance, courage, all of which we possessed in plenty. But it also demanded patience, a quality that enjoys among us perhaps a lesser esteem than it merits. Gonzalo Pizarro was ready to take less sleep and comfort than any of the rest of us. He would do his share and more of bridge-building and of cutting our path with machetes. He would borrow a crossbow or an arquebus to take a shot at a toucan or a parrot, and he would laugh louder than the loudest when he missed or shout with delight when he scored. He was ebullient, untirable, friendly, encouraging. After praising those qualities in our leader I am surely entitled to say that he was not the most patient among us, for his was a mentality that could not tolerate obstacles or delay. And on this march everything conspired to try him.

Sometimes we would imagine, shut away from the sun and the stars in that succulent wilderness, that we were lost for ever. Our Indian guides seemed to mock us as they mocked each other. There were disagreements and hatreds among them, and some were always arguing that we had strayed from our route to Canelos. Very often I reflected how useful it would have been had Orellana been there to talk with the Indians and possibly to advise them to behave more circumspectly before the irascible Pizarro.

After seventy days of such disagreeable marching, when several Spaniards had died from our hardships, we saw our first cinnamon trees. Some were smaller than olive trees, while others were tall and ragged. The flower buds and the leaves had the true taste of cinnamon, but the bark was tasteless.

Pizarro asked: "Where is Canelos?"

"This is Canelos," the guides answered.

He refused to believe them, but he made camp and sent out patrols in every direction with orders to bring in as many Indians as could be found. As we cut our way through the thickets, we cursed those in Quito who, knowing nothing, spoke so extravagantly in praise of this "Land of Cinnamon," and who for long had counted on the glory that would come to their town and to our noble King from the exploitation of Canelos. In our imaginations we had created most extensive and orderly plantations of cinnamon trees, each the same as its neighbour, with Indians in clean garments, sleek and fat, moving about under the gleaming leaves. But such cinnamon trees as we were shown were so scattered and so buried in the forest that it would be easy to travel there for weeks without seeing a single specimen.

Those Indians lived in small and miserable huts, each, like the cinnamon trees, far from its neighbours. Brutish and timid, they went naked (which, I repeat, is sensible enough in a climate so warm and sodden). The men had many wives. They were elusive, for they could slip through the forest as easily as a trout will slide from pool to pool. We captured a number of them, however, and took them unresisting to the camp, where Pizarro, seeking to make friends of them, gave them chaquira (as we called such gifts or bribes) in the shape of blue, green, and yellow glass beads. Then he asked them through his interpreters where we would find country with more cinnamon in it.

They answered that they only knew of those cinnamon trees that were scattered in the forest round us.

Leaving the question of the cinnamon, Pizarro required them to give him news of the country to the east, and to tell him how soon we might expect to emerge into fertile provinces with prosperous inhabitants, plains, cities, and roads.

They answered, one and all, that they had never heard of any such provinces, apart from those that lay beyond the Cordillera (namely Quito). They knew only the dense forest in which they existed. Nor did they continue there from choice. If they moved one way or the other they were attacked by hostile tribes, and those who attacked them were men of the forest like themselves. Many other questions were put to them, but their answers were all the same, without hope for us; and the women were as obstinate as the men.

Pizarro called Gonzalo Díaz de Pineda to his side and asked him for an explanation. He said he had understood that Díaz de Pineda had been to the cinnamon country, and he had also thought Díaz de Pineda to be a man of honour, who would be above spreading false reports about any expedition he might have led. At this Díaz de Pineda became as angry as Pizarro himself. He argued that he had never claimed to have reached Canelos, for when he had been within some days' march of it he had withdrawn after fighting a battle. All he had claimed was that certain Indians whom he had taken prisoner in that action had said that Canelos was not far off, and that beyond it lay fertile and open plains. That, Díaz de Pineda said, was the truth of the matter, and he dared any man to say otherwise. It was possible, he added, that the Indians he had questioned had lied to him in the hope of persuading him to advance and enmesh his expedition still deeper in the forests. This made him feel that he had done well to order a withdrawal, for otherwise he would have needlessly thrown away the lives of many stout Spaniards. At this some of us made exclamations of approval, and these further annoyed Pizarro.

"*I* do not withdraw," he said. "And all Indians are liars, Díaz, as you, who have passed on some of their lies, should now know. At all events, we shall soon wring the truth out of these ones."

He ordered frames to be made, somewhat in the shape of hurdles, and several of the stubborn Indians were lashed to the frames and thus stretched over our fires. They cried out in loud and terrible voices when the pain of the roasting came because, I think, they did not know the reason for their torture. What could they tell him when they did not have the sense to know what he wanted to be told? So a good many of them were burned to death, while others, and there were women among them, were given over to the dogs and were torn to pieces and eaten. Neither from them nor from any who were roasted did Pizarro receive one word of hope. He talked with the other officers for a long time. We did not know what plan they formed, except that we were ordered when they had done to march once more eastward.

We made camp on a smooth stretch of sand beside a river, and while we slept we were roused by the yells of sentries. We jumped up, our swords in our hands, and only our training against night attacks saved our lives, for the river was in sudden spate. A great wave came down its bed with trees and boulders toppling and rolling in it and a high flood behind. Our whole camp being engulfed, we saw out the night on higher ground above the torrent, which ground boulders on its bed as easily as millstones will deal with barley.* And in low voices we brothers of the crossbow spoke to each other of the miseries, the disappointments, the frustrations, that so often outweigh the glories of conquest.

At dawn Pizarro assembled us and briefly ordered us to salve any stores that had not been lost or ruined, and to prepare to march. So we marched on, many of us wondering—since men can never know their destinies, yet are always seeking to peer into them—whether this expedition would ever show profit or amusement. Realizing, however, that we were now marching north by west instead of east, we said, and at the tops of our voices, that the flood had been an act of God, for it had changed the plans of our headstrong leader. On we went, day after day, until he halted us only four leagues † from Zumaco. We were overjoyed at the prospect of returning among our friends. I spent that evening looking through such notes as I had made for Orellana, and I searched in my pack to see that my three dried-up cinnamon buds had not disintegrated.

But in the morning Pizarro, instead of continuing west to the camp of the main body, ordered us to march north. He said he

* Darwin writes in his *Journal* of such a river: "The sound spoke eloquently to the geologist: the thousands and thousands of stones which, striking against each other, made the one dull, uniform sound, were all hurrying in the one direction. . . . The ocean is their eternity, and each note of that wild music spoke of one more step toward their destiny. . . ."

† 15 miles.

would lead us to the province of Capua, and from there we would strike east for El Dorado, as he put it. We supposed that Gonzalo felt the failure of the march to Canelos more keenly than we did, and could not bear to think of us recounting our misfortunes among the compañeros who had stayed behind. Angered though we were by his behavior, when he gave an order all men in their senses knew it was best to obey smartly, and obey we did. I do not say there was no grumbling. There was a great deal of it, and Pizarro was told that the expedition was proving to be that of a Pedro Carbonero.*

It was yet another hard and long march, and before we came near Capua (which some said was nothing of a place, and peopled by ugly, bloodthirsty, and unreasonable savages) we halted on the banks of a river one thousand paces wide, a river more placid yet more potent than any we had yet encountered, a river that flowed smoothly between walls of forest. It was the Coca.

Canoes in groups of ten or twenty slid out on the river and hung there, quivering to the current as fishes do when lying in a pool. We called out to the canoemen and behaved in as friendly and inviting a manner as seemed possible. Pizarro spoke to our guides and interpreters, saying that he would slice off their hands and slit their tongues if they did not at once convince the strange Indians that we were the most benevolent and gentle of beings, and that they would do very well to cultivate our friendship by receiving gifts from us. I do not know what was said, but a few canoes approached and some Indians landed near us. Leading them was one taller and bolder than the rest. The interpreters told us that he was Delicola, an important cacique.† Goñzalo received

* A common expression in the conquest when things went wrong. "I had heard with my own ears that I was a Pedro Carbonero," Cortés wrote in his Second Letter. On what was the expression based? Some have it that Pedro Carbonero was a Spaniard who led a squadron of cavalry through the Moorish lines and was lost with all his men. Perhaps an explanation lies in the proverb: *"Pierre le Charbonnier savait bien où il était, mais il ignorait le moyen d'en sortir."*

† Chief. "Cacique" was the word most frequently used by the Spanish soldiers, who are said to have picked it up in Cuba.

Delicola and his few followers with presents of beads, combs, and some old knives. He greeted the tall Indian as "Lord of the River." Delicola in his turn presented Pizarro with two young alligators freshly caught and alive.

While our two parties thus met amicably, Delicola spoke with our guides. We had no means of knowing what they were saying, except that as he talked he directed side glances at us. When he was questioned by Pizarro about our prospects, Delicola said at once that if we marched down the banks of his river we would get clear of the forests and would come upon rich country nourishing all manner of beasts and crops, which were tended by "tame" Indians, fat ones who hung themselves with gold.

As this was the information that we all longed to hear, we were overjoyed. We congratulated each other and Pizarro, but while he was laughing with us he suddenly stiffened and said to Gonzalo Díaz de Pineda: "Look at the Indian cacique."

"What about him?"

"He is smiling. Did you ever see an Indian smile before?"

"Never. But probably our beards amuse him."

Pizarro was suspicious of Delicola from that moment on. He ordered several of us crossbowmen to keep dogs by us and to watch the cacique, but to do it circumspectly; if Delicola tried to escape from us he was to be shot.

It appeared to us crossbowmen that Delicola was aware of this measure, and that he watched us as carefully as we watched him. But he was a man of dignity, and for an Indian he was exceptionally easy and graceful in his ways, and an agreeable companion.

Taking him with us, we marched upstream until we came to an immense waterfall, and above the waterfall the river poured, deep and gurgling, through a narrow gorge. We felled some large trees to make a bridge. There was some difficulty because none of them would fall correctly across the gap, but at last we swung one into place by using a system of rope tackles supporting the outer end from the upper branches of neighbouring trees. On the other side of the river the ground was open, and there groups of Indians watched us, while some of them seemed to be throwing up defensive earthworks. Gonzalo saw them, and the sight made him laugh, for he was a Pizarro and there was nothing he liked better than fighting.

No sooner was that first tree in its place than he sent twenty-five of the compañeros across it with ropes and tackles, advising them to hurry, without looking down into the rushing water beneath them. One man, more nervous than the rest, went too slowly, lost his balance, and fell. Pizarro said nothing, but glanced at Delicola to see if he had noticed the accident. He had, and so had the Indians on the other side. Some of them went below the waterfall in the hope of finding the dead Spaniard. Now, in dealing with those peoples of the Indies, who always greatly outnumbered us though they were inferior to us in military skill and usually in courage too, we men of the conquest took care to pretend that we were not mortal but were the invincible and superhuman children of the sun; and if some of our number were on any occasion killed or seriously wounded, we always took care to hide them from the Indians. Fortunately for us (and for those Indians), our compañero's body had either been battered into fragments or been caught in some underwater fissure, for it never appeared. So, fascinated as young children, the Indians returned to watch our bridge-building.

Well might they do so, for were there ever bridge-makers to equal us Spaniards of the conquest, who were accustomed to triumphing with the most meagre of man-made materials over the mightiest water obstacles? Those among us who had served under Hernán Cortés said that people in the years ahead would exclaim: "Here are the bridges of Cortés!" as other travellers have exclaimed: "Here are the Pillars of Hercules!" For example, in the province of Copilco, during his march from Mexico to Honduras, Cortés built more than fifty bridges in a distance of twenty leagues.* On the same march, after they had overrun the towns of Tonalá and Ayagualulco, and when the Spaniards and Indians of Cortés's army were worn out, they came to an estuary that all of them but Cortés said was unbridgeable. He set his Indians to felling huge trees, which were to be the floats, and the Indians

* 73 miles.

worked so well for him that his Spaniards were inspired to work even better. When the bridge was finished they rode their horses and drew their cannon across it, and it measured from end to end, this is the truth, half a quarter of a league.*

Compared with such an effort, our bridge across the narrows of the Coca was a toy, though when it was finished it was wide enough and stout enough to take not only our party but also the main body that would follow us with its horses and its herds.

We crossed over and formed up on the other side. And then, if you please, the Indians, who had not attacked us when we were at our most vulnerable and had no prospect of getting among them, came on boldly. Pizarro bade the ten arquebusiers fire one volley. Their joint explosion rolled with uncanny power on the edge of the gorge. From the woods below, parrots rose in a cloud of blues and yellows and then, separating into pairs, flew into the sky downstream. The advancing Indians were aghast. Even Delicola blenched most curiously, and who can blame him? I am no advocate of firearms myself, having a natural and healthy preference for my own handier, more reliable, and more artistic crossbow; but I would rather have the firearms on my side than on the enemy's (and you will remember that I fought against Spanish arquebusiers at Las Salinas). Also it must be admitted that when fighting Indians who have no knowledge of gunpowder the moral effect of an arquebus is at least as great as the destruction it may cause. But to return to the volley: it killed seven or eight, and the others fled, believing that we Spaniards, bearded and in general a trifle bowlegged, had harnessed the thunder to our uses.

After this we came upon a number of small villages, one of which was called Guema. We took some food there and marched out upon a savanna, which we optimistically hoped was the beginning of Delicola's open country peopled by fat Indians. But the grumblers and pessimists among us once more unjustly triumphed. The savanna was only some two leagues long and was surrounded by the same forest against which we had fought for

* 808 yards. Cortés (*Carta de relación*) himself says the bridge was 934 paces in length.

so long, a most implacable and treacherous enemy, and one whose defeat brought only sicknesses and fatigue without glory, satisfaction, or plunder. The savanna of Guema offered little in the way of supplies, and only a few poor Indians lived on it, but Pizarro decided that we had gone far enough from our main body, so we made the Indians build us a good camp there on rising ground, and he sent messengers back to Zumaco, summoning Orellana and the others.

No sooner had Orellana ridden in at the head of the main body (and splendid it was to see horses again) than Pizarro sent Don Antonio de Rivera eastward on a scouting patrol with fifty good men. He was ordered to cut his way down the riverbank until he found more prosperous settlements, and then he was to return and report. Awaiting good news from that sortie, we settled down in camp to pass the time as calmly as was in our natures.

The horses, like most of the compañeros who had stayed at Zumaco, were in surprisingly good condition and carried flesh, which was more than any of Pizarro's party did. It seemed that Orellana had contrived to improve matters in the Zumaco camp. He had instituted a system of payments to the local Indians, and by this means had encouraged them to bring in birds or monkeys or deer or wild pigs almost every day, and as the Captain had soon learned their language, he had made friends with them, which had greatly added to everybody's comfort and security. He had exercised dogs, horses, and Spaniards by holding deer-hunts in the valley, and they had also hunted bears and jaguars.

But although he had looked after his men so well, there were not a few of them eager to run to Pizarro with complaints. It not infrequently happens that a second-in-command when his superior is away feels it his duty to be stricter than he might otherwise be. Orellana had made himself disliked by having inspections of weapons, clothing, and stores and by his confiscation of all the playing cards that had been made from drumskins and his rigid enforcement of the "no gaming" rule. The reason for the rule is sound. We Spaniards, once we sit down with cards or dice or beetles or mice or swimming fishes or tadpoles or chickens or anything else that can be wagered upon, will stake until we have nothing left or until we have stripped all the other players. As the saying goes, we will play away the sun before sunrise. If this occurs in times of peace or idleness, then individuals are the losers, but if on active service the army (or whatever military force be concerned) will be in poor condition to fight because there will be many an arquebusier sans arquebus, and other soldiers without swords or helmets or boots or throat guards, and caballeros minus their caballos. Orellana, then, was only doing his duty. The most conscientious officers always enforce first the rule against blasphemy (another peril, and the most serious of all, to any expedition) and secondly that against gaming. Orellana's men, being well fed and having little work and no fighting to do, had turned their minds readily to almost any forbidden pastime.

So they went to Gonzalo Pizarro and complained that although Orellana had severely punished any poor man who wagered his sword or his one horse, he had not scrupled to use his own personal wealth in gold and emeralds to buy several horses that he fancied. They told Pizarro that Orellana was too straitlaced, and that they were delighted to be once more under the orders of a "real leader." I fear that these babblings pleased Pizarro, who was easy-going and lenient by nature, save when his temper caught fire. And Orellana seemed to receive only pinpricks without praises for his remarkable success in holding the expeditionary force's main body together in the heats of Zumaco.

When I reported to him and described in detail our marches with Pizarro, the Captain honoured me by expressing privately some of his chagrin. He also told me that the wait at Zumaco had passed well enough for him because much of it had been spent in making vocabularies and in practising speech with the Indians. On hearing this, I described the cacique Delicola, and Orellana could not wait, but asked me to bring the Indian at once to his tent. From that moment on they spent many hours daily in each other's company. Orellana was even speedier than I had been in forming a favourable opinion of Delicola. At the same time he decided that the cacique was too intelligent to have the good of us Spaniards at heart and that eventually he would speak to destroy us all. As behoved a loyal officer, Orellana took his suspicions to Gonzalo Pizarro and expressed his fear that when Delicola spoke of good country downstream, and not far down, he was lying in order to trap us.

Gonzalo answered that if his brother the Marquis had listened to doubts and fears, Peru would still be unconquered. If Delicola proved to be a liar, Gonzalo added, so much the worse for Delicola and for all his people, and it would be proper if Orellana explained that bluntly to the Indian. Orellana did so, but received only a smile and the remark that Delicola found us and our ways so entrancing that it would be long before he could bear to rid himself of us. Also, the cacique added, he had no wish to be roasted alive. (And indeed who has, whatever may be said and written of the blessed saints and martyrs?)

While we waited on Guema savanna for the return of Rivera and his fifty men, Gonzalo Pizarro spent much of each day in the saddle. He owned two of the best horses in the Indies, El Villano and El Cainillo, both stallions. El Villano was a pocket Hercules. He stood little more than six palmos,* but he also stood over more ground than would have seemed possible, for he was short-legged, deep-chested, and a devil. Stories of his hard-mouthed impetuousness went from one end of Peru to the other, and it was said that if the horse was hungry, as he generally was, he would eat a dog, or your hand, or a hunk out of another horse's neck or quarters. El Cainillo was a bigger and more showy horse, with more of the Yemen strain to be seen in head, tail, and hocks. He too was dark brown, the best colour, and he too was a difficult and headstrong ride for all the limpid softness in his large egg-shaped eyes. Mounted on El Cainillo in battle, Gonzalo Pizarro was worth a squadron. Neither man nor horse knew fear. Both were exhilarated, inspired, by danger and difficulties. Combined, they were invincible. But we must get back to the savanna. . . .

Gonzalo, swooping round the edges of the forest, bending his mount this way and that to supple its legs, loins, and shoulders, chanced to see an Indian bowman kill a monkey that was jumping from one tree to another. This gave him the notion that the Guema Indians were exceptional archers, and when he was dining

* 14 hands.

with the hidalgos that evening he said so. Orellana, Díaz de Pineda, young Captain Carvajal, and most of the others who had any sense laughed at such an idea. Gonzalo became heated and, sending for Delicola, asked him to produce his ten best archers, and we would turn out against them in a target match our ten most distinguished crossbow marksmen. Then (so it was whispered) Gonzalo and the others wagered heavily on the outcome.

Indians were ordered to build up butts of sods, against which the targets were to be set, and those of us crossbowmen who were chosen to compete spent much time with our weapons, adjusting them to a hair's breadth, testing them, polishing until the bolt slid on its groove as on glass. We refined our target bolts, smoothing and oiling the shafts and fitting perfect feathers.

We were told first to fire from eighty paces at round targets of stretched hide three palmos * in diameter, and in this easy shooting we at once took the measure of our opponents. Whereas nine of us smacked our bolts through so big a target, most of us on or very near the centre mark (and the tenth would have done the same had he not been stung on the nose by a bee), not one of the Indians hit it. Delicola's explanation for this sorry showing was that all his best archers were away on an expedition against a rebellious tribe, and that these were only youths who were overawed by us Spaniards and feared we would punish them should they best us. It looked as though they could never be very accurate with their short bows and their clumsy arrows tipped with bone.

To make things easier for the Indians, similar targets were set up and we took our stand at fifty paces. We crossbowmen were accustomed at such a range to aiming at, and hitting, buttons or oyster shells or silver pieces; all of us pierced our target with a single smack, for all ten bolts flew together, in the centre. But only six Indians hit their target, and of those only two were in the centre.

The crafty Delicola now proposed another test, which he said would tell us more about the potentialities of the two types of arm, and their users, in actual combat. We crossbowmen were

* 27 inches.

each to fire two bolts at one target, and in the time it took us to do it his archers would send all the arrows they could let fly. Since in our last match against the Indian archers we were firing at wooden targets made in the shape of men—in other words, huge targets—and these were set at less than point-blank range (which we take to be rather more than sixty-five paces), we hoped to fire faster than normally. We wound our bows, hung our cranequins on our belts, set the bolts in their grooves, and waited for the Indians, each of whom was sticking arrows, heads down, in the ground all round him. At the signal, which was an arquebus-shot, all of us fired, and while we hastened to wind we heard the constant twang of Indian bowstrings and the exultant whistles of the archers. When all of us had fired the second volley, an arquebus roared, and the Indians were with difficulty persuaded to stop. What a difference then in the two targets! All our bolts, buried deep in the wood, showed in a compact wedge over the "heart." The other target was peppered from "head" to "feet" with arrows. One enemy, then, had twenty bolts in the heart, while the other was wounded in about ninety places, and some of those wounds would have been fatal to any unarmoured opponent.

The Indians appeared to think that they had won this last match, so to give them another lesson Pizarro (who had already paid his lost wagers with good grace) stepped forward. He wore a suit of stuffed leather covered with supple chain mail, a barbote of proof to guard his neck and chin, and a morion. He carried an ordinary round steel buckler. Going to a distance of fifty paces, he asked Delicola to line up his ten archers and order them to shoot one by one at him, Pizarro. This they did, and with the buckler he easily deflected those arrows that would have struck any part of him. Pizarro was adroit and cool, yet I doubt if there were more than ten or twenty among us who could not have done as well because, as I have said before, the heavy Indian arrows are easy to sight, and the danger in battle is rather that the arrows may come in clouds when, as a man cannot shield himself in eight places at once, he must see to guarding his face and must let his armour do the rest for him.

After these amusements, while Pizarro was distributing chaquira to the Indian archers and food and chicha were brought to feast them, Orellana asked Delicola if he and his people ever poisoned their arrows. The answer was that certain tribes who lived a long way off possessed the secret of making such poisons and willingly traded in them when they had more than enough for their own use. Poison was often unobtainable, however, particularly if there happened to be a general outbreak of fighting; and it was always costly, the usual payment for it being with virgins, young children, or canoes.

"Will they not take this stuff in payment?" Orellana asked, touching one of Delicola's gold armlets.

"This!" Delicola answered. "Poison is worth more than this, which can be taken by any man from the sands of the rivers. Poison is the best of possessions. If we have poison, we kill more game to eat, and if we have poison and our enemies have not, we defeat them. Poison is good."

Then Orellana agreed that poison was good—for the man who used it.

CHAPTER NINE

☼

DON ANTONIO DE RIVERA HAD BEEN ABSENT FIFTEEN DAYS when I returned to the camp from a monkey-hunt and saw him there among his men. They were kneeling in the space between two lines of wet green huts while Father Gaspar de Carvajal (who was not related to the Captain Carvajal of whom I have had occasion to tell you) gave thanks to our Lord for the safe return of His children.

When he had travelled a long way, Don Antonio had seen a settlement that impressed him. He reported that it was well built and was set on an eminence overlooking the river, which there was very wide, and that the Indians looked both busy and prosperous. They wore some cotton clothing. The river had been thronged with their canoes, and some of these were filled with maize.

So next morning we marched out of the Guema camp, crossed the savanna, and entered the forest on the path cut by Rivera's men. Don Antonio commanded the advance guard, Gonzalo Pizarro the main body, and Cristóbal de Funes the rear guard. In the centre of the main body those who were left of Pizarro's thousands of Indians from Quito struggled to keep pace with us, and they drove with them the few score of stringy hogs that had not yet been eaten. Orellana led his small group of followers on El Trompetero. The Negroes followed, leading four horses that carried pack saddles holding Orellana's belongings and equipment, much of which had been generously given him by Pizarro, while the rest he had bought at Zumaco. The Negro Number Five had fully recovered from his unpleasant wound, and believed that he owed his life to my surgery, which was certainly not the case. While on the subject of Number Five, I might mention that Orellana had asked him, when he recovered his wits with his health at Zumaco, if he was by any chance a Christian. And his answer had been: "Master, I do not know."

"Then you are not a Christian. For no man who has received the blessing of Christianity can forget it."

"Master, I have received many blessings, but by what sign does a man know when he receives that one of which you speak?"

"It is not only a matter of signs, but of understanding and belief."

"Master, I can believe, for I have listened to Father Carvajal, and like him I believe that good makes good and that evil makes evil, but I will not say that I understand what Father Carvajal means when he goes into stories of the past. I cannot understand why if God came to earth he allowed himself to be tortured and killed, for, being immortal, it would surely have been better for all of us had he remained among us. I can only suppose that he wanted to be in some other place."

"Number Five," Orellana said, "you must not talk like that, and be very careful, or I shall have to punish you. Now I know that you are not a Christian, you had better take extra pains to do your duty in every way."

"Master, it shall be so."

Delicola walked by Orellana's knee, careful that the black stallion should not tread upon his bare feet. Orellana had told us how we must treat the cacique, and like the Captain himself we doffed our helmets when we first met him each day, and again later if we thought it would please him. He was learning Castilian and talked much with the Negroes, whom he readily understood, their speech being slower and simpler than ours. Delicola seemed to be at pains to understand why the Negroes were such cheerful servants to us Spaniards. He would ask them whence they came, and they would answer from the island of Cuba. And he would ask who was their king. They answered that they had no king and no people, and they would laugh as they said it, and perhaps sing. Delicola would turn to me and, pointing at Panama and Number Five, would say: "*Buenos hombres; buenos hombres. . . .*" Then I would tell him that he was a good man too, which was, I believe, the truth, although he was an Indian.

When, after eight days of marching, we came to the settlement that Rivera had seen, I was one of those who went forward with Pizarro, Orellana, Robles, and Delicola to join the advance guard. The river was in flood, and had spread itself over the banks so that the distance from shore to shore would be about half a league.* Three caciques came at the head of armed Indians to parley with us. They were astounded by our appearance, but they seemed pleased with the gewgaws Pizarro gave them, and still more pleased when Orellana began to talk with them in their own language. He it was who brought forward Delicola, at the sight of whom all three at once made profound obeisances and signs of respect and affection. Then (thinking that we thirty-eight of the advance guard were the whole number of unbidden guests) they led us into their village, which was healthily set on its eminence, with enchanting views over the treetops and the wide misty river, and which was bigger and better than Guema, though not so big as Don Antonio had originally supposed.

After looking round the place without seeking to conceal his contempt and disappointment, Pizarro sent back for the main body. When the soldiers kept filing out of the forest, our Indian hosts became alarmed, then sullen, and at the sight of horses and riders all of them with the exception of the three caciques, who were in our midst and in the restraining presence of Delicola, took to their heels, while even those on the river turned their canoes and paddled away.

The caciques began talking to Delicola in a most aggrieved manner and with violent gestures.

"What do they say?" Pizarro asked Orellana.

"They are saying that quartering so many men will ruin them in a week."

"What else?"

"They are saying it would be best to kill us, but Delicola forbids any violence."

"Inform the three of them that we shall keep them as hostages for the good behaviour of their people, and tell Sancho de Carvajal to set guards on them and to be personally responsible for them."

While we were installing ourselves in the houses of the Indians,

* Nearly two miles.

there was an outcry down by the water's edge, and Captain Carvajal came out of the river all filthy with mud and holding one cacique by the neck. The Indian had run from his guards and was about to swim away when Carvajal had leaped on his back and had stunned him as they grappled under water. Pizarro was soon on the bank, and he gave orders that a heavy chain was to be brought and all three caciques shackled to it. He might have been wiser to have had this done inside the village and not in full view of the river. Soon fifty canoes came racing to the shore, and there was a close-fought skirmish because most of us were occupied elsewhere and were slow in running to the help of those on guard. The Indian warriors all but succeeded in carrying off their caciques, but by the time I reached the river they had been put to flight. Nine Spaniards were wounded.

Captain Carvajal now reported to Pizarro that Delicola had been seen talking to the cacique who had tried to escape, and that he had shouted encouragements to the Indians when they attacked. Delicola denied these accusations. I had seen no signs of treachery in him; nor had Orellana or any of the others from Guayaquil. Despite Orellana's protest, Pizarro, without further investigation, ordered that Delicola be shackled to the same chain as the other three. Two farriers came forward and riveted on the anklet. The Lord of the River submitted to this indignity with his usual calm, and when it was done he stooped gracefully to pick up the slack of the chain so that he could walk. Where he went the other three followed.

Next day was a bad one, and by that I do not mean that the weather was worse than usual. Pizarro sent out fifty of us in canoes. He put Cristóbal de Funes in command of all the canoes, and his last instructions were: "Do not return without enough maize for all the horses and the news that you have castigated those Indian dogs for their impudence of yesterday."

Each canoe had two crossbowmen in it, and the remainder of the paddlers were well armed and armoured. Too well indeed, for we soon learned that it was not so easy to manage the canoes as it had seemed when we watched the Indians in them. It was all we could do to keep the things from capsizing and to slowly scratch our way downstream. The Indian canoemen at first retreated, watching us, but after a while, realizing our clumsiness, they began to dart in among us here and there, and we soon knew that it was going to be difficult and dangerous work because a single Indian canoe slid alongside one of ours, overturned it, and speared all nine Spaniards to death while they struggled in the water. A minute later the same thing happened, and this time they killed five Spaniards. I do not think that any of us could have imagined such a thing happening, for it was unheard of in the Indies and in all the history of the conquest that Spaniards should be so easily mastered. Yet the Indians handled their canoes so skilfully that they went five times as fast as we did. And whereas they could stand up and jump about and hurl their spears as readily as though they were on firm ground, we had difficulty in doing more than sway from side to side and splash and shout. Cristóbal de Funes had told us before embarking that if any Indians sought to interfere with us as we went about the river, we were to kill a good number of them, seize their canoes, and generally give them all the lessons they might require. When he gave these orders, Funes had no notion how effective the savages' "interference" was likely to be; and no more had we.

Great was our shame at finding ourselves so weak. The only aspect of the affair that pleased us was that we were out of sight of the village, and most particularly of Pizarro. On the other hand we wondered how we were going to get back there, against the current, and we told Funes that if he had had the wits of a baby he would have led us upstream for a start, to let us get the feel of the canoes, and then we could have drifted back to the village. Whatever we said of him and to him at that moment, Funes was a good leader, and he proceeded to make amends.

Having ordered the canoes to gather until the paddles almost touched, he said, to put us in a fighting mood, that we should be ashamed of ourselves, and that for all we had tried to do to the Indians who attacked us and who had killed fourteen of our friends we might as well have been offering them posies. We were to paddle back to the village in that tight formation and if any Indian canoes came near we would halt, and while the paddlers concentrated on holding the canoes steady, the crossbowmen would fight off the Indians. Then some wag saw that Funes was removing his heavy breastplate, and this person said loudly that one among us, and he who talked of handing out posies, expected shortly to take a bath. Funes turned on him, saying that as a reward for his impudence he would have the honour of being the first to inform Gonzalo Pizarro of the results of our water "victory" that morning. But the man retorted that if it had been a real victory Funes himself would have taken the credit, and since it had been a disaster he must take the first of the blame.

The Indians came at us several times as we struggled upstream, but by doing as Funes had ordered, and by wasting many crossbow bolts, we managed with great difficulty and with even greater good luck to hold them off. Had they once got among us, it is doubtful if any of us would have lived. They followed us to the landing, jeering at us and throwing spears, until a few arquebusiers on shore sent them off.

Hearing the shots, Pizarro came out of the village, and Funes reluctantly mounted the hill to meet him. We saw the pair of them standing above us, Funes talking, and then we heard a roar, and Pizarro came bounding down toward us. He could hardly believe that fourteen good men had been lost with their weapons (three were crossbowmen) and with nothing to show for it. It enraged him that so childish an accomplishment as that of balancing canoes should interfere with his plans. He forgot, indeed, that childish arts are often the ones that take longest to learn. When he had told us how disappointed and amazed he was, he asked for our comments, and the gist of them was that it would take time to learn to be any match for the Indians in canoes, because they had spent all their lives at it.

"Very well," he answered. "What the Indians learn in years we will learn in hours. By tomorrow morning you must be fit to meet them and do your duty."

Then he called the whole expeditionary force down to the water. He asked all who had been seamen, or fishermen, or who had experience of small boats, to step foward. There was no onrush of volunteers. Nevertheless, he said that by the next morning he intended to have sixty competent canoemen, even if there were not six for a start. A line of arquebusiers was set along the water's edge to keep the Indians away, and all the rest of that day, despite the heat and the sandflies, he stood on the bank watching us paddling about, seeking to improve our watermanship. Often he would call in this canoe or that and put another man or two in it from the group he kept standing by his side. When darkness came, we felt that we had begun to make progress, but we had also made many blisters on our hands and our seats, and there was not one of us who had not felt the scourge of Pizarro's tongue.

Next morning at dawn he had us out practising again for two hours, after which we were given food, and then he sent us off downstream. Downstream, you will notice, not up. This was because he had learned that the Indians had some maize plantations in that direction. We let the current carry us down close inshore, and the crossbows managed to contain any attacks until we reached the plantations, where we landed. The Indians went mad, seeing us among their maize and loading it into the canoes. Beside themselves with hatred, they attacked us from the water. But what a glorious difference! Then did the crossbows serenade their impudence. We made such pretty play that we killed not a few, and we convulsed one canoe with a volley so that it overturned near the bank, when, springing chest-high into the water, we put all of them to the sword and captured their canoe. This was better, but all the same we were hard to put to it when, in very close formation, we struggled back upriver, for they attacked lustily and used their speed to such effect that it was like fighting against cavalry. In this water fighting many of us were wounded (I myself had a nick taken out of the flesh of my trigger hand and a gash above the groin), and one of us, a fine swordsman from Burgos and something of a singer, whose name escapes me but whom we called El Rizado because of the untoward frizziness of his fair hair, was killed outright by a javelin that lodged between his eyes, just under the rim of his helmet.

Gonzalo was relieved to see us and the maize and the captured canoe, and to hear that we had killed some Indians (whose number we did not minimize). But he was still incensed by our weakness on the river, and that night there was a conference of officers. After it extraordinary rumours went round the camp, rumours that Gonzalo Pizarro intended to build *a ship*.

At dawn we were mustered and Pizarro spoke to us. When we had conquered Peru, he said, we had used the roads. In that place, however, there was only one road, the river. We must master the river, and it was no use criticizing those who had gone out in the canoes, for they had done their best, and he had chosen them carefully. He had come to the conclusion that canoes did not suit either our weapons or our style of fighting. Therefore it had been decided that we would build a brigantine * on the Spanish model, such a boat as our coasting vessels tow astern in order to have communication with the shore and to save the crew in the event of shipwreck.

Then he ordered those among us to step forward who had any knowledge of boat-building, metal-forging, carpentry, or charcoal-burning. Apart from the farriers and a Sevillian named Diego Mexía, who at some time before he became a crossbowman had plied the trade of carpenter, there appeared to be no artisans, though there were several who had some knowledge of woodcutting and charcoal-burning, while others as boys had been apprenticed to skilled tradesmen, but had run away from that toil to the still harder toil of soldiering. Those who were judged best fitted to direct each section of the undertaking were chosen, and they in turn picked their cronies to work under them. Pizarro then told all the working parties that their boat-building was to be regarded as a matter of life or death, for those, and the success or failure of our expedition, were the stakes. Boat-building, he admitted, was no task for soldiers, but he knew them well enough to say that there was nothing they could not accomplish once they put their hands to it. He would expect the officers and hidalgos to take their turns at the work and, as was their way, to do *more* than their share of it. Only if every man worked himself to a standstill every day would we get the brigantine built before we had drained all the supplies available in that village.

Then he turned to those of us who had been kept out of the working parties. We were to see to the defence of the village and

* *Bergantín*. Not to be confused with the type of sailing vessel we know today as a brigantine. The brigantines in question were later called *galeras*. They were hefty rowing boats that could also rig two masts and travel under sail.

to the foraging. Some were to cut a road through the forest to the maize plantations, which from that day on were to be guarded lest the Indians set fire to them. Others were to make daily sorties in the canoes and, whatever the odds and the losses, were to fight the Indians at every opportunity, for they were offensive and we must never let them imagine that we feared them.

Orellana, I was to learn later, had argued at the officers' conference against the scheme to build a brigantine, and had proposed instead that the whole expeditionary force should turn on its tracks and make for the province of Capua, because from his talks with the Indians he had formed the opinion that if we pushed on to the east we would only struggle deeper and deeper into those infernal forests. But no Pizarro—let it be acknowledged to the credit of that remarkable family—was ever in favour of retreat, and Orellana had been overruled. So now it was he who, with tact and judgement, went about the camp organizing the supplies and the routine of each working party. At such times Orellana was without rival among us, and was the superior of Gonzalo Pizarro, who, though he could and did work harder than anybody else, would fret when it came to planning, because for such ardent souls as he the work is finished before it is begun, and the intermediate stages are too slow.

Men went out to cut wood billets for the charcoal kilns; when these had been built, the heavy and constant rains prevented them from burning. Roofs were built over the kilns, and then they smouldered, sending forth clouds of sweet white smoke. The farriers set up two forges, and as soon as they had charcoal they began to strike long nails for the brigantine out of the hundreds of spare horseshoes carried by the expedition. The woodmen went out to their work, and they said that they had never thought to find so many different kinds of trees, all in a small compass, and that more than twenty of the different kinds would seem to be suitable for boat-building.

So the Indian settlement standing on its bluff over the left bank of the Coca became as industrious as Palos or Barcelona. Smoke, beaten low by the rain, lay over, among, and inside the huts. And as we paddled, and sometimes fought, our way home we would hear singing, the crack and bell-note of smiths' hammers, the duller blows of axe and adze, and the neighing, snorting, and stamping of horses, some of which were used for hauling felled trees into the camp. I did not know much about the building because the more it progressed, the more sour did Diego Mexía, who was in charge of it, become; and the other compañeros were too tired to say much when we returned in the canoes.

It had not taken me long, remembering my childhood days, to find the balance of a canoe and how to take a clean, smooth grip on the water with a paddle. And noting my proficiency, Pizarro gave me a command with five men under me. Two of these were Orellana's Negroes, and there were no paddlers among us to match them for power or dexterity. What if they did not fight? The handling of the canoe was the most important part of any fighting we had to do, and had I not my crossbow and as many bolts as I cared to ask for? When we had been at it for a week, mine was acknowledged to be the best canoe of our small flotilla, though still less swift than those of the Indians, who kept us always on the defensive.

All day every day except Sundays the work went on in the settlement. If anything was done wrong it was done anew. When there were difficulties, it was Orellana who reasoned out the solutions; when the work flagged anywhere, it was Pizarro who showed an example, for no task was so menial that he would not put his hand to it, no load so heavy and awkward that he would not carry it, and when he was not working on shore, he came out with us in the canoes—on which occasions, mercifully few, we always did a great deal of fighting.

Delicola and the three caciques to whom he was chained clanked about the settlement watching everything that was done. Delicola looked, that is to say, because the other three were sullen and would have sat all day brushing insects off their skins had he not towed them about. When Delicola saw the skeleton of the brigantine, its keel, its bow and stern posts, its ribs, take shape, he asked Orellana how such a cage could be expected to float; did we propose to attach bladders to it? He watched the planking being nailed on, edge to edge. It was caulked with cotton, of which there was no lack, for it grew wild there. Instead of tar a kind of resin that the Indians take from a tree was melted down and paid into the seams. While the finishing to the hull was going on, the oars were fashioned and an anchor was made from wood tipped with iron and weighted with a small boulder. Some wished to see our ship rigged for sailing, but Pizarro would have none of that; he insisted that the brigantine was to be fortress, store-chamber, and lazarette, and he annoyed Mexía by saying that he wished it had been bigger.*

One morning, when the friars had blessed the brigantine and prayed over it, we hauled it on rollers down to the river, and some of those in canoes took its bow rope. We asked Pizarro to give his ship a name, so as the stern rested on the bank he touched it with his sword, saying: "In the name of our Lord and of Holy Mary, the Mother of God, and of His Majesty the King-Emperor, I, Gonzalo Pizarro, Captain General of this expeditionary force and Governor of the provinces of Quito, under the authority granted me by my brother the Marquis, Don Francisco Pizarro, who governs all New Castile, name this Spanish brigantine that is the work of our own hands the *San Pedro*, and may the said brigantine bring honour and fame to all who built it and who will man it." Then they gave the stern a thrust, the heavy body floated out high and even, and we towed it into deeper water.

Pizarro would have loaded it then and there, keeping men aboard to bail, but Mexía and the other master builders insisted that such behaviour would be folly—a word that drew a scowl from the haughty Captain General, but then, they were uneducated men who would never have thought to use some softer synonym such as "imprudence"—and they said that the brigantine must be sunk to the gunwales for a day and a night to encourage its timbers to take up. This was done.

We had denuded the maize plantations and were short of

* According to Oviedo, this brigantine would carry twenty men. By that I take him to mean a crew of twenty, and it probably had seven or eight rowing-thwarts. According to Jal's *Glossaire Nautique*, at the beginning of the sixteenth century a brigantine of fourteen thwarts usually measured 52 ft. over-all, 9 ft. 6 in. beam, and 2 ft. 2 in. draught. Perhaps if we estimate the *San Pedro*'s dimensions at 20 ft. over-all, 8 ft. beam, and 2 ft. draught, we shall not be far out.

food, but that evening to celebrate the occasion and because we all believed that the launch of the brigantine signalled the end of our troubles, we ate the last of the hogs and also some fish we had captured from the Indians.

The name we gave to that village on a hummock in the forests was El Barco.*

* The Boat.

CHAPTER TEN

☼

ON FRIDAY—ALWAYS AN UNLUCKY DAY OF THE WEEK—November 11, we loaded the brigantine we had built and left El Barco, the place where we had built it. We ballasted with lance-heads, bolt-heads, swords, lead, gunpowder, horseshoes, axes, and some twenty arrobas * of trinkets for Indians. On the cargo were laid the expedition's blankets, and on these reposed the sick, among whom were the two friars. I heard some say that the friars were sick because they preferred lying down to walking on the bank, but there are always in any company certain characters who, being envious of men of religion, will seek to degrade them, attributing selfish motives to all their actions; in our case the friars had worn themselves out looking after the sick at El Barco, and now they were as weak as any, both of them. Before I have ended my story of our journey, you will hear more of those two friars, and I know I shall not have to ask you to accord them your regard, for it will have been accorded already, and with enthusiasm.

A hidalgo from Valladolid named Juan de Alcántara was chosen by Pizarro to command the brigantine and was given twenty men to row and fight his ship. Now there was a to-do because none of the twenty minded fighting, but most of them objected to rowing because they claimed that it was a menial task and undignified. Alcántara suggested asking for volunteers, and said he would not mind taking some of the best paddlers from the canoes, including (he had his wits about him) my two Negroes. Pizarro refused, however, on the grounds that it had taken a long time to train us in the canoes, and that he meant to keep us there. Argument raged by the water's edge until Pizarro sud-

* 4 cwts.

denly became silent. There was a long pause, and then he announced that any man, no matter what or how he had been born, or how old he was or how young, who refused to row the brigantine when ordered to do so would have his hands lopped off at the wrists.

So the oarsmen took their places on the thwarts, and the *San Pedro* edged from the shore like an over-girthed cockroach. It seemed likely that some of the strange woods used in the building had been heavier than the builders supposed, because the brigantine, loaded with all its cargo, the sick, and its crew of twenty-one, had too little freeboard. They bailed much and often during the first four days, but when the planking had swollen, there was little more trouble of that kind.

Those of us in the canoes had been ordered to travel in a flock round the brigantine. If attacked, we were to entice the Indians close to our mother ship and then slip away to shelter behind it. Soon after our flag had been struck at El Barco, when those in the rear guard were going through the houses to see if they could pick up anything of use or of value, we had an opportunity to test the new water tactics. Pizarro had put six crossbowmen and four arquebusiers among the brigantine's crew, and they took a very heavy toll of the same Indians who for so long, with all the odds in their favour, had been trying to cow us and kill us. When the volleys of the brigantine had thrown them into a panic, we canoemen could not be restrained, and we paddled in among them to explain to them why swords were forged in Spain. In this skirmish we lost one canoe, but captured six from the enemy. We also took a score of healthy prisoners, and these we landed to take their chance as porters with the main body. I might mention that I managed in this little affair to collect some gold ornaments that were of good weight, and the others in my canoe (the Negroes excepted) did likewise, for many of those Indians wore gold about their persons, and from what Delicola told us there is as much gold in that province as there is iron in Biscay. The rivers are so auriferous that to find gold, all an Indian had to do was sift through the sands in the brighter shallows.* The Indians thought

* The gold washings of those rivers were later celebrated.

less of gold than we do of leather, and they laughed at our interest in the metal. Nor were we at that time by any means as interested in it as we were in everyday things such as candles and, of course, food. Our situation was that demonstrated by the true story about Toríbio the Soldier:

While Toríbio was fishing in a river in the Indies, he found a gold nugget as big as his head. "Ho-ho!" he shouted. "I am rich." He did not feel inclined to fish any more, for all that he was hungry and there was little to eat at the camp. Hoisting the nugget on his back, he was leaving the river when he met an Indian dog of the type that is castrated and fattened for eating. And when he saw the plumpness of the animal he dropped his nugget, which rolled down into the river and was lost. Toríbio killed the dog, very well satisfied with the exchange.

After El Barco, we went through a country where there was maize to be taken, and we entered Indian villages where we got fish and some meat. But as we continued downstream the settlements grew sparser and poorer until there were none of them, and our party was advancing day after day through vegetation that left little room for man and showed no traces of him.

I was sorry to be separated on those marches from Orellana, Delicola, and many others, but I was far from sorry to be in the canoe. Mercilessly hot though it was, sitting low on the water, with the sandflies pricking our faces and hands to pulp, it was hotter still for those toiling along the bank, cutting their way through the indescribable tangle of the forest and negotiating creeks or swamps. These last were the worst obstacles, for the horses would begin to sink. While their riders tried to calm them, fearing that the more they struggled the deeper they would go, all of us hastened to cut bundles of reeds or sticks and thus a path would be won.

When it was only water instead of slime, the horses would swim, and most of the men too; but then all kept close together and there was not a single straggler, because the creeks and lagoons were the homes of a host of alligators, some as big as four men. We knew these brutes to be cowards, but the sight of them in the water was so awful as to make any man call on the last flash of courage before he dived in. When a wide tributary had to be crossed, and that was not seldom in each day, Pizarro would summon in the brigantine and canoes to act as ferries. This was especially needed for the Indians, who daily, both men and women, became more miserable and despondent as they shuffled on under their loads. Nor were they overloaded or ill-treated. They seemed to know that, walk how they would, eat how they might, this was their last walk. All of them were lethargic to the state of being dead before they died. When I had to take them in my canoe, it hurt me to see their listlessness. They would get in so quietly, without rocking the canoe, put down their bundles, sit on them, and then, at the other bank, get out as quietly as they had got in. One does not expect them to laugh or smile, one only expects them to look half-human. I do not know if my companions felt as I did, and if they, like me, were uneasy in the face of such resignation. When they looked at me they did not see me, and in their dark, sad, Indian eyes I saw fate—their fate, in any event.

At some of the narrower crossings Pizarro might decide to build a bridge, and then he would send us in the canoes to look for food, sometimes with and sometimes without the protection of the brigantine. Our existence was one of never ending effort. It was work even when we were moving downstream on the flank of Pizarro's march, and all was going smoothly ashore. In parts of the swollen river the current ran as fast as a league and a half in the hour, and at first we often had either to paddle against it to avoid being swept on too fast, or to risk damaging the canoe by taking it close to the bank, where the river eddied among sunken dangers. To improve matters I made fast a rope to a length of heavy chain, and this we towed from the canoe to hold us stern-on and check our way, hauling it quickly inboard when the need arose. We were always watching for hostile Indians, but when we had left the settlements behind, there were no more of them. Indeed, the forest seemed so untamed, unending, and unpromising that we would have been delighted to encounter even the most enraged and bloodthirsty of enemies. Sometimes from the canoe I brought off a shot as a monkey rustled and put its face through the upper leaves, or a toucan danced its clumsy hopping dance on a bough. But what was a bird, or even a monkey, among so many mouths? Hunger was with us, the most pervasive of companions, influencing every thought and action. When the head of the column came to a place in the forest where guavas grew, it would halt, and no order could have moved it. Those behind, sensing that there was something to eat ahead, would run to get there before all was eaten. In truth those guavas were wonderful, and they seemed all the better because there were never enough of them; I can still taste their juices in my mouth.

At night, when the sandflies, after piping "*Hasta la vista,*" silently retired and the mosquitoes began another session of torment, the boats were moored to trees or were beached on sandbanks. Because of the mosquitoes and despite the clammy heat, we went to sleep swaddled like babes or old invalids in a cold climate, and we woke drained of strength, irritable, and unfitted for the day's unceasing efforts and for the morning greetings of the sandflies, enthusiastically taking over their persecutory duties from the mosquitoes.

On Friday November 18, one week after leaving El Barco, we shot out from the mouth of the Coca onto the waters of a yet bigger river,* waters distinctly warmer to the touch than those of the Coca. We immediately hoped, since no change could well be for the worse, that things would be different on the new river and that it would prove to run through tamer and more populated lands. The brigantine came waddling up, and Juan de Alcántara said we must put into the bank to see what Pizarro wished to do. All he said was that we would continue as before. The guides told him that this new river came down from the cinnamon country, so he proposed to call it the Río Canelos, and he devoutly hoped that its lower reaches would prove to be more agreeable than those above.

Day succeeded day, and so far as we were concerned the Canelos was neither more nor less hospitable than its tributary had been. The new river was studded with islands, big and small, and though some of these would have been ideal places for Indian villages, neither sight, smell, nor sound of any Indian did we get.

* Now the River Napo.

On the forty-third evening after leaving El Barco, the two friars went to Gonzalo Pizarro and told him it was his duty to make camp and give his men the following day, which was both Christmas Day and a Sunday, as one of rest and prayer. Gonzalo made no difficulties about this, and to tell the truth it was doubtful whether those on land could have found strength for another day's march. Some Spaniards had been drowned, some had died of sickness, and more had been smothered in the swamps. As for the Indian porters, there were so few of them left that we Spaniards had to fan the horses at night to protect them from mosquitoes and, far more important, from the vampire bats that sucked so silently and deep that were a horse left unguarded even part of the night, he would be drained and near death in the morning.

The compañeros had long been so hungry that as they marched they would pick anything and try to eat it; in consequence many were poisoned and suffered from fluxes of the bowels and vomiting. The last of the hogs had been eaten at El Barco. The llamas had all been killed at Zumaco. Our horses and our dogs and ourselves were all skin and bone, yet we represented between us all the meat there was in our camp that Christmas Day. We would not kill a horse, but a start was made on some of the dogs, while we in the canoes were sent looking for the vegetable they call yuca in Cuba, and for any fish or game we could find. We canoemen could not avail ourselves of the repose offered us in honour of the birth of our Lord and Saviour, but instead we paddled many a weary league that day, and returned to the camp almost empty-handed, for we had only two parrots, a toucan, and five white herons in our canoe.

Later that evening I went to Orellana's rancho, and there I discovered that something important was going on (although I was not to understand its full import until later, when I had ample—too ample—time to think about it).

Orellana, you may remember, had never been enthusiastic about going on downstream. The building of the brigantine had been Gonzalo Pizarro's idea, and it seemed to us that Gonzalo had been wrong in every decision he had made, or that he was dogged by evil on this expedition, or that among us was some man who had the curse on him for blasphemy or perhaps for the Abominable Crime. To return to Orellana: he was always talking with the guides, and he would remember everything that they told him from day to day and thus was able to detect when they were lying. Seldom a day passed but he reminded Delicola (though this did not seem to embarrass the Indian) of his promise, given so long ago to the west of the great waterfalls of the Coca, that there was fertile and easy country on the terrible route we were following with endurance totally unrewarded by comforts or discoveries. Now, that Christmas morning it happened that three of the guides lay dying, and Orellana had conceived it his duty to sit in the shade beside their rancho and listen to their last words. Armed with the knowledge thus gained, he called the other guides, threatened them, and questioned them. Then he went to tell Pizarro what he thought to have learned.

The guides had admitted that we were trapped in a vast region of uninhabited forest. They thought that there was some food where once there had been a settlement surrounded by yuca plantations, and this was at a junction of the Canelos with another important river some leagues downstream. But they were of the opinion that even if our expedition continued to march on at its best speed we would all die of starvation before we came to the yuca. . . . Having told Pizarro this, Orellana offered, if he might take the brigantine and some canoes, to go on until he found the yuca or any other supplies, when he would hurry back to the main body.

Gonzalo dismissed Orellana and at once sent for another interpreter, through whom he questioned the guides and the four chained caciques. It happened that Delicola was in favour all over the camp because he had been responsible for finding us some food when it had looked as though a morsel of roasted dog would be the best Christmas feasting that any of us could expect. He had shown some of the compañeros how to dam the mouth of a creek and where to find a certain shrub whose branches they cut and pulped to his instructions. Then they whacked the waters of the creek with the branches until nothing was to be seen but soapy foam. Within a few minutes many fishes, some of considerable size, floated on the surface either dead or dying. When Delicola had eaten some of the fish to show that although poisoned it was not poisonous, no time had been lost in cooking all that there was. Gonzalo said, and many of us agreed with him, that it was time pressure was put on Delicola and the other Indians, because if they wished, not a day would pass but they could show us where and how to get food. . . . It is possible, though, that the thought of the fish, and its comfort inside him, influenced Pizarro to believe the Indians' story of the yuca plantations. I do not think he would have been influenced by any liking for, or good opinion of, Captain Orellana; and I had better explain why I advance so controversial an opinion.

Orellana's qualities as a man and an officer were not of the kind to appeal to Pizarro. Nor, I suspect—indeed, I know—did Gonzalo Pizarro cast the spell over Orellana that worked so potently with most of us. Perhaps if we look at the two of them individually we shall see why and where they differed. . . .

Gonzalo Pizarro was of no great height, but broad, wiry, and blessed with a manly and exceptionally taking countenance. He seemed always what he was—the bravest of the brave. This was the pattern he set himself, and this, through all proofs of stamina and courage, he brilliantly maintained. Yet it is true that men spend only a few of their days in battle, and it was in battle that the star of this younger Pizarro shone with unmatchable lustre. In battle he had no faults, and those that he showed at other times arose from his virtues as a fighting leader. Of an impetuous temper, even for a Castilian, he was quick with his tongue and too ready, as were all the men of his remarkable family, to impute false motives to others, to suspect them of self-seeking, even of treachery. His hand was as hasty as his anger was quick. It was always dangerous to cross him. His temper together with his pride, which bristled at the merest notion, true or false, of a slight to his dignity or his honour, made this great leader the less great. But great he was, for men would follow him to the death, and would strike the bolder and truer because Gonzalo was beside them—or more likely in front of them. To sum up: what I am trying to suggest is that he would have been an even better leader had he enjoyed a nobler and sweeter disposition. In his private life he was bawdy, pursuing women (though I grant there was little enough opportunity for that in the forests east of the Eastern Cordillera) almost as keenly as they pursued him; in his public life he was turbulent.

How different was his kinsman, the one-eyed knight! Orellana had little personal brilliance. His face was long, ruminative, gentle rather than soldierly, and that despite its scars. His tongue was gentle too, and always clean either of blasphemy or obscenities. He was a man of sober, rather sentimental habits, and if he was ambitious—which he was—his were the smooth ambitions of the governor, the administrator. I should say that he would dream rather of a quiet, well-run palace in its own fertile lands than that his dreams would have trumpets in them, velvet, flashing gems and flashing eyes, and the galloping hoofs of warhorses. Although a good horseman and useful with most weapons and particularly as a swordsman, he did not shine out from the rest of us as did Gonzalo Pizarro—as a Roman god might excel when fighting in the ranks of Romans. Yet from this very brilliance of Pizarro stemmed much of his arrogance and uneasiness; he had had surfeit of praise and glory when he was still very young. Orellana, I am sure, never considered himself to be a man set naturally above all other men unless our Lord for His great purposes should see fit so to raise him. Leadership had flown at and clung to Pizarro, whereas Orellana had always had to work to substantiate *his* authority. And perhaps this served Orellana well in the end, for he had learned to reason precisely, to study the men under him, to scheme with prudence and sagacity.

Two such differing characters, the bold and the prudent, should, you may well say, have formed the ideal complement. I cannot think that this was so. The better qualities of each jarred on the other. Bound as they both were (at the time of which I speak) by their loyalty to the King, by their blood relationship, and by their faith in Christianity, there was not more than tolerance between them. . . . Nevertheless, I would not have expected Pizarro to doubt Orellana's loyalty, and still less his judgement. And if Pizarro entertained no such doubts, he showed discourtesy amounting to personal insult when, after hearing Orellana's side of the story, he called the Indians and questioned them himself. Orellana, who had both his ears—and they were sharp ones—and whose one eye missed less than my two did, certainly did not ignore this act of his Captain General.

That evening Gonzalo sent for Orellana and told him that he was to go on down the river the next morning with the brigantine, the canoes, and sixty men. He thought sixty about the right number because, according to the Indian guides, there was always a chance of meeting war canoes on the Canelos. Orellana must, however, count all the sick among his complement of sixty because Pizarro did not intend to wait there in camp until Orellana returned, but would march on downstream.

When I entered the Captain's rancho, Orellana himself was leaving Pizarro. In the rancho I found Robles, Arévalo the Horseman, Durán, the four chained caciques, and the two Negroes, who were keeping their master's dinner warm. Delicola stood up like the rest of us when Orellana, stooping, came through the entrance, but the Captain quickly asked him to be seated. Then while he ate he told us what had taken place between him and Pizarro. He bade us pay the closest attention, for he intended to take all our Guayaquil party with him, including the two slaves. As the safety of the whole expeditionary force depended on our finding food of any sort and getting it back quickly, it was an affair, he said, of importance and honour.

Delicola, who by this time understood Castilian, asked if he also would be going on the water. Orellana answered that there would be no room for Indians; he had agreed to take the sick Spaniards who could not walk and also the expedition's heavy baggage, since there was no longer any means of transporting either on land; but all possible space must be left in the boats for carrying back such provisions as we might find.

Delicola was unwilling to take that as his answer. He assured Orellana that if room were made for him in the brigantine or one of the canoes we would not regret it, for he would promise to act as guide and cicerone to our party. More than that, he could also undertake to find food where, left to ourselves, we would see none and would go hungry. He, Delicola, knew where the wild yuca groves were at the junction of the river with another, but he doubted if we would be able to find them because they were buried in the forest. Who had got us our fish that day, Delicola asked; and he went on to declare that he could often have provided us with fish, and game too, but he had vowed that he would not find food for Gonzalo Pizarro because it was indecent of one lord (Gonzalo) to put another lord (himself) in chains and keep him thus like a tame bear; it was better, and wiser, to kill enemies than to mock them. However, he said, he felt nothing but friendship for Orellana and would be pleased to help him and all those who went with him down the river; and surely that would be to the benefit of the expeditionary force?

On hearing all this, Orellana left us and went back to ask Pizarro if it would not be wise to take Delicola in the brigantine. But Pizarro merely answered that he intended to keep Delicola near him. On learning this, Delicola smiled no longer, and soon he rose, picking up his end of the chain and the other three copying him. Delicola said good-night, naming each of us and even the two Negroes; and to Orellana he said: "*Buenas noches, mi Capitán, y vaya con Dios.*" I remember this because I thought it odd at the time that he should mention our God, whom he in his sinful ignorance did not acknowledge, but I supposed that he had picked up the phrase and, not fully understanding it, used it as the most graceful at his disposal.

I was not on guard duty that night (it being one of my luckier nights), but what with the heat and the rustling of bats in the leafy roof of our rancho, I could not sleep. At one moment I thought I heard the clank of a chain. I threw off the cloth that lay across my sweating face and listened, but heard nothing more. As sleep did not feel any nearer, I rose and went to the low rancho that Delicola's three underlings had built to cover the four of them. They lay swaddled from head to foot. Reaching down between them, I put my hand on the chain; so, concluding that one of them had turned in his sleep, I went back to my own bed.

In the morning we found that the Indian caciques' rancho contained only four bales of sticks wrapped in blankets. They had stolen the length of chain from my canoe and had laid it between the dummies. Tracking dogs were called and the camp was alerted. Whimpering with eagerness, the dogs led us to the creek where Delicola had showed us how to poison the fishes. Sentries had been posted up the edge of the creek. They had heard and seen nothing during the night. At the edge, where the bushes grew into the water, the dogs led us over the footprints of the four Indians, and here and there we saw the chain's imprint on the mud. The dogs were taken up that side of the creek and then down the other side. There was no further scent, and we could only surmise that the chained men had managed to find a floating tree trunk big enough to carry them down the creek past the sentries and out into the current of the great river. And when we examined the dam that had been built on Christmas Day to Delicola's instructions, our surmises were confirmed; a hole had been made in it at the far side from the camp.

Pizarro, as may be imagined, was in the foulest of humours at this escape, and Orellana, who was theoretically in charge of all the Indians, prisoners and others, came in for outspoken blame, to which, as became him, he offered no defence. So did the sentries, but they could say no more than that it had been a dark night and they had heard and seen nothing suspicious. What then, Pizarro asked, had happened to all the dogs, who usually drew the hatred of the camp by waking us every time a monkey or a snake rustled in the forest? Nobody appeared to answer, but Pizarro had quick hearing, and he paced up to Vayón the Pike and asked him sharply: "What was that? What did you say? Come, man, are you afraid of me?"

"No, Your Worship, and nor am I ashamed of what I said," answered Vayón sturdily. "I merely said that if you give orders to have some of the dogs killed for the cooking pots, you cannot expect their companions to render you the usual services of a night."

"True enough, old friend," Gonzalo said. "And it is a bad thing to eat the dogs that serve us, even if it is a worse thing to eat nothing at all." Then he solemnly declared that he would raze every village in Delicola's territory on our return march to Quito, and would make every man, woman, and child suffer a thousandfold for the cacique's treachery.

Seeing that there was nothing more to be said about the four missing Indians, Pizarro sharply asked Orellana if he had mustered his river party, and if not, why not? Orellana replied that he had chosen those whom he would like to take with him, and among them were four arquebusiers, four crossbowmen, and two slaves who were strong paddlers and swimmers, but he did not know exactly who the sick were, or how many. So Pizarro asked Don Antonio to muster all those incapable of marching. Among them were some exceedingly valuable men of the conquest, including the two friars and Diego Mexía, the Sevillian who had been master builder of the *San Pedro* and who was also, if not a marksman of classical skill, a very fair artist with his crossbow. When the sick, to the number of twelve, had been loaded on the brigantine, Orellana named one by one the rest of us who were to go, and Pizarro gave his orders to us collectively. They sounded simple enough:

We were to get food and bring it back to the main body, and we were on no account to be absent from his command longer than twelve days.

On the riverbank Father Carvajal said Mass and prayed most heartily that we might succeed in our venture and quickly obtain sustenance for our friends. Then we all of us stepped into our separate craft, and in leaving that bank we may be said to have stepped into history, for although none of us guessed it, our destiny was from that moment one that may never be forgotten. This being so, I will give you the names of all who that day followed Francisco de Orellana. We were:

Pedro de Acaray, the Biscayan arquebusier sans pareil whom we called Perucho;

Benito de Aguilar, an Asturian, aged thirty-four, who had seen much service under Benalcázar;

Cristóbal de Aguilar, from the serene and lovely island of Hispaniola, and he was twenty-seven;

Juan de Aguilar, an exceptionally gifted swordsman from Valladolid;

Two by the name of Juan de Alcántara, the one whom I have mentioned before as having the first command of the brigantine, a hidalgo from Valladolid, and the other a soldier from Santiago;

Rodrigo de Arévalo, Arévalo the Horseman, who was from the birthplace of Orellana, the Pizarros, and so many other stalwarts of the conquest, namely Trujillo in Estremadura;

Juan de Arnalte;

Diego Bermúdez, the sailor from Palos who had served us so cleverly in the affair of the tarabita, and whose services, as you will learn, had only begun there and were to be numberless;

Juan Bueno from Moguer;

Alonso de Cabrera, hidalgo, aged twenty-four, from Cazalla;

Antonio de Carranza, from Frías in the province of Burgos;

Gonzalo Carillo;

Father Gaspar de Carvajal, of the Order of Santo Domingo de Guzmán, who also was from Trujillo and was then in his thirty-eighth year;

Rodrigo de Cevallos;

Gabriel de Contreras;

Gonzalo Díaz;

Pedro Domínguez Miradero, from Palos, in his thirty-second year, who was good on the water but even better with almost any weapon on land; he carried an arquebus that was mounted in silver;

Andrés Durán, of Moguer, who had been Alcalde at Puerto Viejo and had joined us at Guayaquil; Durán was the oldest of us, being fifty-eight, which is a great age for a man of the conquest;

Juan de Elena, who had fought under Benalcázar in the conquests of Quito and Popayán, and who claimed that once he had been able to read, but at the age of thirty-three he had forgotten even how to sign his name;

Pedro de Empudia, from Ciudad Rodrigo;

Cristóbal Enríquez, from Cáceres, who tried to seem older than his twenty-eight years and as a result seemed very much younger;

Alonso Estéban and Ginés Fernández, both from Moguer; Fernández at that time was twenty-six, and Estéban was a famous swordsman;

Sebastián de Fuenterrabía, who had once been a fisherman but he denied it, thinking it better to be a soldier;

Alonso García;

Hernán Gonçalez, a Portuguese from the Algarve who had done well in Peru and Popayán, gaining many wounds and much wisdom, and had settled down to spend the rest of his days on a comfortable encomienda near Guayaquil; but at the age of thirty-eight he had flung aside all his well-earned comforts on hearing two words—El Dorado;

Two named Gonzáles, Alexos El Galleguillo, as we called him, and Alvár, from Oviedo in Asturias;

Alonso Gutiérrez, from Badajoz;

Hernán Gutiérrez de Celis, a gentleman of consequence, and not only in his own opinion;

Juan Gutiérrez Vayón, Vayón the Pike, whom nothing and nobody dismayed;

The unlucky Portuguese arquebusier Antonio Hernández, who had clung to us from Quito on, and of whom I think I have already said too much;

Juan de Illanes, an Asturian hidalgo whom many, behind his straight back, called Papa Illanes because he was long-winded and sonorous and always wanted to give advice though he was much younger than Durán, being forty-four at that time;

Myself, Francisco de Isásaga, at your service, a native of San Sebastián, the son, grandson, and great-grandson of soldiers killed by Moors in battle or in skirmish, a graduate of the University of Salamanca, and already, in my twenty-seventh year, a veteran of the conquest and, by common acclaim, perhaps the best crossbowman of Gonzalo Pizarro's array, if not in all Peru;

Juan de Mangas, a robust seaman from Puerto de Santa María;

Alonso Márquez, Márquez the Silent, and a marksman;

Diego de Matamoros (an excellent name), from Badajoz;

Blas de Medina, from Medina del Campo, the birthplace of many a pretty fighter, though this one had a shirking reputation at that time and came with us only because he was sick. . . . But lest I besmirch him unfairly, I must say here that he was only twenty-three when we left Pizarro and he proved himself with us because, like the wood that Indians harden in fire, he was tempered during the ordeals and guazabaras that were to come;

Diego Mexía, of Seville, of whom you know already, a tricky man to deal with, but a clever one—and a crossbowman;

Diego Moreno from Medellín;

Lorenzo Muñoz, yet another soldier from the oak glades that fatten the famous hogs of Estremadura, and yet another born in Trujillo;

Alonso Martín de Noguel;
Alonso Ortiz, from the Maestrazgo;
Baltasar Osorio, a countryman of Ortiz;
Cristóbal de Palacios, a native of Ayamonte;
Pedro de Porres;
Mateo de Rebolloso, a Valencian and a polished fighter;
Alonso de Robles, of Don Benito in Estremadura, he to whom we had owed much on our way to join Pizarro at Zumaco, and to whom we were to owe more in good measure, as you will learn;
García Rodríguez;
Sebastián Rodríguez, a Gallician;
Cristóbal de Segovia whom all, I know not why, called Maldonado; Maldonado was a hidalgo from Torrejón de Velasco and one who spoiled to fight everybody, including his best friends, yet although this personage was always furiously angry about this or that, he harboured no grudges, but allowed them to sail free in action as well as in words;
García de Soria, who was so particular about washing himself and combing his hair and his beard that he was called El Galán;
Two Tapias, Alonso and Francisco de Tapia, both Asturians;
Juan de Vargas, another Estremenian; and
Father Gonzalo de Vera, of the Order of Our Lady of Mercy.

Then Orellana's two Negro slaves were with us, and may, I suppose, be included in our muster roll, and it will be seen that we were, under Orellana, fifty-five Spaniards, two men of Portuguese birth, and two Negroes. Counting our Captain we were sixty.*

This then, Señores, was our company, and I will tell the truth about it, that you may judge of our merits or demerits in the strange course we had yet to run.

* Gonzalo Pizarro (*Letter to Charles V*) says he gave Orellana sixty men. Father Carvajal states that under Orellana there were 57 (Europeans) and 2 Negroes. Domíngues Miradero, when he was seventy-one, had a Judicial Inquiry put through the court in Quito (April 1581). In the official record of the inquiry Domínguez Miradero describes himself as "one of the 57 who went down the Marañón with Captain Orellana." The list of names above is taken from the exhaustive *Descubrimiento* of Toribio Medina.

CHAPTER ELEVEN

THOSE IN THE BRIGANTINE SLASHED AT THE WATER WITH their cumbersome oars, and I saw Orellana, who held the steering sweep, turn to look back at his horses and his dogs; but we were soon carried round a bend in the river, away from our people on the bank and into a silence green, hot, moist, and eerie. The Captain was particularly irked at leaving the bitch puppy that had been born to one of our belicosas, Isabeluca Rinzón, on the way to join Pizarro at Zumaco. That had been in the month of March, and Orellana had just begun to train the puppy in its duties because, as most people know, you should begin to train a bitch at nine months, though a dog had best wait until he is a yearling. Now, as the Captain said, duty took him from his bitch at the most interesting time. But, he added, it would not be for long.

Until that day my crew had been the two Negroes, Márquez the Silent, the two Tapias, and Mateo de Rebolloso, whom I kept next to me in the stern in case there should be fighting, for as I have said before, no crossbowman could ask for a better shieldsman than Rebolloso. Orellana had laid it down, however, that the crossbowmen should travel in the brigantine, and although he left me in charge of the canoe, he took Márquez from me. Arévalo the Horseman took Márquez's place with us, and there was at first some grumbling from the Tapias and Rebolloso, since we had all learned together how to balance the canoe and do things with it, and they feared that Arévalo, who knew nothing about it, would tell us, who did know something, what to do. But before he had taken his seat the hidalgo said that he would do his best to learn to paddle so that he would not be a weight upon us, and that he would loyally take his orders from Bachelor of Arts Isásaga. So this was well settled, though even at the start Arévalo was not strong enough to work as hard as he wished because he had, like many great horsemen, a tall, lanky frame with big hands and feet, and he was by nature "a good doer," a trencherman; the short commons on this uncomfortable expedition had not suited him, and he should have been lying on his back resting, rather than working harder than a galley slave, which was how we all had to work, and for about the same recompense.

Five canoes such as ours travelled around the brigantine, and it also towed five empty canoes to serve as carriers for the food we hoped to find. The current, however, jostled them this way and that, and they impeded the oarsmen; so at the end of the first day those canoes were left in a creek where it was thought that Pizarro's party would surely find them.

Since I know it has been said by some liars and scoundrels that we carried with us gold and emeralds belonging to our friends in Pizarro's main body, I will deny that now. . . . What kind of campaign had we had, what rich conquests had we made, that the expeditionary force should be laden with gold and jewels? Nearly all our private possessions had been lost on our marches, and any valuables that we carried were our own property. Our habit, those of us who were experienced in the conquest, was to keep a few items of value on our persons, generally worn in a small bag under the shirt. For we were unpaid volunteers, we "heroes" of the conquest, and if we came by serious wounds we very likely had to buy such attentions or comforts as might be needed for recovery. Also if, as sometimes happened, we found ourselves in places where we might starve, but where food was to be had at a price, then it behoved every soldier who was not a fool to have that price secreted about his person. Again, although any expedition carried a store of chaquira as part of its normal equipment, each of us veterans carried privately a few articles of barter, beads and suchlike, so that we might if occasion arose do some trading with the Indians on our own accounts. Is any Spaniard prepared to blame us for what I have told you now? . . . We were not mercenaries; we had no pay unless treasure was won and was shared out—less the royal fifth set aside for His Majesty. We had no pay, I repeat, yet when it was a question of buying from Spanish merchants the tools of our trade of war, weapons, helmets, boots, and even the meanest necessities, we were charged prices ten, twenty, or a hundred times greater than those asked in Spain. We were poor men, most of us, but we were honest, and particularly so with our brothers-in-arms. What kind of people can those be who would suggest that we were capable of moving off with the personal valuables of Pizarro or any other of the compañeros on land? Is it likely that any single one of them would have entrusted his portable wealth to us who were leaving on a mission from which we might never return? For the state of the river—setting aside all other difficulties—was enough to show those on shore that our journey back to them would be, to say the least of it, a problem. Swollen with continual rains, the Canelos humped its back, compressing itself to run between sandy shoals. When we pushed out our canoe, it was jostled by eddies that boiled up from the bottom. There would be a down-current to port, a back-eddy to starboard, and cross-currents twisting bow and stern. Even the heavy *San Pedro* was pushed crazily this way and that. . . . I will waste no more breath arguing against such vile and stupid lies and will go on with my story. . . .

Weakened by the sweat that sprang continuously from every part of the body, exasperated by sandflies, we paddled and rowed on. As the sun descended behind us, it shone on the white peak of one of the distant Andes—and that was the last that any of us were to see of those mountains for many a day, while some of us would never see them again. All round us came bellowing and howling from monkeys hidden in the foliage. Then darkness was suddenly upon us, lonely darkness now rustling, now slithering, now with the plunge of a beast, or perhaps of some heavy fruit, into the gurgling river. The Captain ordered the canoes in a screen ahead of his brigantine, and, sounding with pikes, we edged in toward a sandbank, where we hauled out and passed the night. Apart from Arévalo my men were undamaged because they had been doing the same work for a long time and were inured to it. But those who had rowed the brigantine were in a pitiable state. Many had rubbed the skin off their hands, and they were so cramped that they stood on the ghostly-gleaming sand bent nearly double and groaning. At least we did not lack water. The lack of it would have killed every man of us in one such day. While a meal of sorts was cooking, Orellana explained that he would not risk navigating during the night, as we then might pass the food we were looking for; also, as we all knew, the river was difficult enough in the daytime, when dangers could usually be seen and avoided.

We laughed at each other in the morning. Our sweat-streaked faces were mottled with bites, and our eyes were all but hidden in the swollen flesh around them. The river had risen during the night. Two of the canoes were nearly afloat though they had been drawn well clear when we landed.

After two hours of travel on that second day we heard shouts from the brigantine astern of us. Closing the bank, I found a patch of dead water, and we were able to hurry upstream. The *San Pedro* was sinking. The oarsmen, their hands wrapped in blood-soaked cloths, were making flurried efforts to get to the nearest island. Canoes were already taking off the sick men and other encumbrances that could readily be unloaded. Orellana stood in the stern, thoughtful, as he often was in emergencies, with water over his knees and all manner of things floating about him in a wet swirl of Peruvian blankets.

The banks of the island were steep and covered with reeds that cut like sabres. We had to enter the water to haul the waterlogged boat to the mouth of a shallow lagoon, from which herons and egrets rose in their hundreds as we struggled in and beached it. We found that the *San Pedro* had rammed the stump of a tree, and one of the bow planks had been stove in. Diego Mexía, grumbling as usual, took charge of the repairs. When he had cut out the broken plank, he went with it and some of the compañeros to shape a similar piece from a suitable tree. This took them two hours, and during that time I bagged three big herons while Biscayan Perucho, who had somehow managed to keep his powder dry, shot a small alligator. Others found some guavas and pineapples, and caught a number of small and bony fish by driving them into the shallows of the lagoon.

After the launch of the *San Pedro* at El Barco, the prudent Mexía had put aside in a bag any materials left over from the building. He was thus able to produce nails, cotton, and some of the resin we used as tar. In less than an hour after he had begun to hammer we were hauling the brigantine back to the river and reloading it—not forgetting the tail of the alligator, good meat, if rather musky on the palate. From then on that day was a repetition of the first. Several tributaries entered the Canelos from the south, but at none of the junctions was there any sign of yuca or other food.

The third day passed likewise. We stopped with the hellish monkey chorus at dusk, hauled out the boats, and sat down in a circle round Orellana, who said it was time to discuss what should be done. He intended every man to hear what was said so that all might be in accord with any decision taken. Before there was more talking, as we were all famished, the Captain ordered every man to lay out any food he might have. The resulting heap was divided into sixty equal parts. Each took his share, chewing a great deal to make its substance seem the greater. My share was one mildewed cob of roasted maize and half a rotten banana.

Orellana first asked the seamen, whom he had warned at the outset to keep a tally of our progress and our direction, how far we had travelled from Christmas Camp, where we had separated from Pizarro. Their spokesman, Bermúdez, said that we had in the main been covering more than two leagues in every hour, and that we had rowed on each of the three days from dawn to dusk, which in those places is always twelve hours. With allowances for halts they estimated that we were some seventy-five leagues * from Christmas Camp.

Gonzalo Pizarro, Orellana reminded us, had promised to continue down the left bank, that our two parties might the sooner be reunited. But Pizarro's main body, as we knew from experience, could go no faster than two or at most three leagues in a day. We must therefore be more than sixty leagues downstream of the others, and as yet we had seen no food.

It was dark as a Moor's body in a tomb. Now and then a man would throw wood on the fire that it might send out more of the smoke that enveloped us, making our eyes smart and our bites itch. There were hosts of mosquitoes ready to brave the smoke in

* 275 miles. The seamen probably overestimated their speed, a general failing, as all who navigate small boats well know.

order to get at us. They came straight for the flesh, scarcely pausing to emit their whining blood cry or to choose their targets, and in our smoky circle there was the constant noise of slapping, as though we were applauding all that was said and all that remained unsaid.

Our situation was not complicated, whatever else it might be, the Captain went on, for there were but two alternatives. We could turn back and try to rejoin the others, or we could travel on in the hope that if we lived long enough and tried hard enough we would come upon food. It was our duty, he said, to get back, but would we be doing our duty if we went back to them starving and with empty hands when they were looking to us for supplies? Again, would we be able to get back to them? What distance did the seamen think we could travel in a day working upstream against so strong a current?

Bermúdez answered that the distance we had covered in three days with the stream would take us thirty or more days against it.* He added that unless we found something better to eat on the way than seemed likely, such an effort would kill us all.

Then Orellana turned to the hidalgos sitting beside him. How long, he asked, would it take us to march back to the others? Alonso de Robles said that, supposing Pizarro marched toward us and we back up the bank, it would be at least fifteen days before the two parties met. Assuming, Robles said, that we *could* march that distance cutting a path all the way, crossing swamps and building bridges (and what would happen to the sick compañeros?), Gonzalo Pizarro would not be overjoyed to see us on learning that we had abandoned the brigantine downstream.

One whom I will not name cried that Orellana might well have known we would navigate for days without finding anything to eat: why had we not brought more food with us? The Captain answered that those of Pizarro's party were in an even worse case than ourselves because we had the boats—which belonged to the others equally with us. We had left our friends with little enough

* Richard Spruce, the distinguished American traveller, wrote in 1864: "Travellers who have had to creep up South American rivers in canoes will agree with me that . . . an average distance of 10¼ miles a day . . . is over rather than under the mark."

to eat, and it had pained him to accept such meagre supplies as they had spared us.

Another shouted that it would be madness to turn back empty-handed when round the next bend of the river we might come upon abundant supplies. Many took up that argument.

Orellana waited until there were no more words, only the sound of slapping. Then, taking off his helmet as he invariably did when speaking to either of the friars, he invited Father Carvajal to give his views. We knew well enough why the Captain did this. The Dominican was a respectable and intelligent being, and, more important from Orellana's point of view, he was judged to be Pizarro's man. Gonzalo, as he passed through Lima to take up his Governorship of Quito, had met Father Carvajal. The friar came from Trujillo, was in his prime, and was strong, stout-hearted, and somewhat acclimatized, having sailed to the Indies in 1536. He had most gladly accepted Gonzalo's invitation to join his retinue, and the pair had remained on excellent terms.

Father Carvajal now answered, with the good sense we were to learn was almost invariably his, that no profit to God, to ourselves, or to Gonzalo Pizarro was likely to come from our turning back.

At which Orellana asked if it was the common decision that we must continue down the river until we found supplies of one sort or another. That was our choice. At dawn we went with the river again, thrusting our way through the mist that clung to the water. The first hour was always the best; after it the sun with its heat, and the sandflies, would be upon us, making day a delirium.

On the fifth evening Orellana asked Father Carvajal to say Mass as it is said at sea. He did, and it was well done. He laid our bodies, our souls, our lives, and our hopes in the tender hands of our Lord, beseeching Him to deliver us from our torment and to save us from the destruction that none but He in His all-abiding charity could alleviate or avert. Myself I found some comfort in the friar's words, for where else was comfort to be had? We all knew that even if our Lord and Redeemer decided to save us more rapidly than seemed possible, certain among us were too far immersed in sickness and misery to survive the ordeal. In the night some cried out as madmen do when struggling with Satan, while others returned to infancy and whimpered and wetted themselves.

Now the forest passed us, rather than we it. I paddled without knowing when I dipped the blade. We seemed still, a canoe set in marble, and the forest slowly, slowly crept past us, cruel, gorgeous, with vast flowers in its dew-stored recesses and vaster butterflies, and high up under the green awning of the treetops brilliantly clothed clowns, the toucans with their goitred bills, ungainly hoppings, and yelping cry. Once each day when the sun was at its highest and the whole forest was numbed with heat we would stop for an hour. Some of us would crawl into the woods, and the strongest of seasoned soldiers would stumble, bent over staffs like octogenarian cripples. We would grub and grope, and the man who caught a little frog would weep at his luck in obtaining such a feast. The lizards lay stiff, waiting till our fingers came near before they darted off with whispering speed. Monkeys rustled the high branches and peered through, but when weak arms, stiff hands trembling with anxiety, had raised crossbow or arquebus, the leaves closed and the forest, the sun, the sandflies, and the river mocked us.

On the sixth day with a four-pronged bolt I knocked over a kingfisher with speckled wings. When the little bird fell, I flung down my precious crossbow and pounced on the quarry. I was alone, lying on the ground, and I ate the bird raw, feathers, feet, bill, everything. Had any man come upon me then and demanded a share, I might, may God forgive me, have killed him.

The head swam. Movements were slow, and seemed slower than they were. If paddling was purgatory, it was better than the times on land because there was still hope in it. Man is a miracle. . . . None of us but was prepared to go on in hope or desperation until he was dead. Once we saw a *gran bestia,** a fat, juicy animal bigger than a big donkey, swimming the river. At once all the canoes went for it, the brigantine lumbering after. It dived. We waited, shaking so that pikes and paddles rattled against the sides of the canoes. It reappeared some distance up-

* A tapir.

stream. We gave chase, but in vain, for it was strong and as much at ease in the water as on land. Another time the same thing happened with some other amphibious animals that looked like giant rats.

At night we made a fire and set on it the biggest camp kettle, in which we stewed, together with any herbs we could find, belts, the soles of old boots, and pieces of saddlery that were among the brigantine's stores. We might have thought this a splendid stew had we had any salt to put in it. How terrible a lack is that of salt! To think that we soldiers of the Cross in this sixteenth century should die for want of the simple white substance so necessary to man! Ah, Señores, what tribulations we endured in the name of conquest! . . . Our lack will be the more readily understood when I remind you that we cascaded sweat all day; and all night, wrapped up against the onslaughts of mosquitoes and vampires, the same thing happened. Our need for salt was terrible. And there was none.

Many were driven by starvation to a sleep resembling death, while a few, and I among them, found that hunger and fatigue between them banished sleep. It was as though my head were filled with a storming sea of blood. If I lay on my side my lower ear throbbed a tattoo that would have alarmed all Navarre. Father Vera, who fancied himself as a surgeon, advised me that my discomfort was caused by questing blood, raging because I could not satisfy it with food. If I ate, the blood would become docile again and pleased with the narrow walls of its captivity. And he told me, if the pounding became unendurable, to take the point of my dagger and ease a passage for the blood out of my ear. But that I did not do because I was already enduring enough pains for an army after battle, in my one not over-big earthly envelope. So all night through I was tossing in a fret, and all day through I was paddling.

Yes, I could still paddle on the first day of the year 1542, which was a Sunday and the sixth day after we had left Gonzalo Pizarro. I paddled. The Negroes and both Asturians were also paddling. As for the tall Arévalo, he was trying to paddle. But sometimes an hour would go by between one stroke and the next, for he was so weak that he did not know what he was doing.

Little Rebolloso lay in the canoe at my feet, breathing like a fish taken out into the air, and torn by the cough that was always with him, but that grew the fiercer as he grew weaker. Our case was bad enough, yet it was better than that of any other canoe, and we were far in the lead when I felt the weight on my blade grow leaden. Looking forward, I saw that both Negroes, their skins no longer agleam, but scabby, the muscles like frozen snakes on their fleshless backs, were sitting motionless, their paddles laid across the gunwales. Alonso de Tapia had also stopped, and only Francisco and I were doing any work.

I leaned forward and jabbed Number Five's back with the wet edge of my paddle, but turning to me, he said: "Listen, listen, master." I listened, and against the pounding in my head I heard a drum in the forest to the east of us. We made Francisco de Tapia stop paddling, and although he was inclined to be deaf at the best of times, he said that hunger had improved his hearing and that he also heard it. *Food, food-food-food, food!* the drum seemed to sound, and again and again: *Food, food-food-food, food!* We asked Arévalo to listen, but he could not understand us, though his eyes were open and now and then he would plunge his paddle in the water. Rebolloso could understand us, but had no strength to answer.

When the others overtook us, the noise had stopped, and they refused to believe that we had heard anything. Nevertheless, all the rest of that day we were continually stopping to listen, and the other boats too. In the afternoon so many of those in the *San Pedro* had collapsed over their oars that the Captain, after trying to revive them by throwing water over them, decided to land to have a few hours of daylight in which to hunt for roots, worms, tubers, reptiles, palm cabbage, decomposing corpses of small animals, or anything else fit for Christian gentlemen to eat in such circumstances. We made fast the canoes to the brigantine, and the brigantine to some overhanging branches, and with swords and machetes we cleared enough space by the bank.

Sebastián de Fuenterrabía had taken some spools of twine from the brigantine's cargo and was beginning to make a fine-meshed fishing net. He sat on the bank with a wet cloth wrapped round his livid face to keep off sandflies, and his helmet perched on top of the cloth. There were plenty of us to tell him he would be dead before he had made even a part of his net, and that we would all be dead before a fish was caught in it. But he sat there, perhaps thinking of earlier days in his home by the Northern Sea, and his fingers, also going back to boyhood, grew quicker and nimbler as they twisted their little knots. Meanwhile the stew of old leather was bubbling on the fire. There was one dish that could not be overcooked. Nor would a scrap of the "meat" nor one drop of the bouillon be wasted, for if there were some who no longer could face such fare, there were others who could not get enough of it. The mystery of man is that he can usually draw amusement from the most terrible surroundings. There, my friends, we laughed at the vultures. For wherever you make a fire in the Indies those scavengers appear, knowing that there is to be a meal and waiting most ill-naturedly for scraps. They did not get much from us.

As we hunted, dragging ourselves through the forest, continually hung up by slender creepers that in our full strength we would have burst as easily as cobwebs, we thought of meals we had eaten in this place or that, of mounds of firm rice tinted with saffron, of the rosy flesh of lobsters, of the smell and savour of roasted lamb. While we were thus searching for grubs and finding little but memories, the time flitted past and the chorus of the night began.

I wound my crossbow as the parrots flew over the river, two by two, screaming stupidly. The monkeys howled. You would never imagine that a monkey, or any other single animal, could make so much noise: have you heard the bellowing of maddened bulls? Have you heard fifty hogs yell as their throats are cut? Combine the two and you have something approaching the noise I am talking about so calmly. We were not calm about it then, I assure you. We hated them. Their noise was agony. But at last it would cease as though at a signal, and we would hear the thin whistle of the bats as they hunted beetles and moths. The smaller creatures began their choruses: crickets like those at home; treetoads whose voices were the cracking of old bones; owls, and mosquitoes. During a long spell round midnight the only noise was the river. The black water slid on, turned, sighed, and chuckled. Rain fell, and

I walked in it to cool myself. Some hunter, perhaps a big snake, seized on his prey, a monkey, and there was a yell of fear that merged into the pity-sob of death. I stumbled over a swaddled figure, and my loneliness was relieved when it stirred and cried out as had the monkey.

At dawn we had been wakened by the scream of the waking forest. The parrots and monkeys drowned Father Carvajal's words as he said Mass. We climbed down to our seats of torture in the canoe. At noon, when we stopped, we lay on the ground and listened to the slight rustling of small creeping and sliding things moving in the green dampnesses where they found food but we did not. Beetles brighter than jewels clung to trees and allowed us to pick them off. Those who ate them were sick. The only birds we could kill were ciganas, birds that ironically are a kind of chicken except that, gripping with their sharp toes, they run up and down trees as easily as on the ground. There is another "except" about them. We killed but two, and their stench, like that of a tannery, but with a sickly sweetness in it, was so vile that none could touch them. Butterflies live in those forests. If children saw them once they would never wish to look on anything else. Some were of a blue so hard that the eye was drawn to them and repelled; many were yellow; and the most beautiful were transparent, with a hint of milkiness and palest blue or red in their transparency. Why is this transparency so enticing? . . . The Inca Atahualpa told Francisco and Hernando Pizarro that he failed to understand why we Christians, when we had iron which was useful and glass which was lovely, ran about hunting for such ordinary solids as gold and silver. And he begged them to explain why they held diamonds and emeralds to be more precious than glass, either white or coloured. . . . But I wander, like my own wits during the time that I am trying to describe.

That seventh afternoon (it was Monday, January 2) as we floated through the steam bath between the green ranks of forest that every now and then emitted in our faces hot, scented breaths laden with the sweetness and the decay of flowers that sprang, blossomed, died, all in an instant, courtesans dressed to captivate a prince, but imprisoned with the spiders in shaded sepulchres of death in life, that seventh afternoon he whom we called Maldonado cried out blasphemously, and all heard. Orellana told him that he must keep his mouth and mind clean or suffer the consequences, because our case was too near its end to be risked yet further by evil. Maldonado, enraged against fate and its Ruler, but seeing us all against him and ready to do our duty should he repeat his crime, asked sarcastically if the Captain, who had "so cleverly" led us down this river, had thought of an ending for us all.

"*Sí, señor,*" was the answer. "We will follow this river, using up all our strength and asking only the help of God until we die one by one and are all dead, or until we come upon human habitations."

And that same evening, while we were grubbing in the forest, all of us heard Indian drums. At the sound, disquieting enough in other circumstances, despair in any but the weakest among us was turned to expanding and invincible joy. Father Carvajal asked those of us who could do it to kneel among the leaves while he, seated because he could no longer stand or kneel, gave thanks to our Lord.

Orellana, reasoning on more practical and scarcely less important lines, at once set sentries. He did not sleep that night, but continued to urge all who were awake to see to their weapons and also to their armour or defensive clothing, most of which had been laid aside long ago, while fighting another danger. At first light he inspected the crossbowmen and arquebusiers, telling us that in the present condition of our small force almost everything might well depend on us. Five crossbowmen and four arquebusiers seemed too few. He reorganized the crews so that the fighting men would be less impeded by the sick, some of whom could not help themselves in any way. Two of the canoes were left there by the bank as there were no longer enough paddlers.

When we had heard Mass, we went on as fast as we could, helped by the current and by the future, which now looked so much better than before. We had gone two leagues in less than an hour when we were gladdened by the sight of four big Indian canoes coming upstream. The Indians soon put about and fled at full speed, each canoe leaving a fan of ripples as they drove it. They went to warn their people of our impending arrival, and must have done so remarkably quickly, for soon we heard drums from many directions, some near, some distant. Orellana urged us to quicken the stroke, saying that we must at all costs reach the first river settlement before too many warriors had gathered to oppose our landing.

At last, opening a long reach, we saw—oh, blessed sight!—a village on the left bank, the houses built with canes and roofed with palm fronds. Cooking fires were smoking, but the women and children had gone and only the men remained to guard their hearths. Around the village the trodden earth was swept and was clear of weeds. A small inlet evidently served as port. Calling the canoes in close to the brigantine, Orellana steered for the inlet. We wound our crossbows. The arquebusiers lit their matches and loaded with shot (those Indians being naked save for bands of red paint on their skins and tufts of feathers sticking out from holes cut in their ears and their cheeks). Orellana had detailed five men to guard the brigantine. The rest of us were to follow him ashore in close order.

There was no need for exhortation, and he gave us none. Rather was it necessary to restrain our zeal, which far outstripped our strength. We were about to land when Maldonado remarked that steam was rising from the cooking pots, and Hernández the Unlucky, still fussing with his arquebus, said he had scented boiling meat. We jumped ashore and formed up behind the Captain, who, his rusted sword in his hand, walked steadily up the incline toward the houses.

The mere sight of us—our beards, our armour, the bowed legs of horsemen, the brigantine—was too much for them. They did not stand to try us out, and in a breath they melted away, and we were only Spaniards among the houses.

Seeing this, the friars began to help the sick out of the brigantine, and Orellana ordered us all to go to the same task because it was both dangerous and unseemly that any Indian should look upon those poor weak compañeros. Then, in the centre of the village, we ate from the Indians' cooking pots, scalding our hands and mouths, and we drank chicha from gourds they had set aside on learning of our approach. We ate standing, shields on shoulders, swords under our arms. My crossbow was still wound. We expected an attack at any moment. But we ate. Although Orellana and Alonso de Robles kept ordering us to eat slowly and sparingly, they could not stop us—and I doubt if they could stop themselves.

When the food was all eaten, we looked again to our Captain and he explained what was to be done. Those of us who were not posted as sentries lay down fully armed in one of the bigger dwellings, a place that evidently housed a number of families, each in its own compartment. The majority of us were suffering pangs from impetuous greed after days of abstinence. As for me, my digestion may be made of stone, but more likely it is iron. Beside me lay Rebolloso, the Valencian. He had only eaten a little fish and had drunk once from a chicha gourd; but it had revived him and, refusing to admit that he was sick, he was not. He lay at his ease on the earth stamped firm by savages, his round head pillowed on one arm, graceful in sleep as in movement. Near us Orellana was sitting, leaning his back against one of the slender posts supporting the roof. His long face expressed worry, even despondency. But his thoughts could not keep me awake.

CHAPTER TWELVE

☼

IN THAT VILLAGE, REACHED AS THOUGH BY A MIRACLE when even the strongest could have gone no farther, argument and formal business wasted much of our time and our patience. You wish to hear of our adventures, I presume, and could do without parchments and formalities, yet I feel it my duty to go into those matters (in which I played a not unimportant part) with all the clarity that my attainments permit.

First, though, I had better tell you about the Indians. Soon after our arrival Indian canoes crept up the river and hung there to see what we were doing, which was not much, most of us being asleep. Orellana stood forth on the bank above the little port and talked with them until he had persuaded a few to land, albeit timidly. Thanks to his skill with languages, he was able to explain that we were children of the sun, supernatural and entirely benevolent. He gave them some beads, asking them to fetch their Lord, which they did. His name was Aparia, and he was the vassal of another and greater Aparia who ruled a long way off downstream. Some of us therefore called this the village of Aparia, but others called it, as the Indians seemed to do, Imará, and to avoid confusion in my story I will do likewise. To continue. . . .

When Orellana had shown the cacique some of our weapons and the brigantine, he slipped over the savage's oiled torso what had once been a fine Spanish shirt of linen, and hung round his neck a showy string of blue and red beads. Aparia asked how such favours and marks of respect might be returned. Orellana replied that any food would be most gratefully received, and shortly Aparia came to us again with many Indians, all men, carrying maize and other good things, including a variety of meats, birds resembling partridges and turkeys, different kinds of fishes, some of a great size and covered with scaly armour, each scale edged with pink. In the way of condiments he brought the Indian peppers that are plentiful in Peru and also some powders hot to the tongue, which we mistrusted. Among his more welcome gifts were some jars of sweet oil resembling that of the incomparable olive, and this came from the juice of a certain palm tree, as did the oil those Indians use in their lamps, which burn without smoke or stench.

Orellana was agreeably surprised at so promising a beginning, but he warned us all that it was only a beginning, and that the hearts of men are fickle, especially those of Indians. He set double guards by night and single through the day. No man was to move a step unarmed, and all were to sleep fully clothed and ready for fighting.

Early in the morning of the second day at Imará, Orellana sent for me and after taking pains to set me in good humour, as he well knew how to do, he turned to the matter on his mind. He explained that he was still responsible to Gonzalo Pizarro and that it would be more than a pity, it would be dangerous, if at any later date Spaniards could question our behaviour and suggest that it had been illegal. He therefore thought it important that an accurate account be kept of our doings, with notes of his decisions and some proofs of the reasons for such decisions. After this preamble he asked if I would agree for his sake to be his scrivener. I answered that I would do anything for him, but I could not write without materials. He was too much for me there, because he had found parchment, pens, and even ink among the brigantine's cargo. So he sent for Alonso de Robles, Cristóbal Enríquez, Father Carvajal, Juan de Arnalte, Hernán Gutiérrez de Celis, Alonso de Cabrera, and Antonio de Carranza, and when those gentlemen were with us Orellana dictated to me as follows:

> *In the village of Aparia* [sic] *on this important river that descends out of the province of Quijos, on January 4 in the 1542nd year after the birth of Our Saviour Jesus Christ, Captain Francisco de Orellana, Governor's Lieutenant General for the most honourable Gonzalo Pizarro, Governor for His Majesty, appointed Francisco de Isásaga to be the scrivener of this detachment, so that he may bear witness to every happening.*

The Captain and the rest of them witnessed it, Enríquez signing himself Comendador Enríquez, though I never knew in which Order he claimed membership. Then Orellana administered the usual oath to me, and at the appropriate places I said: "Yes, I swear," and "Amen."

All save the very sick compañeros were mustered, and the Captain announced my appointment as scrivener. The wags began to call out this and that about me, but soon all jests were stifled because Orellana at once gave two significant orders: the brigantine and canoes were to be emptied of blankets and other unnecessary stores, to be ready to carry cargoes of food; also most of the maize brought by the Indians was at once to be smoke-dried so that it would keep.

There were many growls. He stood before them, one foot tapping the earth, his solitary eye playing among them, his left hand fiddling with his beard.

When he had savoured the disapproval, he again spoke, saying it was his duty and ours, now that we had found food, to return to the leader and the friends whom we had left starving in the forest. If there were any grievances or complaints, these must be presented to him in logical form, and through me, his scrivener.

Then Robles, Cabrera, and one or two others suggested that, since we were worn out and it would take time to recover strength, we might for that day be excused the work of unloading the boats.

Orellana rejoined sharply that he would agree to this, but would remind all of us that our duty to Pizarro came before our own comforts or inclinations.

The muster dissolved in bitterness, some of the compañeros scowling at their Captain as though he were a monster who plotted their deaths.

After the midday meal there was a meeting attended by all save the sentries and Orellana, who was sleeping in another hut. Even those who could not walk were carried groaning to our meeting. Speaker after speaker stated that it would be suicide to turn back in the hope of finding Gonzalo Pizarro. The seamen said that we would never get the boats back as far as Christmas Camp. Men experienced in Indian warfare said that our Indian hosts, now that they knew about us and coveted our belongings, would follow us upstream and would repeatedly ambush us. In short, many were saddened by the thought that we might be accused of playing Pizarro false, yet all were unanimous that to turn back was impossible. Accordingly a Petition was agreed upon, and I duly wrote it down:

*Honourable Francisco de Orellana: We the caballeros, hidalgos, and priests here with this detachment under Your Worship's command have learned of Your Worship's decision to go back up the river. We maintain that it is impossible to return to the place where Your Worship left Gonzalo Pizarro, our Governor, without sacrificing our whole detachment. We further maintain that such action would not conform with the service of God and of His Majesty, our master. In the name of God and of the King we beg Your Worship not to lead us on so foolhardy a journey. We are assured by the seamen among us that we are two hundred leagues * or more by land from the expeditionary force of the Governor, Gonzalo Pizarro. Coming* downstream *we all thought ourselves doomed to die from hardships and hunger. How much more dangerous the journey* upstream *would be is plain to all of us.*

At this stage some said that the Petition was so much milk-and-water, being in every conceivable detail too mild. They hotly insisted on a change of mood, saying that they would tolerate no nonsense from Orellana. In accordance with their wishes the Petition was continued as follows:

Therefore we summon Your Worship NOT *to take us back up the river. And let not Your Worship take the step of ordering us to do this, since that will make it necessary for us to disobey Your Worship and thereby to show a disrespect that we in no way feel for Your Worship's orders except, as in this case, when such an order would mean certain death and would accomplish nothing. We exonerate ourselves*

* 740 miles.

from any charge of treason or disloyalty in refusing to follow Your Worship on that route. All this we submit unanimously and sign with our names, as will be seen below. . . .

At my request, for I saw that such a document might have repercussions, and I had no wish to be more deeply implicated than any of the other signatories, they allowed me to add a few words saying that they had ordered me, as the official scrivener, to write it down. I also added that all of us were more than ready to follow Captain Orellana *in any other direction.*

Then with heavings and grunts they made play with their rubricas,* and those who could not write their own names chose this friend or that to do it for them. Meanwhile Robles sent men who had signed to relieve the sentries so that they might also sign. There was persuasion, but no compulsion. Then off I went to find the Captain, and found him asleep in a hammock made from palm fibres. These hammocks were everywhere in the village, and we were not slow to note their manifold advantages, for in such a climate they make the coolest, safest, and least verminous of beds. While I waited for him to wake, I compared the muster roll of the detachment with the signatures, and noted down the names of those who for reasons best known to themselves had not signed the Petition. In fairness to those men I will give their names:

Juan de Alcántara of Valladolid, he who at Gonzalo's order had first commanded the brigantine (the other of the same name, who came from Santiago, was a signatory); Rodrigo de Cevallos; Alonso Estéban, the brilliant and ferocious swordsman who has lately won fame in the Araucanian wars of Chile; Antonio Hernández, who was always seeking Orellana's favour, and often with a success that did credit to neither; Juan de Mangas; Diego Mexía, ever ready to counter public opinion; Alonso Martín de Noguel; García Rodríguez; and one of my canoemen, Alonso de Tapia. Eight names out of fifty-seven.

When I added the names of those who had signed to those who had not, I saw that there was one too many. The explanation was that the other Portuguese, Hernán Gonçalez, in his enthusiasm

* The flourishes accompanying signatures.

had signed twice, doubtless reasoning that two signatures would have double value. Since it was written, I had no authority to alter it, and I thought Orellana would be unlikely to notice it. I sat down in the silent hut, watching the sleeping Captain, and I dozed.

The shadows were longer when we both awoke and looked at each other. Without speaking, I handed him the Petition. He sat on the ground and read it from the first word to the last.

"Gonçalez signed twice," said he, and then: "Fetch me Antonio, Antonio Hernández."

The eyes of all the camp were on us as the arquebusier followed me back to the Captain's hut.

"Captain?" he said when we both stood before Orellana.

"Why did you not sign this Petition?"

"The Captain said he wished to go back up the river."

"Well?"

"Therefore those who signed have pledged themselves to disobedience. Where his Captain leads, Hernández follows."

"My little escopetero,* well spoken! You are a better soldier than many who profess to look down on you, for the highest virtue in any soldier is selflessness, and the next highest is discipline, by which I mean regard for, as well as obedience to, orders. Before you go, one more question. Do you think you will die, Antonio, if you go up the river with me?"

"I leave the thinking to my Captain," answered the reptile.

Orellana sent him off, but when I made to follow him I was called back. Orellana's smile had gone as he reread the Petition.

"Why such roughness of language?" he asked.

I answered that I had only written down what I had been told to write.

"You signed it," he insisted. "Therefore you approved it."

Alonso de Robles appeared at this opportune moment to warn Orellana that Indians were arriving in canoes, and that several of them were hung with feathers, bones, gold, and other finery. So the Captain hurried out.

Aparia had brought three other caciques to look at us. He said he would have brought more, but the remainder lived too far

* Musketeer.

away to come so quickly, and one or two were extremely sorry but they were otherwise engaged on slaving raids, or hunting virgins, or killing their neighbours, or making chicha (which meant drinking it).

Orellana entertained them with a speech in their own tongue, or at least in an approximation to it that they gave every sign of understanding. He spoke of our white-skinned King-Emperor, Don Carlos, over the Northern Sea, and how he was to be King of the world because he was the terrestrial instrument of the one God, who was indivisible, all-powerful, and universal, a charitable deity, generous to the weak, compassionate and merciful. . . . That is what Orellana claimed to have said, but from the savages' behaviour you would have thought he was cracking the neatest of jokes. Then the Captain called Father Carvajal and asked him to give God's blessing to those valiant warrior chieftains who came to us with peace in their hearts. He also introduced to the caciques Cristóbal Enríquez, Alonso de Robles, Antonio Carranza, and Maldonado; and our hidalgos, although they were a trifle filthy and their cuirasses somewhat rusted and dented, behaved with invincible good manners and showed lofty interest in their new acquaintances, who, I regret to say, were more impressed by the looks of the black men, Panama and Number Five, when they arrived on the scene carrying between them a red leather chest holding beads and toys, which Orellana distributed. Then Aparia made a speech.

He said (according to Orellana's understanding of it) that there were extremely rich provinces farther down the river, and that the richest belonged to a king called Ica, though that province was set somewhat back from the banks and the flooded lagoons. He also warned us that if we pursued our journey downstream we would meet ferocious peoples whose joy was fighting all strangers, and the most to be feared of all were the women warriors of Queen Coñorí. Aparia therefore advised us not to go on downstream, but rather to go back the way we had come.

When the Indians were gone, Orellana told us all to follow him to his hut, where, although I complained of fatigue in my trigger hand, he dictated the third of that day's documents, an affidavit to the effect that he had—on behalf of Gonzalo Pizarro—

accepted the submission of the caciques, who had "come to a peaceful understanding" with him. It was made plain—since such details are important to those who further our conquests by sitting in the Office of the Indies in Seville—that the Indian leaders he named had come without persuasion or rough treatment on our part. When all of us had signed the affidavit, the scrivener was at last free to go and get something to eat.

We passed that night of January 4 in a state of uneasiness. None knew what Orellana intended to do. My ears grew tired of questions from those who expected me to know everything—and to tell them all I knew.

After we had heard Mass in the morning, Orellana called me away from the others. For once I followed him reluctantly. He took me to where the mist was thickest and the water swung past, restless and clouded. I sat beside him on the bank, and for a while, fingering his beard, he watched the Indians arriving with fish and maize for the camp. They were so eager about it that one would have supposed them to have been working for Spaniards all their lives. Orellana was in an ill humour, and his voice and looks betrayed it. He had lain awake most of the night. Although I cannot vouch for his exact words, I can vouch for the sense of them, and our talk went like this:

"You are an educated man. Do you intend to make your life henceforward in the New or the Old World?"

"Captain, if God grants me the choice, I choose the New. I have forgotten what the Old was like."

"And you wish to return to your encomienda at Puná?"

"I was well enough there. But I will go wherever there is most profit."

"Good!" he said. "I liked that. It was honest. Adaptability to circumstance, belief in himself, these a man should cherish, for they ease his passage through life. . . . Now listen to me, Bachelor of Arts. Here on this river I am offered the opportunity I have long desired—an independent command, new lands to open up. But there is a twist to it, for if I grasp opportunity and turn it into reality, I must seem to desert Gonzalo, and thus I shall put a stain on my honour."

"There is always a twist, Captain. When Cortés marched

into Mexico, did he not first have to cut the tie of duty and kinship binding him to the Governor of Cuba, who had financed him? Or take Francisco Pizarro: did he not deceive Diego de Almagro, his first companion in the venture to conquer Peru, and was that deception not what caused the fighting between the two (in which you and I bore our parts) and Almagro's death? Yet both Cortés and the Marquis are honoured and respected. And rightly so. Their deeds will surely enrich and transform even the few mean and dubious sentences in the history they have made, both of them."

"Cortés and Francisco Pizarro have attained the status where wrongs are forgiven. Ordinary men cannot expect to have the genius of a Cortés or the determination of a Francisco Pizarro. . . . Now, my friend, I want to ask why you signed a Petition cast in terms insubordinate to me. Have I ever wronged you? On the contrary, once when you were wounded I saved your life. Again, when you had a diseased foot I would not leave you, but put you on a horse and brought you with me. At Guayaquil I set such wealth as I could in your way, and trusted you. I had cause to believe that you might hold me in affection and esteem."

"Captain, I do."

"Yet the simple Hernández, for whom I have done so little, proves to be more loyal than my Bachelor of Arts."

"He proves to be a fool."

"Explain yourself."

"By failing to sign the Petition, the Portuguese, of whom you seem to think so highly, was only making your duty the more difficult. You would not be acting responsibly in ordering us back upstream, since such an order would be insane and pointless. The Petition makes this clear. And with the Petition inside your shirt you are cleared of any charges of disobedience, disloyalty, or self-interest. . . . Do you suppose that Gonzalo would go back upstream in such circumstances? Not he! Nor any other leader I can think of. . . . If the best of us, such as Robles and Father Carvajal, to take two significant examples, had not signed, the Petition would have been valueless—and your dilemma the more severe. . . . So I say that your 'loyal' Hernández is a fool."

"For all your reasoning," he answered, "I say that there is room and to spare in this world for such 'fools' as Hernández." He sat with his eye swivelling downriver on the current, like a man watching squadrons of horse canter by. "Look at that water, Bachelor of Arts. Where does it come from, and where does it go? What lands does it penetrate, what peoples drink from it and navigate on it, what beasts live in it and beside it? . . . I suppose you are in the right, all of you, though I am more moved by the sentiment of one Hernández than by the ambitions, the reason, the selfishness, and the violence of the others. What option have I? The brigantine is heavy and draws too much water to negotiate the shallows where the current is less strong. We would have to go upstream in canoes. But then we could not defend ourselves against Indian attacks, and we cannot trust these, or any other, Indians. They watch us too eagerly. Today we are new to them. When our strangeness has worn familiar, they may become dangerous. . . . How much food could we carry with us up the two rivers? How much of it would be left when we managed—*if* we managed—to reach Gonzalo? And where will Gonzalo be some ninety days from today? Certainly far from where we left him, but in which direction? . . . Would he and his men even be alive? I doubt it. . . . Can I divide so small a detachment as this? No. If I left a few men here, they would be massacred. Yet I could not leave the brigantine here unguarded; Gonzalo would blame me for that, and rightly. See how the Indian dogs covet it," he said, pointing at the port. "Look at them. See them gape at it. We must guard the brigantine as we guard our throats, for it and our lives are indivisible."

Thus I knew, Señores, that Orellana intended to go on downstream, and that we were destined to perish in obscurity or to be a probe for yet another of the great conquests. A thought to make Castilian blood sing.

"Where do you think Pizarro is now?" he asked. "What is the talk of the camp?"

"If he has not turned back for Quito or Capua, he must be on the point of it, for where can he find food? He will be eating the horses now."

"My Trompetero. I shall never buy his like again. . . . True enough, but there is another possibility. Gonzalo and the others could launch themselves on the river as we did. They may be building another brigantine, or two."

"Mexía is with us," I reminded him.

"Mexía never built a boat before, and he had assistants at El Barco. They would not be so lacking in resource that they could not build another. They have enough iron in their shoes for the nails, and enough meat in the horses to keep them alive while they build. No, we must hope that Gonzalo is boatbuilding, and we must wait for him here until we are sure he is not going to reach us, by land or by water."

"How could he come by land? It is impossible."

"Everything is possible to a Pizarro. He might stumble on a source of food that we, hurrying by in the boats, failed to see."

"Such a journey would take many months."

"Yes, months," Orellana agreed. "Now, scrivener, to business. Put this preamble into your own words:

"You came to me with the Petition yesterday. I took note of its content and of the signatures. Today, January 5, I gave my Answer. I admit that it is impossible to go back upstream—'impossible' is a bad word, but I think we must use it, for no other will quite do. Therefore I am ready, most regretfully, to look for another route on which we may serve the King. But I give this Answer to the Petition only on the condition that we wait for Gonzalo Pizarro here for two or three months. . . ."

"May I make a suggestion?"

"What is it?"

"Supposing we cannot, for one reason or another, wait so long, your 'two or three months' may put you in the wrong. Better to frame the Answer so that you will not be caught out by it."

"Lawyer! Very well, then, put down 'two or three months or until we can no longer hold out here.' Then (do not take this down) we must keep the compañeros busy, very busy indeed, if we are to keep them waiting here, so this is to be added to the Answer: we will build another brigantine here so that if Gonzalo arrives with the main body or any remnant of it, we shall be able to go downstream under his command, and if he does not come, then we will go down it ourselves—in Gonzalo's name. . . .

Well, there is your Answer to the Petition. Go and frame it for me. When you come back with it, we will find witnesses, and then I shall give you more to do, for you also must be kept out of mischief. I know you. I must keep *you* busier than any of the rest of them—the dogs."

I assumed that his last remarks were in the nature of a friendly joke, though I knew it would be some time before he entirely forgave me for signing the Petition, but when I took back the Answer to the Petition fairly written out and with the verbosity advisable in any official document, he at once required me to take down more orders that seemed to show he did think Pizarro might reach us at Imará. The new order was that any man who happened to have weapons, clothing, valuables, or utensils belonging to any member of the main body was to hand it or them over to Captain Orellana before dusk on the following day, the 6th. Anybody failing to comply would be liable to the penalty for theft (removal of his hands), and it would be an offence of the same nature should his friends, knowing of his disobedience, fail to denounce him. This order had to be proclaimed, so when I had written it I got Juan de Mangas, who had a voice like the sea booming in a cave and who could read, to go with me round the camp together with Alonso Martín, who could strike a roll on the drum.

The proclamation was read in the centre of the village, then down by the port, and those who bothered to listen after the first few words were in no mood to think it important. What they wanted was news that Orellana had regained his senses, as they put it, and this was not long delayed, because as we were about to proclaim for the third time, and that time beside the cookhouse, our audience vanished. Robles had announced that he intended to read out the Answer to the Petition. Thus we were free, Mangas, Martín, and I, to repay ourselves for our conscientious performances with some joints of monkey so tender and so delicate in flavour that they would not normally have come our way. The monkey was slowly roasting on a spit, and the technique for eating it was to cut off one of the better pieces and if it needed a little more cooking to thrust it for a minute or two into the embers, which gave the meat a somewhat salty tang.

Orellana spoke to us that evening about what he called discipline-and-dignity. He began by saying that we need not imagine, because he had agreed not to go back upstream, that we could put all responsibility on his shoulders and at the same time tell him what he had to do. He said he had been deeply angered and offended by the tone of the latter part of the Petition, which, he maintained, smacked of mutiny and, even worse, of womanish panic. He would say no more about the matter provided there was no more of such offensive talk or behaviour; if he had further cause for complaint, and it came from a majority of the detachment, he would relinquish his command; but if only a few men made trouble, he would punish them without mercy. Our situation was still difficult, and his conception of his duty as our Captain was to hold us together firmly. He would go to any lengths to do this, and we must get it clear in our minds that he was going to command as he wished, and never as we wished, for a commander who strove to please his men instead of leading them was worse than useless.

He then discussed our behaviour toward the Indians of Imará, and ordered us to behave as though they were our hosts. If at any time the cacique Aparia came among us we were to stop whatever work we might be doing, stand up straight, and doff our helmets. There was to be no traffic with the Indians for gold or anything else, and whatever we might feel about them and some of their habits, we were to behave with friendly and unsupercilious dignity. Neither by signs nor by pictures was any inquiry to be made as to why none of the Indian women returned to their village. If any women did come, no Spaniard was to touch them, or speak to them, or even look at them. Above all, we must remember that the Indians watched us every minute of the day. We should behave always, even when we thought ourselves unobserved, in a manner likely to win and keep their respect.

Turning to the question of building a second brigantine, he said that the first task would be making more nails. As there were twelve sick men who were entirely bedridden, the two friars were nursing, six men were on guard by day, and both Negroes were on duty in the cookhouse, only thirty-eight of us remained to do the work, and we also had to take our turn of the double guard posted at night. Who would be the overseers?

Alonso de Robles offered to take charge of the charcoal-burning. But by whom were the nails to be struck, as there was no farrier among us, and Arévalo, who had sound knowledge of such work, as of everything pertaining to horses, lay in the dark unable to speak or even to eat? Surprisingly enough, since he had refused to sign the Petition, the hidalgo Juan de Alcántara was the first volunteer, and the second was the Galician Sebastián Rodríguez. They said that with God's help they would do their best to give us all the nails we needed, and good ones. Orellana, who must have been gratified by this show of good will from Alcántara, one of the best of Gonzalo's men, thanked them both warmly and said they would be rewarded—and not only in heaven.

Diego Mexía was, of course, the man to supervise the carpentering, but he made excuses (and they were anything but graceful), pointing out that he had been weakened by his hard work at El Barco and that some kind of ague attacked him continuously with fits of hot shaking, and his skin was blotched and was peeling in places, giving him a most odd appearance, like that of a mangy turkey. Worse even than the rest of us, Mexía craved salt, and although we were eating well at Imará, salt was the great lack. Orellana joked with him, trying to rally him and reminding him gently that it was his duty to use his undoubted skill for all of us. But Mexía sourly rejoined that he had no ambition to be a Martín Lopez,* that he did not think Imará a suitable place for boatbuilding because the forest round the village had been cleared by burning to make plantations, and that, from what he could see, there was no good hardwood at hand such as had been so plentiful at El Barco. Even then Orellana was patient with him and merely said he would go into the forest with Mexía to investigate supplies and the problems of cutting and hauling.

* "Martín Lopez, who built the ships for Cortés on the lake surrounding Montezuma's city of Tenochtitlán, was a master craftsman. First he built two very speedy craft, and when we returned after the [disastrous defeat of the] Night of Sorrow, thirteen more, but one of these was no good."—Bernal Díaz: *Historia Verdadera.*

Some said that Diego Mexía should be ashamed of himself and that he was behaving like a wayward girl, because he had not minded supervising the building of the *San Pedro* and ordering everybody else about, including Gonzalo Pizarro himself, but that he had "pretended" to be sick all the way to Imará to save himself the labour of rowing that same brigantine down the river. Others, however, and they were in the majority, said that Mexía was right, and why should we break our backs building another brigantine? They said that the Indians were our friends, and that therefore, when we had rested and laid in supplies and the sick compañeros were on the way to recovery, we should continue downstream in the *San Pedro* and the canoes. Orellana ignored such talk; by that I do not mean that he knew nothing about it, I mean that he pretended not to hear it.

The spirits of our party were fallen to their lowest ebb. They had been high immediately after our arrival at Imará, but had speedily dropped in spite of the excellent supplies of food. To make things yet more dismal, that night two of the compañeros died. When Father Carvajal had given absolution to Sebastián de Fuenterrabía and Diego Moreno, he called several of us, including Orellana, to sit with them in their last moments. Poor Fuenterrabía had worked on his fishing net while he lay at the point of death and had finished enough of it to be useful in small creeks. He had bequeathed the net—and this seemed very strange—to Hernández the Unlucky. According to the friars, Hernández had been continually hanging about the sick men's hut, doing them trifling services, and it seemed likely that he had been after more than a bit of fishing net, which apparently was all that he got for his pains. We could ill spare either of these good men, and we buried them sadly in a deep grave inside one of the huts, working without lights lest the Indians should see what we were doing.

There followed twenty-four hours of rest from all save guard duties, for it was Twelfth-night, and not a merry one for those of us who had enjoyed bright childhoods and remembered our eager anticipation of the Three Kings and the gifts they had brought us. That day two more of the sick, Juan de Arnalte and Baltasar Osorio, slid rather than plunged into the sea of death.

As the number coming under the care of the friars and excused from all work was daily increasing, we began to fear that we had a plague among us. We still had some of the sarsaparilla we had brought from Guayaquil, and there were camomiles among Pizarro's stores in the brigantine. Potions from these good herbs did much for some, but nothing for others. The friars, and particularly the skinny Father Vera, who was tolerant of weakness in others, did their duty, praying their voices away and taking little sleep. One of our detachment (whom I will not, or rather cannot, name) was the possessor of a certain charm that was said to have cured many of the sick and badly wounded in Benalcázar's campaigns. This charm was used day after day, and some said it had more good effects than any other remedy. All the same, we lost at intervals three more compañeros. First, Juan de Aguilar, then Alonso Gutiérrez, and last of all, not long before we left Imará, Arévalo the Horseman. Arévalo had been one of the weakest from the beginning, but had held out more stoutly than any. When he went, he was but a big skeleton, and so light that a child of six could have carried him to his grave. May he rest in peace, for there were few like him. Amen.

Thus, without fresh wounds, but merely as a result of struggling against the climate and privation, we lost seven good men in that village, and our numbers were reduced to forty-nine fighting men, two friars, and two Negroes.

Turning to more cheerful subjects, Juan de Alcántara and his assistant made a tolerable forge by setting a steel buckler inverted on legs and improvising a bellows from the soft leather of a pair of high boots. Then the toil of making nails went on to the point of exhausting us all. Some may incline to imagine that this voyage of ours was a period of repose, that we merely sat in boats and were carried eastward by the natural flow of great rivers. I assure such people, who must be landsmen as well as fools, that boats of any description voraciously consume the energies of those who man them. The climate at Imará, with air steamy and thick as lentil broth, made a man sweat away his strength if he lay still in a shady corner, and was far from conducive to hard work—or good temper either. Now we were drenched by sudden downpour, now melted by the heat of the vertical sun, now half-stifled by clammy mist, and always irritated to the point of madness by insects. Several men collapsed each day on their way back to the village from wood-cutting for the charcoal kilns, and it soon came to be that less than half of us were doing all the heavier work while the others took over guard duties and such tasks as working the bellows. Despite deaths and difficulties, Señores, in twenty days two thousand long nails and several iron fittings had been forged out of horseshoes.

On Monday, January 9, Orellana gave me more writing to do when eleven caciques, including one called Irimara, who seemed to be more important than the others, came to pay their respects, and we made out an affidavit that they had been taken over in the name of His Majesty. But it almost seemed that the caciques had looked at us and had not greatly liked what they saw, though we had nearly cracked our cheeks with smiling at them, the ingrates. For as our days of labour dragged by, the Indians came less and less until, as the end of January drew near, none came at all. The sudden stoppage of supplies was not so serious as it might have been. Orellana, who had been talking with the Indians every day, had realized that they were getting tired of our presence in their village, and he had built up reserves in the time of plenty. But how long would the reserves last fifty-three mouths? And it is almost impossible to keep food from the ants and weevils in those places.

Those who had reluctantly accepted the Captain's plan to wait two or three months at Imará began to say we must move on. We had not liked the continual come-and-go of the Indians, but we liked their complete absence even less. Among the more violent characters I heard mutters of rebellion, and some of these, for his own sake, I repeated to Orellana.

"Exactly what are they saying, Bachelor of Arts?"

"Some say— You would wish me to be frank?"

"I would."

"Some say that you intend to stop here to cosset your precious honour and waste our lives."

"Go on."

"I have heard it said that you are so afraid of Gonzalo Pizarro that you will never stir from here."

"Anything else?"

"There is another opinion that you have too much property in Peru, and that you fear you may lose it if you do your duty and lead us, your men and your servants, to safety."

I may say, in justice to myself and to Orellana, that he never asked for the names of his detractors, nor would I have given them. Also he was, as are all our best officers and dignitaries, very approachable, and much of this criticism was spoken to his face. He was, I think you will admit, in a situation where his authority had to be supported by guile and tact, and he was bound to consider the will of the majority.

On the last day of January, after Mass, Orellana offered a reward of one thousand gold pesos to any six Spaniards who would venture upstream with a well-provisioned canoe in a last attempt to see if Gonzalo Pizarro was within reach of us. He said he would send with the six his two Negroes, the best paddlers in the camp. There were no immediate replies to this offer, which indeed was greeted with barely muffled derision. The Captain told me later that three men whom he did not name had come forward secretly; but they were only willing to make the attempt if he would, as well as the Negroes, give them three crossbowmen. By thus throwing away three out of his five crossbowmen Orellana would have ruined his detachment's chance of survival. So it would seem that those three, whoever they were, wished to curry favour, yet made their offer negative by demanding the impossible.

Accordingly on February 2, which was Candlemas, the feast day of the Purification of Our Lady, we embarked once more in the brigantine and the canoes, rejoicing to leave the Indian village of Imará, which had been our salvation.

CHAPTER THIRTEEN

☼

FOR MEN OF ACTION ONE DAY SHOULD NEVER BE THE SAME as another, and variety is to life what salt is to meat, and flint is to steel, and love is to a woman.

When we had reached Imará, we stepped from the boats hoping we would never sit in the confounded things again. When we left Imará, however, we joked and sang and shouted for joy as paddles and oars bit at the running water. We were on the move, and life once more was a gamble, its twists and its endings known only to God.

Imará was thirty leagues * astern when we came to the junction of the Canelos with another great stream that entered from the right.† Nor was the meeting of the two by any means orderly, for the one fought the other with much roaring, clouds of spume, beds of foam, and many watery commotions.

Orellana said we would halt above this dangerous place and negotiate it the next morning. There were few to disagree with his decision until it became known that he intended to go up the new river for some distance, looking for the head settlement of the cacique called Irimara, who had visited him some three weeks earlier. He would not argue about it, but merely told us that Irimara was all-powerful on the next long stretch of river, and that if we could claim his friendship we should be fed and entertained for the next hundred leagues or so instead of starving as we had done between Christmas Camp and Imará. Maldonado and a few of the others were not to be stifled, and they began to voice their discontent until Bermúdez the sailor went unobtrusively from person to person saying that the new river was in such spate that there would be no chance of our mounting it, even if our lives depended upon doing so.

* 110 miles. † The River Curaray.

In the morning we were soon among the broken water. The current of the new river was even fiercer than we had supposed, and it hurled along with it numerous floating trees of great size. There were whirlpools that had to be avoided. Orellana had ordered the canoes to stay close to the brigantine, but canoe after canoe, in danger of swamping, had to allow itself to be swept downstream, while in the sternsheets of the *San Pedro* Orellana stood yelling encouragements to the oarsmen. At last even he saw that they were beaten. He pulled the brigantine round with the steering sweep. Those at the oars, worn out by their efforts against the stream, then had to pull more strongly than ever to save themselves from the dangers off-lying the banks. Thus did the new river settle the question of our courtesy visit to Irimara, and most of us were inclined to bless it, for during the rest of that day we passed grim country, seeing on the banks nothing but desolation.

The left bank, crumbling and low, had been washed away in long sections by the flood waters, which expanded on that side in endless vistas of lagoons, with trees growing out of the water like bristles on the skin of a hog. The higher right bank had been populated, but every village was a black heap of ashes sodden by the rains. We at first supposed (I speak for myself and my crew) that Irimara's subjects had burned their homes and withdrawn lest we should visit them and do them injury. But when we halted for the night, other possible explanations were advanced by Papa Illanes, who was always seeking to reason things out. His suggestions were:

1. That Irimara's tribe was at war, and a victorious enemy had moved up the right bank, sacking as he marched.

2. That the region had been attacked by pestilence and therefore the Indians had destroyed their villages hoping that the area would be healthy again when the river subsided and the season of the great fishings came round once more.

3. That it might be the custom of certain riverside Indians to build new villages each spring in preparation for the turtle-hunting and the fishing, then burn the villages and move into the forest for the hunting and trapping of the rainy months.

For all we knew, Illanes was capable of making suggestions

throughout the rest of that night, since once he began talking he was as hard to stop as a stone-mouthed stallion. But Orellana interrupted to say that since the villages were burned, talking would not rebuild them, and we must get a full night's sleep because we were going to get no supplies in those devastated areas beyond those we could find for ourselves.

This we were better able to do, for we were stronger in health than on our disastrous passage to Imará, were less out of tune with our peculiar surroundings, and had bought with beads at Imará a quantity of Indian nets of palm fibre with which we could fish shallow creeks and the entries to lagoons. Then Hernández the Unlucky had the net bequeathed to him by Sebastián de Fuenterrabía, but nobody expected him to make catches. We were indeed, for the Captain's taste, too keen on hunting and fishing. He insisted many times each day that we must hasten on to the next inhabited region because the Indians for a distance of several hundred leagues probably knew that we were on the river, and if we delayed too much they might suspect us of being weaklings or cowards or, worse still, they might conclude that we intended to settle for ever in their country.

We stopped occasionally to search the burned villages. Some had been inundated until the cultivated plots were more like carp ponds than fields. Nevertheless we found peppers and yucas. These last were the yucas bravas, smaller than the yucas mansas found in Peru, which are harmless and can be eaten like the potatoes of Quito when they have been boiled or roasted. The juice of the wild yucas is poisonous, and before we could cook them we had the labour of squeezing them to pulp and expelling all their liquid. To call the resulting fibre appetizing or even palatable would be the grossest flattery, but when we had fish or meat and some gravy to eat with it, yuca was better than nothing and took the place of bread.

It is time I said something about the weather, which had a great deal to say to us. . . . We had by no means entered anything approaching a dry climate, though it was not so wet as on the skirts of the Cordillera. Sometimes we had a day and a night without rain, and even on wet days there would be periods of sunshine. We came to expect what we called the noon storm. At noon, or shortly after, the eastern sky would darken. The darkness lifted until it hung overhead. Then we would hear the rustle of the east wind in the treetops, loudening and deepening its sound as it combed through the forest, nearer and nearer, until with a growl it would be with us and the rain falling in streams. Half an hour later both rain and wind would be gone, and all was quiet for a little. Then the insects would all sing (and sting) in chorus, and we imagined we could see and hear flowers expanding and shoots shooting, while butterflies big as roosters rose in the washed air to shake out their dazzling wings. All but our arquebusiers welcomed these diurnal showers and looked forward to their freshness, particularly as they swept our attendant clouds of biting insects over the sterns.

Now and again we would get a light morning breeze from the north-west. On such days we did not expect rain. Those in the brigantine would rig a crude square-sail of blankets to take some advantage of the fair wind. But one day we learned how treacherous the north-west breeze could be. . . .

Midday. The sky is china blue. Green forest walls on either hand rise to the height of the trucks of a seventy-gun ship, and in the rigging of lianas climbing to and falling from the tops we occasionally see monkeys, some with the faces of cats, some big as wolves, others small as pigeons. Above the banks, in the steaming shadows, are orchids, tree ferns, canes in groves with festoons of pale-spiked leaves. There are palm trees like women, their hair falling over bended necks, their throats decorated with great single flowers. All this is still, heat-frozen, under the relentless sun. Those green walls, that simple china dome of sky, the rippling back of the potent stream—one thousand paces wide here—might be beautiful; not so to us * who stifle while small torturers drain our blood. To the sandflies are now added other enemies no

* The English naturalist H. W. Bates says: "There is something in the tropical forest akin to the ocean in its effect on the mind. Man feels so completely his insignificance, and the vastness of nature."

The German traveller Hermann Burmeister says that the contemplation of a Brazilian forest depressed him because the vegetation revealed "a spirit of restless selfishness, eager emulation, and craftiness."

less vicious. A fly smaller than a pinhead * settles unperceived and sucks until he swells; the hole he makes festers and the skin around it blackens. Aiding these are bigger sabre-flies † that fly boldly in, slashing us with their long, horny noses, so many squadrons of winged midget Moors. We paddle out of unison, now one of the crew, now another, having to defend himself against slashers, bloodsuckers, biters. Each paddle stroke is an act of abnegation. But the canoe slides on.

Ciganas balance on branches over the water. Cormorants and duck pace the summits of those sandbanks that still show above water. It we had their wings we would rise till the forest lay green below us and would follow the silver paths of great rivers to the greater sea, and cross it to Cuba or Hispaniola. Hispaniola-ola-ola, as the song has it, where the women are lovely, and warm-hearted, and always lonely. . . . Smooth are the backwaters as green mirrors, save where they catch the sky and then they are blue. One heron stands by the edge. He seems to shimmer because the air trembles with heat. He lifts one twiggy leg, cocks his narrow, serious head, the head of a verger. Egrets, puffy and light, sit beside the river. Perhaps they sleep. . . . But something is amiss.

The sky turns swiftly from blue to yellow, yellow to green, green to a reddish darkness. The deep water begins, most mysteriously, to tremble under us. We paddle closer to the brigantine, whose crew are looking uneasily about them. Bermúdez from Palos tells the Captain that shelter must be sought, but where it may be found he does not know and cannot guess until from the north-west comes a rumbling as though of cannon assaulting a bastion at very close range. We turn from midstream and, bending over oars and paddles, make all speed for the right bank, which should offer a lee—if we can reach it. The first gust. It is hot as steam and so powerful that our canoe is hurled sideways, while ahead of us the heavy *San Pedro* lists until the lee gunwale ships water, the weather oars flog the air. Any loose things in the brigantine, including a dozen live parrots kept for the pot and some Peruvian blankets, are torn out and whisked away across

* Piums. † Motucas.

the sullen and heaving river. After the gust, a pause, of which we make the fullest use, panting with our efforts. We are all near the bank when the wind comes off it again, stronger than before. The river instantly builds up a sea. I am a Biscayan, and I know a sea. This one is soon covered with hissing foam and a swell runs under. As we make the bank two canoes founder. We are safe in a creek. Both Negroes and other strong swimmers plunge in to help our friends in the water. The upturned canoes are dragged inshore. No lives lost.

Now the palms, so still before, vibrate and screech. The stouter trees bend and jump as the hot blast bears on them. Rending timber, shrieking wind; it is bedlam. We lie on the mud. The wisest of the herons and egrets do likewise, facing the wind, bills dug in, thin legs outstretched behind them. The clever ones only have their feathers disarranged; others, who try to stand, are whipped away, mere puffs of tumbling feathers. Raindrops beat at us with the impact of grape.

The sea grows darker, higher, until one great wave comes round the bend upstream, moves diagonally across the channel demolishing all islands, sand, trees, everything. The wave strikes the bank opposite us. There the trees bend until their heads nearly touch the ground, then spring back bravely. What catapults! No walls could withstand their missiles. But they are loosening their roots. The weakened earth gives way. Long pieces of that bank and forest, monkeys, birds, smash into the storming water.

More suddenly than it came, the storm is over. When we understand that the wind has travelled on, we busy ourselves, laying about among the recumbent herons with sticks and swords. We find three big, hairy monkeys, as dead as dead can be. The waves still run high on the river. We make a great stew of heron, monkey, bananas, peppers, and yucas. We eat until all is finished, and while we eat we look at and listen to the other bank, where destruction has set up its own rhythm. When the edge of the forest falls, it sends out a surge of water that flies against the sea, then recoils in a backwash so irresistible that it brings down the bank, the trees, again. So it goes on, as though it will never stop. Had we turned to that bank when the sky first darkened, the forest in its fit of disintegration would have turned us and our boats into a nourishing soup for fishes and alligators.

When we have travelled three leagues from that place, we still hear the thunder of the falling banks. The river is dangerous, covered with floating trees, and the current much swifter than we have known it.

Sunset comes. The howling of monkeys. The screeching of parrots flying high over us in their monogamous formations. The hooting of frogs. None of us care to approach the forest on either hand, for we know it to be as vulnerable as before it had seemed strong. Diego Bermúdez makes fast the *San Pedro*'s bow rope to a floating rosewood tree, an immense jacaranda. We in the canoes paddle in and make fast to the brigantine fore and aft, chickens coming under the mother's wings. The jacaranda tows us down the wide river. The tree is not one of the recent casualties. It has floated many hundreds of leagues from its perch under the mountains. Its branches rise from the water like arms, and they are garlanded with convolvuli fragrant in the dew of evening. In every crevice of the tree, sand and leaf-mould have gathered and flowers live. Our tree is more gracious than the tame garden of a duchess.

Panama and Number Five go out among the flowers on the wide trunk, make fire there, and cook the soup. We are far from the banks; no mosquitoes smell us out. We pass our gourds to the tree. When we have eaten, we pass them to the Captain, who fills them with chicha from Imará. Tongues are loosened. In the lapping stillness of night, we listen to the good talkers who know how to put words to their thoughts of home, of the comedy of life in the Indies, of the great, the sad, and the ridiculous moments of conquest. Somebody sings. Who is it, with the voice fruity as the bilges of a sardiner? It is Juan de Mangas, from the sweet port of Santa María.

Quién vos había de llevar
¡Oxalá!
¡Ay, Fátima, Fátima!
Fátima la tan garrida
Levaros he a Sevilla

Teneros he por amiga
¡Oxalá!
¡Ay, Fátima, Fátima!

The singing and the talking turn to yawns. Father Carvajal thanks God for our escape and for the food He brought us in the storm. We lie in our boats to sleep, the dew falling cool upon blackened skins, forming in clusters of pearls on uncombed beards. The expedition travels on its exploration—asleep. *¡Ay, Fátima, Fátima!*

Strengthened by a night without either sentry duties or mosquitoes, we awoke to hear the seamen saying that we had travelled twelve leagues * attached to the jacaranda. As we were very dirty and there was soap in the brigantine, we went out on the floating tree to wash our bodies, while some, myself among them, dived into the river. I will not pretend that I enjoyed the experience, and I was no sooner in than I was pulling myself out. Indians at Imará had told Orellana that it was safe to swim in midstream but that near the banks there was danger from a small fish † that enters man's penis to cause torture and death. The Indian fishermen went to their work naked save that their penises were sheathed against this most horrible of water menaces. Those of us who swam regretted it. We were chilled and shaky (although the water had been warmer than the air) for the rest of the morning, and we felt the noon heats more than usual. We concluded that it is unhealthy to bathe in those waters.

My canoe and the one commanded by Pedro Domínguez Miradero were in the lead when we sighted two Indian pigs swimming for the left bank. We gave chase, and Domínguez Miradero cleverly made his paddlers steady the canoe while he still more cleverly with his silver-mounted arquebus put a ball through the eye of one of the pigs at fifteen paces—a brilliant shot or a very lucky one. While it floundered, they came over it and stuck it with a pike. Meanwhile its companion (probably its wife), swimming and diving, made for the shallows, with our canoe giving chase. My crossbow was ready, for I was not going to be outdone by Domínguez Miradero, who was no friend to me. Hit through

* 44 miles. † The candiru.

the shoulder as she drew herself out, the sow fell back into the water. The war bolt was buried deep, yet the brave animal found courage and strength to stand up and turn on us. When we had killed it, the Negroes jumped into the water and, each taking two legs, heaved it up the bank. Orellana shouted to us that we were to skin the pigs, cut out the stinking warts on their backs, butcher them, and wrap the joints in damp leaves. The other compañeros wanted, as usual, to fish. Orellana said he would take them downstream and would stop to cast the nets at the first likely place under the left bank, where our two canoes were to join them.

The butcher work completed, we paddled downstream in company with Domínguez Miradero's canoe. All afternoon we paddled, and the farther we went, the more we wondered where Orellana and the others might be. Why had they gone on so fast? Were they making game of us? . . . Night fell. At Domínguez Miradero's suggestion, we lashed the canoes side by side. Half the crews paddled, watching for the campfire of the Spaniards, while the other half slept. Morning came without any sign of them. We landed on a sandy spit and roasted some of the wild pig. There was nothing wrong with the meat save that we were in no mood to think any meat good. None of us said so, but all knew that if we did not find the others we were doomed. We were ten Spaniards and a pair of Negroes, too few to beat off any determined attack on water or on land. To make things worse, we were ill-supplied in every way because the *San Pedro* was our storehouse, and the Captain inclined to keep everything under his personal supervision. Our joint defensive armament consisted of my crossbow and Domínguez Miradero's firespout. I had eighteen bolts, and no metal heads for making any more, while the arquebusier, even more improvident, was very short of powder.

We were all sure that we had not passed the brigantine. Therefore it was ahead of us. Would we find it? The river was so split up by islands that it was impossible to say which was the main channel.

All day we paddled on, saying little. When we came to two channels of equal width our canoes separated, to rejoin below the island. These separations racked our nerves and strained our voices, for when we did not find the other canoe where we expected it we would begin to shout. That night we landed at the upper end of a big island, where we found good wild bananas. A guard was set and a great fire was kept burning. Domínguez Miradero and I were still on terms. The emergency was so grave, so unexpected, that we did not trouble to decide who had the higher authority, but worked together like twin brothers. While we were conferring in the dawn we saw deep tracks by our feet and knew that a jaguar had been moving round the camp during the night and had been within a few paces of the sentries without alarming them. We supposed that the flood had trapped him there, far from either bank. Or perhaps he had been brought downstream upon a floating island. Under different circumstances we would all have combined to hunt him. But we were in no mood for amusement or unnecessary excitement.

Few of us had much hope left that we would see the brigantine again. Streams joined the main river from many directions, and one tributary glittered as the waking sun touched the sand of its bed. What if the glitter was gold? We paddled on. Many an unspoken vow must have been made among us, many a promise of alms, of pilgrimage, many a supplication to Our Blessed Jesus Christ and to Mary His noble and most Holy Mother.

In the early afternoon, fifty-four hours after our separation from the others, we saw boats ahead, looking like three beetles crawling between and under the vast walls of forest. They were Indian canoes. We hid for a while, drawn in under overhanging branches, and when the Indians had disappeared downstream we paddled to a small, hummocked island that we thought we could defend. We were nearing the island when the brigantine with its attendant canoes came round a bend two thirds of a league upstream. We knew the *San Pedro*'s waddle, and there was no doubt among us. On the other hand, those with the brigantine saw only two canoes, and while they doubted, prayed, and hoped, they did not know that it was us until they were nearer.

Unbounded the rejoicing, unbounded the recriminations, on both sides. The period of separation might have been years instead of days. It seemed that soon after they had left us skinning our pigs, they had gone into the mouth of a creek to fish, assuming that we were watching them, had seen them go in there, and would soon join them. When they realized that we must have passed they had wasted much time looking for us in different channels, just as we had looked for them. Orellana decided that we would land and haul out the boats to give our reunited party one whole day of rest. When we were ashore he said:

"Gentlemen: Although we say God helps us, which He does, or fate is on our side, which it should be, the truth is that we must help ourselves. . . . Because we assumed this latter stretch of the river to be uninhabited we all grew careless, and I do not exclude myself, for I must take most of the blame. Our expedition has been degenerating into a fishing outing. From these two days of ceaseless worry we will draw three lessons. Firstly, our ever-watchful Saviour saw fit to bring us together again, which I hope to be an omen of success. Secondly, from this day no canoe is ever to be farther than a crossbow-shot from the brigantine. Thirdly, at the earliest opportunity we will build a second brigantine and dispense with canoes altogether, and this time I assure you," looking at Diego Mexía, "when I tell you to build, you will build whether you like it or not." Then he asked the Dominican to say Mass, which was done.

We had a day of talk, sleep, fishing, and shooting parrots (which without doubt were created to be eaten by man because their flesh surpasses that of any bird reared for the table or commonly shot as game). That night something happened that at the time raised a commotion, so I will tell you of it.

Monkeys are shy animals, most difficult to shoot, and the Indians in those places go to endless pains in setting monkey ambushes. You may therefore imagine my excitement. . . . I was on sentry-go. It was about three in the morning. I saw a biggish body move near the top of a tall tree. I kept my eye fixed on the place, and had to wait a long time before the moonlight, piercing the upper leaves, revealed another movement. It was more than flesh and blood could stand. What I was doing was entirely contrary to all regulations governing the behaviour of sentries, but I wound my crossbow, reasoning that if I missed, nobody would know I had fired, and if I did not miss, a body would fall to the ground, two or three compañeros might turn over in their sleep, and that would be all. I waited for the next movement and, seeing it, took instant aim and fired. Then hell broke loose. As I had foreseen, a heavy body hurtled down, breaking branches as it fell. What I had not foreseen was that the "body" was roaring and yelling like ten thousand fiends. Behind me I heard the camp springing to arms and the Captain gathering his men round him. Before me, clutching at the bolt that had mortally wounded him, was a monkey, a great hairy red-coated brute of unimaginably ferocious appearance. He had a swollen pouch under his chin, and from the pouch he produced his terrible noise while he glared at me and gnashed his long and dangerous teeth. Something had to be done. Half-sick, half-afraid of the monkey, and wholly afraid of Orellana, I seized hold of a heavy branch and beat the creature's head in. Long after he should have been dead and cold, he was still writhing and making his noises. Next day I was forgiven the night's disturbance by most of the compañeros because the brute made excellent eating. I had to take their word for it, Orellana having punished me by condemning me to five days' rations of nothing but yucas and water.

When he said Mass that morning, Father Carvajal had reminded us that it was February 12 and St. Eulalia's Day. It was the tenth day after leaving Imará village, and it was to be a memorable one. In the afternoon two great rivers appeared to join ours, from the right, but as we went on we saw that this was not so, and that these were two branches of one enormous river. The dark waters of our Canelos were swallowed up at the confluence, where a strong east wind blew, and we wallowed and splashed in the ochre-coloured chop of the new river. Once truly out near the middle of it, we began to understand its vastness. Although it ran with a steady current at a speed estimated by us at a league in the hour, it was more sea than river. For all their size and power, the Coca and the Canelos had been rivers running through forest. This new river dwarfed the forests. They were mere fringes that it allowed to cling to its banks. And perhaps because of this change in scale, or because of the new freshness in the air, the forests looked more uniform, less luxuriant, less ferny, than those we had come to know so well. The river came out of the sky astern, ran east between two dwindling lines of forest, and poured into the sky ahead. Gone were the stifling confines of the big tributaries we had followed. On those great waters we saw what we had not seen since the upper slopes of the Eastern Cordillera, the unrestricted play of sun, wind, rain, and cloud. It was as though blinkers had been taken from our eyes, and pads from our mouths. But if the new-found glories of space were invigorating, they were also daunting, and we were glad when evening approached and the Captain steered the brigantine for the left bank.*

No sooner were the boats made fast to trees than he spoke to all of us, saying he believed we were on the road to famous discoveries and eventual refuge. These, he said, must be the greatest confined waters on earth, and we were the Christians chosen to explore them and to stake our lawful claim to them in the name of His Majesty.

"And of Gonzalo Pizarro?" asked some jester at the back.

"And by the authority of the Governor and Captain General, Gonzalo Pizarro," Orellana continued, his single eye darting among us. He confessed that while we were navigating the other rivers, powerful and wide though they had been, he had sometimes feared they might fling themselves over precipices or vanish into awful holes or storming tunnels. It was unimaginable, he went on, that any void could contain this phoenix of rivers; if it poured into a hole, it would drag all the earth with it into the same hole and to perdition. We could assume that as we went down it, the river would increase in girth and would water more prosperous lands, yet already it was big enough to contain every

* "As we sat in the stern of the vessel [a river steamer], at night, looking up this vast river stretching many hundreds of leagues, with its solitary shores and impenetrable forests, it was hard to resist an oppressive sense of loneliness."—Mrs. Elizabeth Cary Agassiz.

"The march of the great river . . . in the untamed might of its turbid waters . . . was awful. Its waters looked angry, sullen, relentless; and the whole scene awoke emotions of awe and dread—such as are caused by the funeral solemnities, the minute gun, the howl of the wind, and the angry tossing of the waves, when all hands are called to bury the dead in a troubled sea."—Lieutenant William Lewis Herndon, U.S.N. (usually an unrewarding traveller, a mixture of taciturnity and cockiness), on reaching the Amazon from its headwaters.

river in Spain, could they be gathered into one, and those of France and Italy for good measure.* He therefore thought it must be the river whose mouth had been discovered in the year 1500 by the Castilian explorer Captain Vincente Yañez Pinzón, who called it the Fresh-Water Sea. Other servants of His Cæsarean Majesty, the Captain said, had subsequently arrived at the mouths of this river, which spanned many scores of leagues and spewed far out into the Northern Sea, so that several days' sail from their landfall mariners had only to lower buckets into the sea to obtain drinking water. And the river, he knew not why,† had come to be called the Marañón.

No Castilian, no Christian, he said, had witnessed the glories and riches that surely existed on the banks of so notable a river. We must bear ourselves as worthy servants of Don Carlos, fear-

* Vastness of the Amazon: "All the United States could be packed into the Amazon valley. The Amazon itself drains one million square miles more than the Missisipi."—James Orton.

"The valley of the Amazons is . . . a plain some 700 or 800 miles wide and between 2,000 and 3,000 miles long, with a slope so slight that it scarcely averages a foot in 10 miles. Between Obydos and the sea, a distance of about 800 miles, the fall is only 45 ft.; between Tabatinga and the seashore, a distance of more than 2,000 miles, the fall is about 200 ft."—Professor Louis Agassiz.

The rise and fall of the Amazon between wet and dry seasons "is certainly not less than 40, and probably often 50 ft.; if therefore we think of the huge water surface rising 50 ft. annually we shall gain an idea of the immense quantity of water. . . . We cannot take the length of the Amazon and its main tributaries at less than 10,000 miles, and their average width about two miles, so that there will be a surface of 26,000 square miles of water raised 50 ft. each year. But not only this surface is raised, for a great extent of land on the banks of the rivers is flooded to a considerable depth."—Alfred Russel Wallace.

"The basin covers an area of 2,722,000 square miles, and affords 13,738 miles of safely navigable communications."—*South America Pilot.* But the same Admiralty publication (1945) goes on to state: "The river was first *as*cended by Orellana in 1541."

† Nor do we know why to this day. According to Medina, the river was so named in February 1513 by Juan Rodríguez, a pilot. From 1515 on, the name Marañón was in common use, and the river was marked on certain charts, the mouth being shown in approximately its correct latitude.

ing nothing, daring all, in a voyage of discovery that, if God saw fit to allow it a successful conclusion, would bring honour and profit to each and every one of us.

"And to Gonzalo Pizarro?" asked another voice from the back.

Then Bermúdez and the other seamen said that they too had heard of this Marañón and had seen its egress marked on pilots' charts of the Indies. They said that its mouths should be within sailing range, granted good weather at sea, of the pearl island of Cubagua. That would mean sailing up the coastline to the northward, then westward past the dangerous Dragon's Mouth that gapes some distance above another great river,* but one considerably less great, by all accounts, than the pulsing monster, Marañón.

Nine days later we saw Indian canoes among some islands clustered off the left bank. A considerable village on *tierra firme* was deserted, but opposite it, on the biggest of the islands, Indians stood round some huts. Those in the brigantine rested on their oars in the offing. The Captain ordered the canoes inshore, enjoining us not to land and not to lose our tempers if there should be signs of dislike or offensiveness among the Indians, but to withdraw at once for further orders and the support of the brigantine.

The Indians were hideous. Their skins were blotched with some leprous disease and their mouths were painted black both inside and out. They wore claw necklaces, and nothing else save for great bouquets of flowers, leaves, and feathers, which stuck out from their ears, whose lobes had been stretched into thin sacks that brushed their shoulders. They looked, in short, like the hounds of death. Nevertheless they were as friendly as they were ugly, and they brought us splendid gifts, parrots, and turtles of a size and weight that astonished every man among us. They asked us by signs to go across the channel and make ourselves at home in the empty village. This we did after rewarding them with some handfuls of pretty beads.

The turtle steaks were rich—perhaps a trifle too rich for our digestions. When darkness came, sentries were posted and the rest

* The Orinoco.

of us lay down to sleep off the turtle, but found it impossible because of the noise the sentries insisted on making. When I went out with some of the others to complain about this, the sentries galloped around us, shouting and whirling their arms. One had gone into the river with all his clothes on and was using his helmet to cascade water over his head. The reason for these unsoldierly outbursts? Merely mosquitoes. When I say "merely," I do not belittle the sentries, for in a minute we were all behaving like them. The Captain told each sentry to take a bunch of fronds and swish his companion; it was of little use. Building up the fires, we loaded the boats by their light (not forgetting the turtles, each of which was a full carry for a strong man), and we moved far out over the river, where there was a breeze. We were able to get some sleep while only two men rowed in the brigantine and one paddled in the stern of each canoe, but there were many alerts because Indian canoes were afloat, and some came very near us, though only, it seemed, out of curiosity.

In the morning we landed at another village that Orellana thought better sited, for it was on a point, and got the benefit of such air as went up or down the Marañón. The Indians were friendly enough, and gave us all the food they could spare. Orellana got out his vocabularies and soon was able to talk to them. They told him we had reached the lands of the great overlord Aparia, and that we would see no more burned villages. News of our approach had gone before us. They had heard of our hairiness and that we did not get drunk (this they thought both unmanly and foolish), nor go and squat in the river after meals, nor paint ourselves, nor bore holes in our faces to serve as flowerpots and feather vases. They also kept repeating the Castilian word "*oro*" in a mocking manner. When Orellana heard this, he became exceedingly thoughtful. At length he took me aside where nobody could see or hear us and said: "Dearly beloved Bachelor of Arts, be good enough to tell me the meaning of this, for well do I know that if Acaray dreams of Doña Beatriz or if Carillo sleeps badly because of a thorn in the second toe of his left foot, you know all about it in the morning."

I conceived it my duty to tell him how at the village of Imará, despite his orders to the contrary, a few of the compañeros who coveted the gold ornaments worn by the natives had gone among them bartering, and repeating: "*Oro? Oro?*" thinking that that, of all words, must be comprehensible to all peoples. The Imará Indians had laughed, but had occasionally produced ornaments, nuggets, and small bags of gold dust.

Orellana required me to give the names of the men who had thus bartered. I refused, on the ground that they would suspect me of betraying them and might kill me for it, and also that in so bartering they had meant no harm. But on receiving his promise that he only wanted the names for his own edification, would make none of them public, and would punish nobody, and on hearing him swear an extremely complicated oath and mention his honour, and say that he would have my crossbow taken away from me and keep me scrivening for the rest of my life if I did not comply with his wishes, I obeyed. He was astonished at some of the names.

That afternoon there was a muster and Orellana inspected our weapons. He was moved to anger at the state in which he found them, and it may have been that he was especially incensed with each of the parties named by me earlier. He ordered them, and others, to take some of the spongy stone that floats in those rivers,* which we collected when we saw it, to rub the rust away, and then to treat the steel with turtle oil and sharpen the blades. Then he made a few unwelcome observations.

"Gentlemen: When I give an order, it is for the security and profit of us all. He who disobeys is a traitor and deserves no mercy." At this there were sounds of general agreement, and after looking to see who agreed most heartily, he continued: "At Imará certain among you pestered Indians for gold, and you bought gold with beads and other articles that could and should have been kept for exchange against more useful commodities. These Indians revere gold as little as you revere weevils or dung.

* Pumice stone. "Fishermen twice brought me small rounded pieces of very porous pumice stone . . . messengers from the distant volcanoes Cotopaxi, Llanganete, or Sangay. . . . The stones must already have travelled some 1,200 miles. . . . The Brazilians believe them to be solidified river foam."—H. W. Bates, on the Upper Amazon.

Next time you are starving on this river, try to buy food from them with gold. You will get none. . . . I knew of this treason when it happened at Imará. I knew which of you were the guilty ones. I did not punish then because you were weak from suffering and saddened by the deaths of seven brave friends. I will not punish now. But I insist that my order was a just and sensible one because here, hundreds of leagues from Imará, the Indians are aware that some of us lust for the gold that they in their ignorance despise. They laugh at us, and that is dangerous. So take care, gentlemen. Do not imagine that I am blind in *both* eyes, or that my mercy and patience are all-enduring. That is all I have to say."

This caused some commotion in the camp, and after a while that quarrelsome man from Torrejón de Velasco whom we called Maldonado came before me looking as sour as a hungry priest. He would not let me pass, but called me by scurrilous names, including "spy" and "informer" and worse. Then he made to strike me, and in self-defence I put my hand on my sword hilt. Instantly we had both drawn and swordplay began, while those around, nothing loath for entertainment, formed a circle. I told Maldonado that I would not tolerate his bullying ways, and that nothing could save him. He told me he intended cutting me into morsels, beginning with my ears and my nose and continuing to other even more important parts of my anatomy. Maldonado was a fine swordsman, very volatile, with a wrist of steel. He had, however, one weakness: his wind was poor and he was a garrulous fighter. Now, as he worked away at me, he recounted parts of his life history:

"Was it to be insulted by such scum as you that I went to Nicaragua in the year 1519 and was the right hand of Captain Martín Astete when we opened up the Desaguadero? Now I propose to open you up—*take that!* . . . You were not at the conquest of Quito, but I was, and Benalcázar knew it. . . . *Would you?* Was it not I who, after Popayán, defeated the Indians below the Sierra de los Alcazares and captured all those women and porters and enough supplies to— *Dog! give way!* My lance played its part in the founding of Timaná. *Ah, fledgling, first blood!*"

At that moment he had managed to nick my right ear, and as

his footwork was very polished and he had the longer reach, I could do little in the way of retaliation until he got short of breath. I rejoiced to hear him waste it in boasting.

"Did I or did I not help Juan de Cabrera to found the city of Neïba?"

"You did not," I answered.

"Liar! If I did not do as I said, how in God's name did I become Regidor at Neïba with a grant of two hundred Indians and—"

"Boasting will not save your skin."

"Insect!"

Then Orellana came running from a hut, followed by Alonso de Robles and Papa Illanes. Drawing their swords, they separated us and ordered others to hold us tightly by the arms.

The Captain demanded an explanation. I said Maldonado had known no better than to pick a quarrel by offering me unendurable insults. Maldonado said my version of it was the truth, and that he had called me informer because I had told the Captain which men had obtained gold at Imará.

"Such duplicity was more than I could endure," said Maldonado, "because this wretch was himself concerned in the barter, as always when there is gold in the offing; and he obtained more gold than any three of the rest of us put together. If you disbelieve me, have him searched."

"I will have nobody searched," Orellana answered. "And it happens that I knew Isásaga was one of the guilty men, so how could he have betrayed the rest of you?"

"Then why did you pick on us for the state of our arms, yet not on Isásaga?"

"Your sword, with which you are so free about our own selfish business, was blunt and rusty; Isásaga's crossbow was as clean as the day it left the forge at Mondragón." Then he made Maldonado apologize to me for his insults, and he made me apologize to him for having drawn upon him. And as punishment he took away our swords and set us both to cutting out and cooking turtle, which was a greasy, hot, and tedious operation, and one for which I was ill-suited, but Maldonado, with his airs of hectoring grandeur, even less.

In the morning I asked the Captain if he had believed Maldonado's lies about me. His answer was that he believed no accusations against any of his men, and that as for the matter of the gold at Imará, he had forgotten who was concerned in it and who was not. He added that he would tolerate no more bother between Maldonado and myself, because one or the other would get killed, and he could spare neither. I assured him that we had become good friends while we sweated together over the turtles. This was the truth, and Orellana believed it readily, for he remarked that Maldonado's aptitude for forcing quarrels on others was only exceeded by his aptitude for inducing them to forgive his outrageous behaviour. And he also said: "I cannot help liking Maldonado; but whenever I do not like him I hate him."

We stayed three whole days in that village, whose name I never heard. Orellana was in two minds as to whether we should go on or whether, since the people were friendly, we should build the second brigantine there. But he reasoned that it would be bad manners to stop thus at the frontier of the great Aparia's domain, and that we had best go on to find Aparia himself.

He was disappointed and mistrustful when on the morning of our departure those Indians who had cheerfully agreed to come with us downstream as guides did not appear and could not be found. We all feared that this presaged a bad reception when we arrived at the centre of Aparia's power, where he would have had ample time to gather and prepare his warriors. But Orellana put a good face on it.

At that time the Marañón was continually disturbed by east winds, with midday squalls of rain and wind that whipped up a steep head sea. We kept to the shoreline in order to have the shelter we needed in the squalls, and also to continue testing the temper of Aparia's people. The villages were prosperous by Indian standards, drunken, and at peace. At least once each day we lay to off a village and the Indian men waded in to barter food for chaquira. We made such excellent bargains that we came to believe we were destined to grow fat. Maize we got wherever we stopped, and it was most welcome after something of a surfeit of yucas. They sold us quantities of fish, many superb turtles, which they imprisoned in muddy fenced enclosures to provide fresh meat during the winter, and guacamayos, big fat parrots with green and red feathers. The Indians kept their guacamayos as pets and as providers of feathers for facial embellishment and ceremonial robes. They doted on the birds. So did we, but after a different fashion. To avoid giving offence, we never wrung their necks until we were out of sight of those who, with sincere protestations of affectionate sorrow, had sold them to us for beads. The one disconcerting aspect of these encounters with the populace was that we saw neither women nor children. The men kept them hidden. They could not have known the envious reputation we Spaniards hold in such matters, but instinct probably warned them that their wives might become amorous at the merest glimpse of us—though a little discernment would have been required on their part because they would have seen nothing but hair, eyes, and a few patches of bite-, sun-, and wind-tormented skin.

On Sunday, February 26, some canoes came out to meet us. We closed our formation, and when Orellana had had a good look at them, he called them nearer and spoke with the Indians in their own extraordinary language. They gave us ten or a dozen enormous turtles. We were already overloaded (in every sense) with turtles, but Orellana thought it would be unwise to disappoint them, and he ordered them to be paid with beads. Talking with them again, he learned that we were near one of the main settlements of Aparia, and that the great man himself was there and would like to see us. They agreed to lead us there; and since they led us out of the main channel, without them we would have missed the place.

We saw a large and well-built settlement on firm ground sloping to the river. Canoes were drawn up the length of the beach, which was thronged with hundreds of warriors. When we were two crossbow-shots from the place, our guide canoes sheered off, paddling for their lives. Orellana would not let us try to stop them. He ordered us to go on steadily, making for the middle of the settlement, and told us to have our arms ready but concealed.

When those ashore saw us approaching in this placid manner, as though we were merely on the water for our own enjoyment, they responded to some command given by voices, drums, or trumpets—for the din was very great—and all leaped into their canoes, coming at us in two flanking columns. Athletic and well-armed dogs they were, and their speed in canoes was miraculous. They grimaced and yelled at us, wondering if we would show fear. Needless to say, we gave them no such easy satisfaction. Landing in good order, we formed up facing the water. Orellana stood, as did we all, stiff and silent, his hands at his sides. From throat to knee he was sheathed in plate that had been well scoured and then polished with oil by the two Negroes. He stood before us a man of steel, and at the sight of him eight paces out from our steady ranks the Indians gradually reduced their hubbub and paddled nearer.

He spoke to them, suggesting that they should not ask for a fight, as they would regret it, and saying that they should leave their canoes. For a while they showed no sign of agreeing to this, and we said to each other that if they wanted trouble it would be more profitable to shoot them while they were still afloat. Finally, however, they all came in with a foaming rush and stepped from the canoes as though they were four-wheeled carts. Their watermanship was something that you, who did not see it, could never imagine. Whereas any of us, even one of the Negroes, would board his canoe gingerly, a hand on each gunwale, an Aparia Indian would leap in, and while the canoe surged out under the impetus of his leap he would stand on one leg, scratch his bare posterior with one hand, and scratch his head with the other. So now they were all quickly round us on land, and when it was plain even to such dunderheads that we had no intention of starting a fight, though we were willing to finish one, they opened their throng and their aged overlord came through.

He rapped a knuckle on Orellana's breastplate and drew back astonished. He looked at my crossbow, fingering the smooth wood of the tiller, the hempen string, the steel bow with its coating of grease that came off on his hand. The crossbow was wound, and I held the trigger firmly down lest the old man should do himself damage. Then he asked Orellana what was the thing's purpose, and I was told to fire one bolt at a slender tree some sixty paces away. Aparia cleared his rabble to give me a path to the target. I chose a bolt with its feathering set in a spiral. Off it whistled, and the Indians, save Aparia (who thought it fitting to look unimpressed), ran to the tree and tried in vain to pull the bolt out. Aparia then looked at Perucho's arquebus, putting his venerable head on one side to hear more loudly the hiss and splutter of the match. When Orellana told him that the arquebus was a machine to call forth thunder and lightning, the Indian begged to be excused a demonstration.

Aparia asked permission to be seated, and signed to Orellana to do likewise. We stood behind Orellana, and Aparia's men, all of them shifting and jittering and pushing, were behind him. Some were ordered to bring us gifts out of the canoes. It seemed that he had been equally ready to kill us or befriend us. His offerings were all edible: turtles, sea-cow flesh, fishes, roasted birds resembling our Spanish partridges, but twice the size, roasted monkeys, monkeys broiled with their skins off, and jaguar meat. Aparia knew in advance what he wanted in return: a knife. This was ceremoniously presented to him, together with a long string of fat multicoloured beads and two large yellow-silk bows. Beads were also distributed among his followers, after which Aparia required Orellana to state our purpose in being there in his country.

According to the version he later gave me for my records, Orellana answered that we were the servants of Don Carlos, King-Emperor of Spain and other great lands and peoples without number. It was by His Majesty's order that we were travelling down that river until we reached the sea. We offered our friendship to all peoples of the river because our God was the Prince of Peace, for all that He was the most powerful and indeed the only true God. Where the power of other deities was single, His was a thousandfold, and where their mercy, love, and pity were as a single leaf, His goodness was all the leaves in the forest, uncountable and ever growing, freely bestowed on all who acknowledged Him.

The elderly Indian listened to this discourse with a most knowing expression, and when he had considered it he asked Orellana to repeat it. Aparia now swung half-round on his hams and looked at those behind him as though saying: "See how clever I am. We shall soon know if he is telling the truth."

Orellana patiently repeated it all. Aparia then said that he believed him and would command his people to be friendly and to help us in every possible way. He would put that settlement at our disposal for as long as we cared to stay, and as proof of his good faith he would leave ten of his sons with us if Orellana would likewise hand over ten of *his* sons as hostages. The Captain replied that all of his sons were elsewhere (which was true enough, for so far as I know they had not yet been born), and that it was forbidden by our religion that we split our ranks, because we worshipped as a community at every moment of the day and the night. He added that there was no call for so great and good an overlord to give us any proofs or hostages, for we could see into his heart and, liking what we saw, trusted him as we trusted each other. Further, he said, we hoped to create in that settlement a work of magic in the shape of another boat even finer than the brigantine drawn up on the beach.

Aparia said he would be most interested in our magic, but he would advise the Captain not to lead us downstream, but rather to turn and go back. He said that many ferocious and evil peoples lived below his territories, and that they would certainly overwhelm us. Like the other Aparia, the one at Imará, he then warned Orellana of a tribe of women warriors, whom he called the Coñupuyara.

When the old man had done, Orellana answered that no Indian should believe that our strength corresponded to "*los tres gatos*" * under his command, for although we were few, we feared nothing and nobody because our Lord protected us and granted us powers so tremendous that if any chose to molest us we would annihilate them, though it would grieve us to do so.

The palaver was ended. Aparia went off, well satisfied with it and with his beads, his bows, and, above all, his knife. He looked to us like any other Indian, though older than most. We were to learn by experience that he was one who held by his word. We never had cause to threaten him. He behaved well, I think, because his country was prosperous and he had many fat wives, because he was strong with the true strength that begets gentle behaviour, and because he was touched that Orellana

* "The three cats": the handful of men.

could converse with him in his own language—of which he was as misguidedly proud as any Frenchman. That Orellana so quickly found the key to Aparia's generosity was to be of untold benefit to us all, for in that settlement we were to build and launch our ship of war, the *Victoria*. I dare say this *Victoria* was so ugly that sailormen would choke with laughter if she lurched and tumbled into Cartagena roads, but she was to earn a place in history as important as that of any great ship with its painted sails, its tiers of guns, and the scented exquisites upon its towering poop.

CHAPTER FOURTEEN

OUR STAY IN APARIA, AS WE CALLED THE SETTLEMENT, was to be a long one of fifty-seven days, and the most profitable of the whole journey.

We began in righteous fashion by erecting on the stretch of stiff clay we called the Plaza de Santiago a big cross made of hardwood rabbeted and bolted. The plaza was our church except when rain drove us into one of the huts, where a smaller cross was set up. Orellana ordered us to be exceedingly devout at Aparia for two reasons: firstly, that until we got there we had not done our duty by our Lord as He had done His by us; and secondly, that it behoved us to let the Indians see that Christians were earnest in their devotions.

On the morning following our arrival, the Sevillian carpenter repeated publicly that the task of building another brigantine was repugnant to him. He thought he had more than done his duty by building the *San Pedro*. A precious lot of thanks that had earned him! Rather, when things went wrong, had the brigantine's crew cursed it, and him, its builder. So let some of the so clever critics build the new one, and then we would see which was the better brigantine. To this outpouring of southern disgruntlement Orellana responded unctuously; and when he finally on behalf of the King and of himself prayed Mexía once more to lead the craftsmen, he obtained a grudging acquiescence. As soon as Mexía had taken the first step, one thing led to another, and he became able and energetic, though anything but cheerful. Orellana assigned to him the best hut in the village, and on the smooth floor of the hut Mexía drew the shapes with his sword. Then he went into the forest and marked certain trees that must be cut for planking, others for the stem, stern-post, and keel, and yet others for the frames. The woodmen were divided into groups, and each group was given its task of cutting and delivering in the rough to Mexía's hut.

It was soon apparent that as he had designed a brigantine somewhat larger than the first one, the two thousand nails made at Imará by Juan de Alcántara and Sebastián Rodríguez would not suffice. Alcántara offered to begin again at the forge, but Orellana decided that the first essential was to store inside the perimeter of the village all the wood we needed both for the building and for charcoal-burning. Then, he said, by throwing up earthworks we might be able to continue with our work even if the Indians turned hostile. And he drove the work on with very potent exhortations. All seemed to be going as well as could be expected until after Mass on the first Wednesday, when Orellana asked us to stand for a minute and listen to him.

"I will be brief," he said. "And then you can get on with your work as usual. . . . We must now regard it as impossible that we shall again see the Governor, Gonzalo Pizarro, before the end of this detachment's mission. We are agreed, I think, that it is our duty to go down this river and open up new lands. As we have lost all contact with the Governor, from whom my authority is held, I think it right that I should resign my commission; and this I now do, in the presence of all of you."

We were so unprepared for business of that nature that we did not understand what he wanted, and someone called out, asking for an explanation.

"I mean," Orellana answered, "that I am no longer Gonzalo Pizarro's Lieutenant General, and therefore I am no longer your Captain."

He dismissed us. We woodmen went off to the forest. In the course of the morning, when I was sawing down a tree with Mateo de Rebolloso, Robles came to us. He sent Rebolloso away, coughing as usual, and himself took the other end of the saw. It was dark in the forest, and cooler than outside, but the insects were damnation. Our saw was hard to pull through the close-grained, sticky wood. Robles, small, thin, wiry, and very black-haired, worked like a demon. I was thankful when he said it was time to rest. He took some guavas from his knapsack, and we shared them, sitting on a felled trunk.

"I want to have a talk with you now, Bachelor of Arts, because I am going to see the Captain, whom you know better than most of us. . . . Had you any warning that he intended to resign?"

"He is tired of working for Gonzalo Pizarro, and sees no sense in it. But I think there is more to it than that."

"What, then?"

"Between Imará and this place Orellana decided to burn his boats. Wait and I will explain. . . . He is related to the Pizarro family, which family rules Peru, where Orellana is a man of property."

"You mean that, supposing Gonzalo returns to Peru from his disastrous expedition, the Pizarro family, forgetting past services and the tie of blood, will take back Orellana's benefices—Guayaquil, Puerto Viejo, the emerald mines, and so on?"

"Yes, but the Pizarros are too powerful in Peru to be well liked in Spain. That is to say, they may enjoy the esteem and good will of the populace, but not of the Office of the Indies, nor the court, nor the King himself."

"So if we get down this river, Orellana will go to Spain?"

"Yes, to ask the King for a governorship."

"He will be at a disadvantage there," Robles said.

"How so? If he leads us to safety, he will have won great renown."

"My dear Bachelor of Arts, you who are so wily in day-to-day affairs plainly know little about courtiers. Another's renown only makes them jealous, unreceptive, and dangerous. He who goes soliciting among them if he comes from the Indies is expected to bring them at least a shipload of inducements in the shapes of gold, jewels, strange and amusing dwarfs, coloured women, unheard-of beasts, and opulent robes. Even if we are lucky enough to find riches as we go down the river, we are too few to exploit our luck. So the odds must be that Orellana will arrive in Spain a poor man. Now, poverty is a most unfortunate condition at any time and place, but it is disastrous at court. Favours there must be asked from strength, amigo, and by strength I mean riches."

"Very well. You know more about the court than I do, for I have never seen it, and am never likely to. . . . But it is plain what Orellana wants now. He wants to be reinstated as our leader without being tied to the name of Pizarro."

"His authority was already good."

"He was mortified by the threats in the first Petition. He was angrier than he seemed when he learned that some had disobeyed him and bartered for gold at Imará. Then there are some of Gonzalo's men among us. The Captain wants to know how he stands with them."

"Why did he not resign at Imará when we were having all the other fuss?"

"Because the future looked even more uncertain then, and because Orellana then hoped, or feared, that Gonzalo would launch himself and his men on the river and would find us."

"Hoped?" Robles asked.

"I think Orellana sincerely regrets our separation from the main body. He is of gentle birth, and to him honour comes first. You do not deny that, do you?"

Robles said: "I am not criticizing him, Bachelor of Arts. Thank you for our talk. I have the business clearer in my head now, and think I know what should be done."

"And what is that, may I ask?"

"I will put it to Orellana that he should consider very carefully the implications of resigning Gonzalo's commission. In my view, he has acted impeccably up to now, for he has often made it clear that he is acting in Gonzalo's name and is prepared to share any of the credit we may earn with our absent commander, who is Gonzalo. Then if, as you suggest, Orellana intends to ask favours of the King, such favours are problematical, and I should be surprised if in the aggregate they were worth a quarter of Orellana's holdings in Peru, which he owes to the Pizarros."

"He will not listen to you."

"Very likely not."

At the meeting called by Robles that evening, the general attitude of the compañeros was one of bewilderment and—because they had no relish for being puzzled—of annoyance with Orellana (who was not present). Papa Illanes was the first to speak.

"I hold, gentlemen, that the Captain's resignation is a promising omen," he began.

"Let us listen to sense, not to parables," interrupted Maldonado.

"Give him a hearing," Robles said. "But please do not be too long-winded, Illanes. We are in no mood for speeches."

"In acting as he has done," Illanes continued unperturbed, "in discarding the authority vested in him by Gonzalo Pizarro, Captain Orellana follows the example of numerous successful leaders of the conquest. Give me leave to cite but one example—that of Hernán Cortés on the expedition that was to add the realms of Mexico to the empire of His Cæsarean Majesty. Cortés, you will recall, had been sent to the Mexican coastline by Don Diego Velásquez, then Governor of Cuba. All that Velásquez sought from the expedition was trade and immediate profit. But the soaring genius of Cortés envisaged a more noble aim. So when Cortés had decided where to build his base and had founded la Villa Rica de Vera Cruz on a bare and hostile coast, he resigned into the hands of the municipal authorities and justiciaries the appointment he had received from Don Diego. Did it matter that those authorities had just been appointed by Cortés himself? I think not. They duly exercised their powers in obedience to his wishes. They took away his position of subordinacy to the Governor of Cuba and promoted him to Captain General and Chief Justice, responsible only to His Majesty. The whole thing was done legally, and who can argue today that it was badly done? For Cortés was one of the greatest generals that soldiers of any race ever followed, and by contrast with him Diego Velásquez would seem no better than a huckster. . . ."

But Juan de Alcántara, the hidalgo from Valladolid, was now on his feet, and he asked with ice in his voice: "Does Juan de Illanes intend to say by implication that our Governor, Gonzalo Pizarro, the noblest lance in Peru, is a huckster?"

Before Illanes could answer, Robles told Alcántara that of course nothing of the kind had been intended. No man among us, Robles said, who did not admire Gonzalo Pizarro. It was more than unfortunate that we had been separated from Pizarro, but, being separated, and finding ourselves far down these immense rivers, we had to acknowledge that Orellana was entitled to ask for his own command. How could we expect Orellana to go on working as Pizarro's underling when Pizarro himself was not there to take at least his share of the responsibility? There was none of us but Orellana fit for the task of leading our party. To give but one example of the Captain's remarkable gifts, here we were at peace with Aparia and his subjects, whereas had our leader been more hasty, more nervous, less of a student of Indian customs and tongues, we should have had to fight Aparia's people instead of being feasted and housed by them. Robles therefore submitted that we should at once draft a Summons, showing it to be the will of everybody that Orellana be reinstated as our commanding officer, answerable only to the King.

"Have you done, Alonso?" Alcántara asked. "Because I have not. I maintain, whatever gloss you may try to put on it, that this Illanes has insulted our Captain General Gonzalo Pizarro, and that he has by implication called him a huckster."

"I did nothing of the sort," said Papa Illanes. "I called Diego Velásquez a huckster as compared with Cortés. I might have said the same of myself or almost anybody else."

"Before returning to that matter, as I intend to do," Alcántara said, "I would point out that I have loyally supported the Lieutenant General, Captain Orellana, in our vicissitudes since we left the Captain General because I have thought Orellana to be right and just in all his decisions as well as a brave and resourceful leader. But I do not agree that he should now throw aside his allegiance, or banish the name of Gonzalo Pizarro from our thoughts and from any credit or glory we may earn if we succeed in going down this river. There must be some among us—I know there are, I see there are—who agree with me. We should go on in Gonzalo's name. That is the least thing we can do as soldiers and men of honour, because fate chose that we should leave Pizarro in the middle of those forests with nothing to eat, and by now he is very likely dead and watching us from heaven."

"More likely from some other place," said someone.

"What if Orellana will not agree to lead us except on his own terms?" Robles asked. "We must be practical, gentlemen. Surely we are agreed that we want Orellana and nobody else as our leader. In my opinion his resignation is normal under the circumstances. I have talked it over very fully with him, and I feel we must comply with his wishes and give him our unanimous support."

Alcántara spoke of our consciences and of the love some, if not most, of us bore for Gonzalo Pizarro, whom one of our number had seen fit to call a huckster.

"I deny that," Illanes said.

"Then you are a liar."

"Retract those words, Alcántara," Papa Illanes said, his face showing concern and even pity, "for I have no wish to kill you."

"May I suggest," Alcántara said to Robles, "that we adjourn this meeting while Illanes and I arrange with the good friars for a safe passage to heaven, because it is certain that before an hour is out either he or I will be speeding on the way there?"

Alonso de Robles answered that, sooner than allow a duel for so slight a reason, he would have both hidalgos tied up for the night and would continue the meeting without them.

Then Hernán Gutiérrez de Celis said that Robles was perfectly correct in maintaining that Juan de Alcántara had roused himself against Illanes for no adequate reason. "Alcántara must now withdraw from his intransigeance," said Gutiérrez de Celis. "Alcántara has no right to kill Illanes. That is my right."

"Explain yourself," Robles said wearily.

"Illanes did not call Gonzalo Pizarro a huckster."

"Agreed."

"He called Don Deigo Velásquez a stay-at-home and a huckster."

"What of it?"

"Don Diego Velásquez is the son of my mother's cousin. He is my cousin. He is no huckster. *Ergo,* Illanes is a liar, and must pay for his lie and his insult with his life, since fortunately I am here to defend my family's honour."

"Before I dissolve this meeting that has been the greatest waste of time and words ever known," Robles said, "does anybody else want to kill Illanes?" Then I heard him explain to the two friars that they must on no account give absolution to Illanes, Gutiérrez de Celis, or Alcántara, for that was the only gentlemanly way he could think of to prevent them from doing each other mischief, though he would take other precautions as well.

There was argument all night. We heard voices when we went to sleep, and voices wakened us long before dawn. At five in the morning Robles called us all to another session. He, Illanes, Gutiérrez de Celis, and Alcántara were full of yawns, and their eyes stared with sleeplessness.

Illanes got up and said he had been very wrong to call so distinguished a man as Don Diego Velásquez, formerly Governor of Cuba, anything but an honourable Castilian and a fine soldier; and he apologized publicly for any offence his simple delight in speechifying and in drawing dramatic contrasts might have given in any quarter.

Gutiérrez de Celis got up and said that on behalf of his kinsman he accepted Juan de Illanes's apology in the spirit in which it was offered.

Juan de Alcántara got up and said he had stated his views about Gonzalo Pizarro the night before. While he still held those views, he was in full agreement with Alonso de Robles that there was only one among us fitted to command, and that we must agree to have him as our Captain on his own terms. He, Alcántara, would therefore take his part in drawing up the Summons to Orellana, and would undertake to sign it, provided there was nothing offensive in it.

The night, therefore, had held a diplomatic triumph of some magnitude for Robles, who had somehow found a way—and it cannot have been easy—to make three fiery men see sense.

Robles now rose and said he hoped no other man had a speech in his head. The night before, he added, Papa Illanes, who never found his own voice unmusical, had been tempted to make a few harmless remarks concerning (if he, Robles, remembered aright) the orthodoxy of legal illegalities, and as a result of these remarks blood had nearly been spilled and ten hours had been passed in fierce and unfruitful arguments. Therefore, Robles went on, we must now discuss the terms of the Summons, which he thought should be short, bold, and unequivocal.

Ah, but those men were prolix when it came to setting things down in writing! The wordage of their Summons was so flatulent that I most certainly shall not repeat it to you, but will paraphrase the content, taking it for understood what wristy pains a scrivener upon active service might be required to bear. The first section ran to six hundred words, and with the affidavits and certificates I had about double that number to set down. Thus is learning sometimes penalized, and in the most unexpected places.

They began, then, by relating our story from the moment we left the main body, not omitting details of their sufferings and of previous to-dos and documents when Orellana had proposed taking us back upstream. They went on to declare that they understood Captain Orellana's reasons for resigning. Then they acknowledged their debt to him, and they required him "to keep us in peace and order as you have done up to now, and as in other places you have looked after and led greater numbers of Spaniards." Whereupon they elected him their Captain in the name of the King "until such time as His Majesty shall otherwise decree." (They did not explain how His Majesty, who had no means of knowing that we, or any other of his loyal subjects, were embarked upon the discovery of that unexplored river, could communicate his royal wishes in the matter.) They added, but in language much more careful than that of the Imará Petition, that if Orellana did *not* accept the responsibility that they insisted was his and his alone, he would be to blame for the outrages, quarrels, and even murders that might well break out among us when discipline dissolved and there was no clear leadership.

As soon as the Summons was ready and all but the two friars and myself had signed it (forty-seven signatures), I took it to Orellana, who, without comment, dictated a few sentences to the effect that he accepted the command of our expeditionary force (it was no longer a detachment) in the name of His Majesty. When I had written the Answer out, there was a ceremony. Prayers were made. Then all placed their hands in turn on Father Carvajal's big missal and swore by God, by the Holy Virgin Mary, by the sign of the Cross, and by the four Gospels, to believe in Captain Orellana and loyally to serve him. Orellana in his turn swore by the same authorities to do justice in the name of the King and to lead us as we should be led. Mass was then said, rather longer than usual, but without unnecessary dallying because Father Carvajal was no tortoise, and in general without skimping anything he got through Low Mass in twenty minutes, doing the whole thing better than many priests who take thirty-five or forty. How can I state those times so precisely? Because Father Carvajal had an hour-glass, and what is more, he used it. Others of his calling might well do likewise. The hour-glass was also useful to the seamen when they were estimating our speed through the water.

I spent much of the day putting the Summons entirely in order, and recording the ceremony of swearing-in, and certifying it. Orellana found me when I had about finished and asked me why I had been so long absent from my wood-cutting. He told me to put the parchment along with the others in their leather box. I remarked that if we continued to accumulate legal documents at such a rate, we would soon have one for each member of the expedition.

"But now we can have done with them," Orellana said. "No more documents. These will suffice. Our deeds from now on must speak for themselves, and when all is over let those of us who survive put words to fit them—if we think them worth so much trouble. As for you, Bachelor of Arts, you are a good scrivener, but I must remind you that today you are a wood-cutter, next week you will be a charcoal-burner, and of course you will always be a crossbowman."

Thus, in strange places, were those parchments covered with ink that today and for all tomorrows repose in the Archives of the Indies at Seville, a few squares of yellowed parchment among so many. If a poor clerk passes them once a week as they moulder on their shelves, that must be an event of magnitude. Thus we had to act, we of the conquest, with our thoughts hinged on the bureaucrats of Spain and their reactions, fusty and crabbed, to our martial exploits. We are a nation borne down by written reports, testimonies, affidavits, judicial inquiries, and estimates; but we are a great and virile nation, and we write the reports, etc., etc., as ably as we do all else, which means very well indeed.*

* "We must also bear in mind the routine formalities of those days in America, when everything was reduced to a file of papers, when the most insignificant vessel did not put to sea without a scrivener on board, when the smallest event of everyday life was recorded in a notary's office. To whom would it occur today to have

Now enough of written reports, and let us get back to building our brigantine. . . .

By the seventh day we had hauled into Aparia's settlement all the timber that would be needed. Mexía said (and no doubt it was true, for he was given to understatement) that for every variety of tree grown in Spain from the Navarrese frontier facing the perfidious French down to the place where the giant rock of Gibel-Tarik juts at the mouth of the channel connecting the two seas, there were hundreds of varieties crowding in round this village on the bank of the Marañón. In cutting the timber, Orellana had sought the advice of Aparia and his head men, who only felled trees for canoe-making at certain stages of the moon, for they maintained that if felled at other times the timber would soon rot or be devoured by ants or boring water creatures.* We did not know the names for the woods Mexía chose, but the keel was of a kind of ironwood, desperately hard to cut and fashion, while for lightness the planking was made of a wood resembling cedar (though taken from immense, branching trees whose leaves were oak leaves). Certain men began to saw out the planks, while others were set to making charcoal and assisting the blacksmiths, who could still draw on a plentiful store of horseshoes.

From the day he accepted the Summons, Orellana was even sharper in the watch he kept on us. One day, for example, Cristóbal Enríquez, a young gentleman normally overfull of airs and nonsenses, did not bare his head as, going about his work, he happened to pass the cacique Aparia. The Captain took Enríquez to task before all of us, informing him that if he thought too highly of himself to be polite to the King of those whose hospitality we

---

a Judicial Enquiry covering his past services put through the Court? And yet, what was more common than this among the Spaniards of the 16th century and even a part of the 17th? The great mass of papers that, as a result of this procedure, has come down to us from those times is precisely what forms today the wealth of the Spanish Archives."—Toribio Medina.

* "To this day the Amazon Indians will cut the timber they need for their building purposes only in the last quarter of the moon." —Bertram T. Lee, in Medina: *The Discovery of the Amazon* (American Geographical Society, Special Publication No. 17).

enjoyed, he must think more of the expedition, because his rudeness might well mean the difference between success and failure. Enríquez went pale with anger, though he was too proud to make excuses, and he dared take no offence because he would have found no support even from Maldonado and the only-good-Indian-is-a-dead-one brigade.

Do you imagine that it was easy to work there? Then let me tell you that we worked through almost interminable rains interspersed with spells of blistering sunshine that turned our world into steam. In daylight we were so plagued by the small bloodsuckers and the sabre-flies that a man could not work well unless two others were swishing at him with fans made from the tails of grey eagles, which were used by the Indians for a like purpose. In addition, many of us suffered from a worm that burrowed under our skins and there rapidly swole to form an agonizing carbuncle. Then at dusk the mosquitoes flew at us like lovers and we must sleep wrapped up against their painful kisses and the more serious embraces of vampire bats the size of partridges and covered with black fur. They had spears on their noses, huge ears, black eyes that glinted horribly, and their faces always were grinning. There were also smaller bats, grey and comparatively inoffensive, at least in appearance. Those animals have some devilish power, for none of us ever saw them at work or even felt them until they had done, when we would wake to find an uncovered toe or hand running with blood where the vampire had drawn his fill. We were, in consequence of these night discomforts, most eager to go out into the early-morning freshness, but our tempers were uncertain, and our language was apt to be foul. We were a group of men not particularly homogeneous or harmonious, thrown together by what we regarded as ill luck and shut away in those forests where no white man had been before us.

Father Carvajal daily reminded us of our duty before God, and sought to prove that if we felt ourselves isolated or forgotten, it was not so, because God's eye was ever on us, and because we were in the presence of the Blessed and Sacred Virgin, whom we pleased by our worthy efforts and whom we distressed when we were angry with ourselves and others and the accursed insects to the point that we made beasts of ourselves, or fought, or wrangled. The Dominican preached every Sunday at Aparia as well as each saint's day and on Maundy Thursday, Good Friday, and Easter Saturday. His words were always pithy, and were variegated within the proper bounds of simplicity. If he asked many favours of our Lord, he also made generous promises, and in case anything should have been overlooked he often listed our sufferings and tribulations. He worked so hard at it all that it seemed probable that God would grant him, and through him us, special grace. It was evident, indeed, that the friar knew his life depended upon our efforts in Aparia, and he was determined to be no whit behind with his own specialized contributions. Orellana, as I have said before, was persistent in seeing to it that each one of us attended to his devotions, and Father Carvajal was heartened by the earnestness with which we apparently strove to catch and understand his every word. We had reached Aparia four days after Ash Wednesday, and before Lent was out we had all confessed to one or other of the friars. On Sundays and Good Friday we did no work.

I think Orellana was right, and that our constancy with our humble devotions made more impression on Aparia and his Indians than anything else we said or did. They were also surprised by our industry; but this they did not admire, for they were the laziest set of hounds imaginable, and no man among them would dream of carrying a gourd weighing no more than an orange if there was a woman to carry it for him. The more they saw us round the Cross, the greater did its power seem to them, so that the Captain had to prevent them not once but many times from profaning it by killing animals in its shadow and pouring offerings of chicha, or even aguardiente, over its base. Here there was argument between the two friars, each making the most of his case.

Father Vera was angered by the Indians' spontaneous approach to our religion. He said they should be punished for attempted defamation of the Cross, and should without delay be instructed in the Christian faith. Father Carvajal, the plumper, the more practical, the more human of the pair, and the more worldly without being less devout (if that is possible, and I think it is), said that the Indians meant no harm and should not be blamed for attempting to worship as their upbringing told them to do and in the only manner that they in their ignorance understood.

Orellana took Father Carvajal's part, insisting that the first essential in the way of serving God was to press ahead with building the second brigantine, and that in his conversations with Aparia and the lesser caciques he was doing his best to encourage them to wish for instruction in our faith. He said it would be useless for one of the friars to stand up and teach, expecting him, Orellana, to translate each sentence, because the language of the Indians had many limitations. Apart from their needs or comforts they seemed to the Captain to be empty-headed, and this was reflected in their talk. So far as he could make out, they had no word for glory, none for honour, and none for gratitude. He had found it impossible to explain to old Aparia, the cleverest of them, the meaning of eternity or of virtue. How then, he asked, could they begin to understand the spiritual beauties and truths of a religion founded on gentleness and virginal purity? He told us other things about the Indians' language, illustrating his remarks with the words—and the blanks—in the vocabularies upon which he worked so assiduously. What remained in my head as remarkable was this: in those weird forests the people used the words "papa" and "mama," and far from mixing them up as one might have expected, "papa" meant father, "mama" mother. Father Carvajal's opinion on this was that God was already at work, shaping the Indians' thoughts, guiding their tongues. Orellana, who knew Indians better, said that he could find no traces in them of respect or affection for parents, or aged people, or children, or husbands, or wives. He thought it more likely that those two simple words were nearly universal, and that they were so because, by reason of the structure of the human throat and tongue and the difficulty of making the first pronounced noises as distinct from bawling and squalling, those were the words that children of all colours and races first brought out when they found the blessing of speech—which can also be a curse.

When Aparia had decided that we were men dedicated to our own unfathomable God, and when he had had time to observe the bonds of discipline in which we were held by Orellana, he sent women to the camp to cook for us. Every morning from then on, ten women, most of them with babies, came carrying baskets slung on their backs and held by thongs of bark round their foreheads. One woman's baby had died, so instead of it she carried a thin monkey with shaggy dark hair and a long tail. She suckled the monkey when her friends gave suck to their babies, and when she put it down, it would follow her faithfully, unless it saw something it could steal. Aparia's hunters brought us many monkeys to eat, and this shaggy, long-tailed kind was about the best of them. Its flesh was like beef, but sweeter and more nourishing.

It seemed to us that Aparia had chosen the women carefully. They were married women, and a good deal uglier than their husbands. In those places the men do nothing but hunt, fish, eat, dance, and drink. The women help with the fishing, dancing, and drinking, and it is they who do all the labour. In such a climate this has a speedy effect on their bodies, and they are worn out soon after they are born.

Aparia also offered to lend the Captain a few score of *women* to help us with the heavy work of dragging timber. Orellana refused, thinking that it might give rise to incidents, and he ordered me and one or two others who knew of Aparia's offer to say nothing about it to the compañeros.

The Indian women took their baskets to the bakehouse, an open, roofed space with clay ovens. Maize was roasted for us or was pounded and baked into bread, which made good eating when it was seasoned with the peppers that grew profusely round the huts and with a kind of saltpetre, made from ashes, which was better than no salt at all. The bread had to be eaten the day it was baked, and for a while we found it difficult to store any maize either on land or in the boats, until the bakeresses showed us how to hang it in baskets suspended on ropes that had been smeared with a kind of gum no ant would go near, and how to smoke the baskets morning and evening by lighting green-wood fires under them.

Though they had maize, which we much preferred, the main food of the Indians was yuca. They prepared it for us in its most useful form, roasting it in hard grains that would keep for weeks without rotting. They also fried it in turtle oil or sea-cow fat, chopped herbs into it, and with some fish or meat or turtle eggs made quite splendid croquetas. I have already mentioned our difficulties with the wild yucas, but since we were doomed to eat enough of this root (which resembles the humble parsnip) to suffocate us under more normal conditions of life, I feel justified in telling you how they prepared it and made their chicha from it.

The Indian women peeled the yucas with sharp stones and flung them into a trough of water, a hollowed tree, where they lay softening. They were then grated on the rasping tongues of big fishes or on boards in which sharp pebbles or bits of shell had been embedded. The resulting pulp was packed into long tubes made of plaited fibres with a loop at the top and another at the bottom of each tube. The upper loop was hung on the branch of a tree, and through the lower one the bakeress passed a long and stout stick. One end of the stick went into a hole in the tree trunk, and the woman perched herself astride the other end. Then, by flexing and relaxing her legs as though she were a child on a seesaw, she levered on the flexible tube above her, and at each downward stroke poisonous juice came out of the tube and dripped into the tray set beneath. Such juice as remained in the pulp would leave it as it steamed in the ovens. . . . You will agree, then, that this is a vegetable demanding much work in preparation even before cooking begins. The work does not end there when chicha is to be made. To perform this labour of love (for the Indian woman is as addicted to intoxication as is her Indian husband), the yuca pulp is boiled, and while it is boiling, the women chew mouthfuls of pulp and spit it into the cauldron. The human saliva is enough to make the liquid work, which process begins when the boiling is over and the chicha is put away in covered earthen jars. When it is to be drunk, it is taken by the fistful from jar to drinking gourd and is stirred in water with the fingers. . . . Any beverage prepared in so brutish a manner might be considered unfit for drinking. Not so. It seems to go well with the climate and the foods of those places, particularly with the yuca flour, which has a parching effect on the roof of the mouth.

The turtles that when we first saw them so astonished us soon became commonplace, for they are part of the Marañón landscape. Any village had its enclosure where from five hundred to a thousand wallowed in water and mud. The turtle-hunting season is in the summer, in August or September, when the river is at its lowest. The creatures then swarm on the sandbanks to lay their numberless eggs, which they bury in the sand. As they return to the water, the Indians fall upon them, killing many and turning others over on their backs. These last have holes bored in their shells and, strung together, they are towed after the canoes to the village enclosures. Two breeds exist, but the smaller kind, which is said to make the better eating, refuses to live in captivity. All the ones we saw were as big as targets.* From two of them we would take more fat than is got from a well-fed full-grown bullock, fat as good as any for cooking. When we killed a female, we might find as many as two hundred eggs in her. Some thought them better than hens' eggs, though they made much gas in us. It was some time before we caught the trick of making a tortilla with them, for if the eggs are put in whole, the mess will not thicken, but if only the rich and greasy yolks are used, the result is good.

From the Indian women we learned different ways of cooking turtles. Perhaps the best of these was a stew made by cutting the breast flesh in slithers and cooking it with bananas, palm shoots, and yucas, in the shell. This was improved by the addition of small river-fishes like eels and fresh-water prawns, and it had to be well seasoned with peppers. Another fine dish consisted of broiled haunches eaten with the pungent Indian sauces that we came to like. They made these sauces with some exactitude, and matured them like gherkins in jars. One sauce was yellow, and was made by boiling the poisonous juice of yucas; another was so hot that it burned mouth and stomach, and this effect was got by cooking certain kinds of ants. But the gastronomic marvel of Aparia came when the bakeresses carried in some salt, which they said had come in canoes from deposits on the bank many days' journey upstream, and they then made a sauce into which

* 3 ft. by 2 ft.

they pounded the bones and flesh of small salted fishes. It was good enough to make a Biscayan mouth water.

An Indian paddled to the beach one day with a vast creature in his canoe quite overflowing either gunwale. This was a sea-cow, and although we had eaten quantities of the meat, since the spearing of those animals goes on in winter, we had never seen one whole. Twelve of us carried it ashore; eleven would have been too few, for it was slippery, was longer than the tallest man, and was as round and fat as three pleasure-loving abbots rolled into one. The colour was that of dull iron, with pale blotches on the belly. It was a female, and had two small breasts between the fins that took the place of arms or forelegs. Hinds it had none, only a flat tail. Its head was small, its eyes even smaller, while its ears were holes no bigger than the eye of a sailmaker's needle. There was no neck, the head being merely a prolongation of the rounded body. When we slit open the body, we found that its droppings resembled horse dung, which seemed strange in an animal that never left the water. The Indians said that the male has testicles and a penis, and therefore I suppose it should be called a sea-bull, though we always lumped the sexes together and spoke in the aggregate of *vacas marinas*. Perhaps this was because the animals are deficient in courage, for although they are of such size and apparent strength, a stout blow struck at any part of them will suffice to kill them, and they show no fight. They live in the deeps, but swim to the banks to eat the grasses and green-stuff, lifting their heads out of the water to feed. When he has killed one, the Indian fisherman sinks his canoe under it. He bales until the canoe floats, and then paddles home. The meat is twice as rich as, say, mutton. Some of us said it tasted like veal, others pork, and others that it had its own taste. We were shown by the Indians how to slice it and preserve it by rubbing in salt or saltpetre. Thus treated, it would keep for thirty days without putrefying (or so Aparia maintained, for our appetites always outstripped any wish to experiment in such directions). The Indians made most of their tools, spades, hammers, and so on, from the bones of those strange animals.

We saw alligators at Aparia, and would have seen more had

we been there later in the year. The Indians ate the small ones, and the big ones ate the Indians when the latter were drunk, and therefore careless. One or two monsters always lay near the beach, watching.

Had it not been for Orellana's wisdom in such matters, it is likely that we Spaniards would have been at odds with Aparia's men. Now they were glum and emotionless. Now they were dancing about, shaking their spears, throwing dust over themselves and us, grimacing, yelling, in the most aggravating fashion. The Captain explained, however, that we must regard them as children and should remember that they were merely drunk when they were obstreperous, and suffering from the after effects of drink when they were surly. They were good hunters after their own kind of game, and we came to appreciate their art with the bow, which was largely a matter of judging distances, since they fired into the air and struck with a dropping arrow whose weight rather than speed of flight made it penetrate. In this way they were able to kill swimming turtles and big fishes, using long arrows barbed with bone. When the arrowhead penetrated, it came free from the shaft, which was secured to it by a roll of thin twine. Picking up the floating shaft, the canoeman drew in the fish as though he had caught it with a baited hook; a very pretty thing to see.

The wives of our Spanish fishermen are clever with their hands, and so were those savage Indian women. They wound strong ropes from palm fibres, and heavier, coarser ones from lianas. We were able to furnish the brigantines with cordage of this make, and it withstood hard usage. There was nothing they could not weave out of palm leaves, from a roof to a pretty basket. And they were expert potters.

Four unusual Indians came to look at us in Aparia. Taller than the tallest among us, their skins were soft and almost white. They wore their hair long and carefully combed. It hung down to their belts, which were of soft leather studded with gold. They said they were the servants of a great lord in the hinterland to the east, and Orellana supposed this lord to be the King Ica of whom we had heard before. They had come to see if the stories they had heard about us were true. The strangest thing about us was the hair on our faces, and even their phlegm could not hide their astonishment at these lusty sproutings, natural in us, unnatural in them. Giving them trinkets and beads and a knife for their King, Orellana asked them to inform the King that he would be most warmly welcomed by us all and that we asked nothing better than to have the pleasure of receiving him at Aparia. The four strangers went away in the night, and we neither saw them nor heard of them or any like them again. But we often spoke of them and of King Ica, wondering if he might be El Dorado.

At length the time came when we were caulking the brigantine with cotton brought us by the Indians, rubbing the planking smooth, and painting it with a substance made up of different resins. Even the agreeable promise of such work did not hearten one of us, Alcántara from Santiago. He died in Aparia on April 4, apparently more from weakness that made him drowsy than from any ailment. We buried him secretly that night, and next day, which was Tenebræ Wednesday, the new brigantine was ready.

Diego Mexía said that if it floated down by the head or with a terrible list it would not be his fault and we were not to blame him, for although he had done his best, the work had been forced upon him. The Captain gave to Mexía, though he was but a plain man (if a crossbowman), the honour of launching the brigantine after the friars had named it, and of himself choosing its name. It flew into the water as though eager to be there, and after a preliminary lurch floated high, easy, and trim as a duck—or so it seemed to us. Then loud were the rejoicings, and even Mexía, who had hidden his eyes when the first splash came, managed to raise a smile. The Indians thought our new boat the greatest wonder beneath the skies, and Aparia, having asked leave to step aboard, sat there nearly a whole day with five of his head men and a couple of tame monkeys that shared his affections.

The new brigantine was both bigger and stronger than the *San Pedro,* for although it was not much longer—the seamen judged its waterline length to be 19 goas *—it was beamier and

* 23 ft. 9 in. According to Jal: *Glossaire nautique,* the goa—"*Mesure de longeur fort en usage dans les ports de l'Italie et de la Provence pendant le Moyen Âge et depuis*"—was 3 palmos, or 27

had considerably more freeboard, and it had nine thwarts to take eighteen oarsmen as against the *San Pedro*'s seven thwarts. As soon as we could get the Indians out of it we sank it to make its planking swell, and then we hauled the *San Pedro* high up the bank.

Somewhat cheered despite himself by the triumph of the launching, Mexía set to work repairing and strengthening the smaller brigantine. He slightly raised the bulwarks to make it more seaworthy and easier to row. Any doubtful planking and two or three of the frames were stripped and replaced by new. Then all the seams were recaulked and paid, and the outer planking was tarred with our substitute for tar. Over the centre well of each brigantine, leaving just enough room for the oarsmen on either side of it, Mexía rigged a light framework on which the Indian women wove a roof of palm leaves fashioned like the practical and beautiful roofs of their own huts. This meant that we should have some hope of keeping stores dry and that sick men or those resting could find shelter from the sun or the rain. Two jury masts were shaped, one for each vessel, and square-sails were sewn from the Peruvian blankets that were an invaluable part of our equipment. We hoped thus to be ready to take advantage of favourable breezes, though the wind seemed to come constantly upstream, and the seamen said this was the same easterly that came regularly over parts of the Northern Sea and even crossed the Peruvian Cordilleras to the Southern Sea.* From a springy white wood, Mexía and his helpers made forty good oars and many thole-pins.

Orellana had the bakeresses at work from dawn till dusk preserving meat and ramming it into stoppered jars. Other jars were filled with maize and with yuca grains. The women also made for each brigantine a flat earthenware fireplace. This meant that we could cook on board with charcoal, if we had to. Nothing, in short, that forethought and hard work could provide was forgotten.

---

inches. Capitán de Navío Don Julio Guillén, director of the Museo Naval in Madrid, says that the *Victoria* had nine rowing-thwarts.

* The south-east Trades.

During this time, Orellana took those of us who were not helping Mexía and put us to work in other ways. He decided who was to travel in each brigantine, and that he would jettison all the canoes. Separating us into two squads, he gave us exercises in tactics and laid down rules as to how the brigantines were to be fought, when they should fight side by side and when bow to stern. He made each arquebusier and each crossbowman train two other men in the use of his piece, and it was understood, if any marksman should be incapacitated in action, exactly who would take up the piece and use it.

We crossbowmen made many shafts, feathering them and fitting them to warheads, of which, most mercifully, we had a huge supply. They had been struck in Peru, a country where there is no iron, so they were of copper. And although copper warheads would have been imperfect against French knights, they were good enough against Indian warriors, for skin can never be as tough as plate. We fitted our bolts with real feathers, since there was no lack of them in Aparia; in other places we often used leather or waxed parchment instead of feathers, and there was a certain advantage in it, those materials being less liable to damage than feathers when the made bolts were packed away in quantity. In Gonzalo Pizarro's admirable stores we found Valencian hemp in plenty, and from it we made spare bowstrings, waxing them right through so that the damp could not affect them. Aparia's Indians supplied us with beeswax good enough in every way save that it was black and was therefore unsightly on the white strings. The small bees that provided this essential nested on the ground. Their honey was not so scented as that of Spain, but it was very sweet, and for that reason we ate a great deal of it.

During those last days at Aparia, Orellana officially appointed Alonso de Robles to be his Lieutenant and his successor should he be killed. Although this appointment could not have been bettered, for Robles was popular in every quarter and in his small frame packed more energy and sounder judgement than any of the rest of us, perhaps even than Orellana himself, there were among the hidalgos some mutterings of jealousy or damaged pride. Those who complained suggested that Robles had been set over them because he came, like the Captain, from Estremadura.

It is true that Estremenians hang closely together (and this is not the only way in which they are inclined to be "close"), but none could honestly deny that Robles deserved his post and was in every way worthy of it. He was given a band of picked swordsmen, all experienced in close-quarter fighting with Indians.

The plan was that when we came to hostile places, Robles and his men would storm ashore to take food or prisoners, while the brigantines lay ready to give covering fire or to land reinforcements. For this reason Orellana laid it down that Robles's landing party would travel in the *Victoria*, and the command of the *San Pedro* he gave to Maldonado (or Cristóbal de Segovia, to give him his full name). Perhaps it was wisdom thus to keep the quarrelsome caballero occupied, since he was one who might eat his fiery heart out and make trouble if he had no responsible position, and he was an unsurpassed fighter in skirmishes or when situations seemed hopeless. At the same time it seemed foolhardy to leave Maldonado somewhat on his own and without the shrewdness of Orellana or the steadiness of Robles to restrain his impetuosity.

When both brigantines were afloat, we began to say we had been overlong at Aparia. But Orellana refused to leave until he was certain that everything was in order, maintaining stubbornly that we might not find another stopping-place as good and as safe in all the rest of our journey. And fate was to vindicate his judgement, as you shall hear.

CHAPTER FIFTEEN

✲

ON APRIL 24 WE PUT OUT FROM APARIA'S SETTLEMENT, where, with God's help, we had so greatly strengthened ourselves. The weather was good. The Marañón ran strong and smooth. There was no wind. We delighted in the strangeness of the new brigantine.

After rowing all day we landed at another settlement, where old Aparia was waiting to feast us and to bid us good-bye. We spent two nights there, and all the intervening day was one of eating and drinking with the Indians, who were dressed for the occasion in feathers, flowers, and gold. To while away the time, Lorenzo Muñoz made a small racecourse with mud walls, and he with several of us who enjoyed such sport raced crabs in it for wagers. The Indians became interested and would dearly have liked to risk a few of their gold ornaments had not Orellana intervened, explaining that it would lead to trouble because the Indians had never been taught how to wager and lose.

The Captain had overheard a few of the compañeros saying that since we were nearly done with Aparia and his people, it might be sensible to take from them all their gold ornaments, and they were prepared to do it by force of arms, which would have been a queer recompense for all the kindnesses we had had at their hands. Orellana warned them severely, telling them that Aparia's territory extended another eighty leagues * downstream and that it would be foolish not to concentrate on retaining the cacique's regard until the last second spent in his company. It was our duty, he said, and in our own best interests, to make all the friends we could on that river. When news of our voyage reached Spain, His Majesty would send a great expedition to take posses-

* 290 miles.

sion of the Marañón and all its peoples, and if we, the forerunners, could but travel in friendship, the region would be the more easily pacified. He had the chaquira chest brought out from the *Victoria,* and after making a speech in the Indian tongue he distributed presents, giving to Aparia himself a sword with a gilded hand-guard that had belonged to Arévalo the Horseman, the best accoutred of the eight who had died.

We went on down the river, leaving Aparia in ecstasies at our goodness; but the women were hidden away in the villages we came to. The men were willing enough to trade food for trinkets, and we made good and peaceful progress until, finding the villages deserted, we knew that we had crossed the frontier.

The days passed wearily for me. I missed my canoe and the joys of independent command. I did not relish the long spells each one of us had to take at rowing. The nights were always wet, and we slept in the huts of empty villages, setting many sentries, as we knew we were being watched.

One evening after dusk we came upon a solitary Indian fisherman, whom we took aboard, thinking that he might make a useful guide. We towed his canoe astern of the *Victoria.* He showed no interest in us or our doings, and whether we laughed or sang or quarrelled was all the same to him. He sat with his head lowered, his hands on his thighs. When he ate, he flung the food into his mouth with flips of his hands, and those of us who tried to copy him for amusement would miss our mouths altogether. Then he would wait like a famished dog until he was offered some chicha, the only thing in the brigantine that had the power to excite him. Some of the compañeros made game of him by drinking themselves and pretending that he was forgotten. Once the gourd was in his hands, he drained it and held it out for more. On seeing that there was no more chicha for him (and he was ready to go on drinking it all day long, though he felt the effects of it much more than we did), he would lower his body up to the neck in the water, then drag himself back aboard and go to sleep.

He never guided us to any place where we might find food or shelter, though he understood what the Captain said to him and replied reluctantly to a direct question. On the fifth day we were all tired of so sour a guest. Orellana did not punish him (as many would have done), but ordered him to be put in his own canoe and pushed off. Then he looked at us with interest for the first time. He stared after the brigantines, his paddle wagging lazily in the water, and he was still there, a speck on the yellow flood, until the distance became too great for us to see him.

Fifty men (fifty-two counting the Negroes) take a deal of feeding when they are in full work, and we had not been stinting ourselves since Aparia, where, with regular and copious meals, our stomachs had regained their normal sizes. One Friday evening, finding no village, we landed in a cove and lit a fire. All that we had to eat in sufficient quantity was sea-cow, the hinder part of a sizable animal. Orellana was not with us, for he and Robles and six others had walked off down a track that led inland from the cove. We were going about the business of fending for ourselves and were doing no harm to anybody when, if you please, Father Carvajal and Father Vera began to call us names, and say that we were evil men destined for perdition. Did we not know, they asked, that it was the day of the week on which the Crucifixion of our Lord and Saviour was done? And were we prepared to dishonour our whole venture by eating meat?

Papa Illanes replied that sea-cow was fish, not meat, and that the compañeros were in no mood to be robbed of the only sustenance available after they had toiled all day at the oars, most of the time in heavy rain.

At that Father Vera, instead of listening to reason, flung himself upon the meat, clasping it with both his long, thin arms, and he said that if we put it on the fire we must put him too. Meanwhile Father Carvajal caught hold of a pike, and taking up his stand beside his brother friar, recumbent on our much-needed supper, the Dominican said we might kill him if we were such profane beasts, but that for his part he would do his best to defend himself.

On hearing that, Papa Illanes went running off down the path to find the Captain, while the friar made practice jabs and parries with his long pike, and the men of violence among us began to speak of putting both friars to cool off in the river, or of belabouring them with the flats of swords, or of treating their thumbs with bowstrings.

When Orellana and the others came back, Father Carvajal, being unused to arms, had easily been overcome and was lying on the ground, firmly trussed. Father Vera was still astride the slippery tail of the sea-cow, while certain of us strove to drag him off it that we might hack it to pieces and lay the pieces on cane grids to cook. First Orellana made us untie Father Carvajal. We feared that he would side with the friars, as was his habit. But it proved otherwise.

He said that the sea-cow, being entirely a water creature, was a fish, just as the whale is a fish, and so is the seal. Then he asked the friars if they were prepared to see their friends and children fainting with hunger. They said they were, if the alternative was to see us eating meat on a Friday.

He reminded them that it was for the greater glory of God that we sought to extricate ourselves from that river, and that God certainly had the intelligence to know that we could do but little in His name if we did not eat. They answered that it were better to die of starvation than to profane our Lord's holy memory by eating meat on a Friday.

Orellana told them that the sea-cow flesh was still in a fit state to be eaten, but that by morning it would assuredly be putrid. Nothing he might say could budge the friars, so the Captain declared that it was his right and duty to give orders, and the well-being of his men was his responsibility. He had therefore decided, whatever objections any among us might raise, to leave this matter in the hands of the Omnipotent. He would throw his sword in the air; if it fell with the maker's name uppermost we would go hungry, whereas if it fell the other way it would signify that our Lord, taking into consideration our arduous circumstances, gave us His blessing and said: "Let the sea-cow be eaten."

His sword fell in such a way that the sea-cow was cooked and eaten. But the friars would not touch it, preferring to make do with some fish (of which there was enough for the pair of them). When they heard us chewing, which we possibly did more loudly than usual, they continued to predict ill from our gluttony, as they termed it.

The flooding of the river was such that it seemed to have no true course, but to pour down over a vast plain. Everywhere sections of bank were being torn adrift to form floating islands. For days on end we saw no villages, and the rain constantly stabbed down on us. It was hard to find any place to land, and we spent nights cramped in the brigantines. At the end of this period of wetness, short rations, and sleeplessness, on Saturday, May 6, the day of St. John Ante-Portam-Latinam, something happened so extraordinary that I would hardly venture to describe it were it not vouched for by all the others, and by Father Carvajal in a written deposition.

We had stopped to spend St. John's Day at a place where the bank was high and covered with trees. Diego Mexía fired at an iguana on one of the trees, and the nut * jumped out of his crossbow, falling into the deep, yellowish, and turbulent water of the river's edge. An ivory nut can have a hole drilled right through it and be held in the stock by thin lashings of gut, but our nuts were made of horn, and each had a shallow hole in either side. Into these holes went two screws, and Mexía had failed to notice that one of his had been lost and the other had worked loose. The nut has to be the most precisely made part of the whole crossbow, since it must turn with absolute smoothness in its socket. We had neither spares nor the means of making them. The loss of Mexía's nut meant the loss of a crossbow, an extremely serious matter. . . .

But that same afternoon while Gabriel de Contreras, half-asleep, was dangling a rod from the bank, he landed a fish five spans † in length, and when the fish was cut open for cooking—this I swear—we found the crossbow nut in its belly.

The importance to us of this miracle will be understood when I tell you, as I am about to do, of the next part of our journey, which was our entry into the country belonging to a cacique known as Machiparo. The Captain had learned from Aparia that Machiparo ruled a potent and bloodthirsty people whose hobby was war, and that beyond his territory lay that of an equally bellicose ruler named Omagua. The pair often worked together to

* The nut is the firing-catch of the crossbow. It holds back the string and releases it when the trigger is pressed. See diagram, page 340.

† 45 inches.

defend themselves or to take slaves from other tribes. Machiparo was said to have fifty thousand warriors, all men of middle age, with thin moustaches but no beards. The young men had to be content with fishing and hunting and criticizing the exploits of their elders until they were old enough to be deemed ready for the pleasures of battle.

It was a day of misty rain such as often comes during the Marañón winter, from January to May. Machiparo's first village was set high above the riverbank. It gleamed white against the darkly glistening forest, and the houses had domed roofs that gave them the peaceful and agreeable air of beehives. A flotilla of canoes put out from the bank and flew upstream to meet us. We had no time to count them. They were longer than our brigantines, each with paddlers fore and aft, the well being filled with spearmen and estorica men. These had shields so big that the bearers could shelter themselves from head to toes. Made of the treated and stretched hides of sea-cows, the shields were tough, as we were about to learn.

Our brigantines were kept close together; the inner oars sometimes clashed. The *Victoria* had the starboard station, and its three crossbowmen, myself, Mexía, and Márquez the Silent, were posted on the starboard side, as were the two arquebusiers, Hernández the Unlucky and Biscayan Perucho. The canoes spread out in a crescent, those on the flanks paddling their fastest in order to close round us. When they began to hurl estoricas, the Captain gave orders to return their fire. We crossbowmen at once began to damage them, firing as fast as we could crank and aim, but the arquebusiers were a disappointment because, with all the wet weather we had been suffering, not one of them could get a shot away. This was a pity, since our crossbows dismayed them, and if the noise and smoke and lead of the arquebuses had been added, they might have fled, thereby sparing us much blood and anxiety. Our shooting was interesting, though; when my bolt struck one of the big shields truely, it went right through with a smack, but an oblique hit would glance, and as often as not would strike down another enemy.

More canoes continually darted out from the shoreline, and each new lot would paddle in at speed to try its luck. Between the five of us crossbowmen we managed to keep them away until one canoe grappled with the *San Pedro*. The first Indian to lay hold of the gunwale had both hands hacked off by Maldonado, and the compañeros sprang at the enemy with pike and sword so fiercely that they wounded many, while the rest shrank back or dived into the water. After that no more came very near us, but they remained well within range and the shooting continued while Orellana at the *Victoria's* steering sweep pointed our bows for the shore, where the warriors were formed up ten deep to beat us off.

As the keels grated, we crossbowmen concentrated our fire to clear a space on the shoreline. The sword-and-shield men led by Robles landed and cut their way forward. Thanks to Orellana's exercises at Aparia, there was little need for orders. Each of us knew what he had to do, and did it. My task was to remain with the Captain and guard the *Victoria,* which was necessary because, seeing their homes in danger, the dogs in canoes came at us again and again. Márquez and I made some shots so remarkable that the Captain, with many other matters engaging his attention, had time to praise us. The little Valencian, Rebolloso, acted as my shieldsman with his usual grace and dexterity, and he was equally useful with his sword though sickness was rife in him, and when he could find the time he would spew blood.

With what fury those Indians fought! There can be little doubt that with a modicum of Spanish training Machiparo's tribe would make the steadiest of infantry. Many of them wore their own kind of armour, the whole body being covered with small sheaves of toughened hide. They gave our men blow for blow, using their long spears and sword-shaped hardwood clubs with judgement. Where they went wrong was that they wasted breath and lost balance and cohesion by dancing about, jostling their neighbours, and yelling. With the slope and weight of numbers in their favour, they held our swordsmen. Where one Indian fell, there were ten others to take his place. But hand-to-hand fighting today is a matter of science in the first place, courage in the second, and the wounds were all on the enemy's side. Robles and his men were fighting economically, and when Biscayan Perucho, always the most reliable arquebusier, got his noise machine to function, our line increased its pressure and began to advance steadily uphill. Loud were the cries of wounded Indians who had to turn or die. The fight was of their seeking, and we had no more pity for them than they would have had for us.

Robles sent back a message to say that he was making good progress and that the village was full of food—turtles, meat, fish, and biscuit. Accordingly Orellana told Maldonado that our headquarters would be in the few houses down by the river, and he was to take twelve of his *San Pedro* men and bring us back supplies of food, but not to venture too far away from the river.

Only ten of us fighting men, together with the friars and the Negroes, stayed by the brigantines, and we were glad to see Robles returning to us at the head of his men, several of them wounded. He said he had pushed the Indians back for half a league without reaching the end of the houses, which in places were thickly set in clumps with narrow paths between, and in other parts were widely spread among fruit trees and shrubs. While the Negroes prepared food and the friars dressed wounds, Maldonado's party returned, each of them carrying a big turtle and Maldonado carrying two. Full of himself, and vastly cheered by a chance to show his leadership—which was admirable, even if it did not equal his own opinion of it—Maldonado said he would go out foraging again with the same men. Knowing then that Maldonado was somewhere above us among the houses, and seeing the river empty of hostile canoes, we eased some of our harness and rested.

Despite Orellana's warning, Maldonado had ventured too far away. He was in the upper fringe of houses when he saw "an army" of Indians coming to attack him. Although he later put the Indians' number at two thousand warriors (probably no underestimation), Maldonado appealed to the ancient Castilian valour that has never been known to falter in the face of an enemy, and he attacked them with his twelve supporters. In the close alleys between the white houses he was able to hold his own. At such moments he was in his element, and though two of his men were badly wounded, he drew such efforts from himself and the remainder that the Indians retreated, leaving their wounded. When Maldonado had killed all these, he set his hard-breathing men to collecting more food, and they obeyed him cheerfully, even the two wounded. But soon the Indians were at them again, advancing this time behind a wall of their huge shields. The Spaniards were pushed back, and took their stand shoulder to shoulder in a narrow space. Six of them were now wounded. Maldonado himself had a spear-thrust in his left thigh and a blow from a club across the face. Some of his men demanded a retreat to the main body, but he would not entertain such an idea, for he would never return to us admitting himself bested. So he rallied them.

Meanwhile the Indians, knowing their way about their own settlement, had decided to attack in two places at once. Creeping up a ditch, they fell upon one of our outposts and struck down four of the five Spaniards there. But the fifth, Cristóbal de Aguilar, held the lot at his swordpoint and most lustily shouted the alarm, while his companions ruefully got to their feet one by one and likewise fell upon the Indians. (I will say now that this Aguilar was an unusual person. The handsomest of Orellana's party—indeed, the only Adonis among us—he was the son of the Licentiate Marcos de Aguilar, who sired him from an Indian woman of outstanding loveliness on the island of Hispaniola.* Some have it that children of such mixed parentage are twisted and lack courage. But Aguilar was brave and unselfish. At this time he was twenty-seven, and he had proved his worth in the conquest of Popayán and other extremely hard fighting.)

Orellana was the first to hear Aguilar's shouts and the clash of his swordplay. He ran to the place, sword in hand, while we followed. When we had eased the trouble there, we saw that the houses we had occupied were surrounded, and that the Indians, several hundred strong, were mustering in an open space near by. After sending some of the wounded to guard the brigantines with the friars and the Negroes, we cut down small groups of the enemy, making our way toward their main force. Then Orellana called on blessed Santiago, and without more ado we fought our way into the centre of them. The Indians surpassed themselves, and there never was fiercer work than in this small battle, which lasted for two hours until they left us the ground. All of us had done our duty in the encounter. We had no choice, for it was a

* Haiti.

matter of survival. Those few whom we had thought to be weaklings or men with little stomach for close fighting acquitted themselves properly. Young Blas de Medina, for example, who had come to Peru at the age of sixteen, and in seven years had got himself a reputation for skirting and shirking, lost his sword in the melee but rushed in among the brutes with nothing but his dagger and fought with such spirit as to amaze us all. He came out alive, covered in blood, and wounded in both legs and in the chest. Eight others were wounded there, and after the heat and speed of the fighting we judged ourselves very fortunate.

Orellana then led a strong party to find Maldonado, who had withdrawn with his men into a house and had continued to kill Indians as they tried to force the doorway. Luckily for him and his Spaniards, their enemies had not the wits to burn the roof over them. A sorry sight Maldonado's party presented when they came back to us. Pedro de Empudia had to be carried in and laid down gently, for he looked to be in ribbons. He was only one of eighteen badly wounded, and I do not think there was another fighting man who had not mixed his blood with that of Machiparo's Indians. I know I was sticky all over, and felt as though I had been drubbed for twelve hours with wine staves.

Friars and Negroes set about washing wounds in river water and smearing them with turtle grease. Some of the compañeros were out of their minds with pain, and the charm I have mentioned before was used with some success. (As this method of healing is forbidden, and is even punishable under the terms of reference of the most admirable Holy Office, I declare that I do not know who used the charm, or who said it could be used, and nor did I see it being used—in short, I had nothing to do with it.)

When one of the sentries, Diego de Matamoros, called to us that Indians were gathering in a gully near us, Orellana told Cristóbal Enríquez to take two arquebusiers, two crossbowmen, and eleven swordsmen and drive the Indians off. Enríquez was a haughty young gentleman of a good Cáceres family, a man with a long neck, a longer nose, and a still longer pedigree. He had seen only three years' service in the Indies, with very little action, and was so eager to become a noted officer that he was desperate to show to advantage, particularly in Orellana's eye. There was nothing to dislike about Enríquez, but as he was excessively solemn about his soldierly ambitions, we had a great deal of amusement at his expense. His manners were as distinguished as his dress was ragged, all tapes and strings, and buttons and buckles undone. Being a greenhorn, he was less good at "finding" useful apparel than more seasoned campaigners, and he was too proud to ask for anything. For this reason, because he was such a haughty scarecrow, we called him El Pulido, which was funnier than attaching that nickname to one of excessively good appearance. He now led his men off most keenly, waiting only until Hernández the Unlucky and Perucho had lit their matches.

Very soon we heard shots and all the hurly-burly of a fierce set-to. Orellana bade us rest where we were until Enríquez sent back news. He had much sympathy for the young hidalgo's military aspirations and did not intend to interfere with him or hurt his pride. A runner, Matamoros, soon came in to report that the Portuguese arquebusier had been badly wounded, and that Enríquez needed more men because the enemy were in great numbers. Orellana told him to go back and ask Enríquez to withdraw little by little, concealing the move with sorties, counterattacks, and ambushes. Then he ordered us to load the brigantines with the food taken in the settlement and finally the wounded, each of whom was swathed in blankets and carried on the back of a man, to be dumped in the brigantine like a sack of maize. There was method in it, for had the Indians seen so many wounded Spaniards who could not even walk, they would surely have been emboldened to rush us.

You will have heard, Señores, that it was always easy to lead us of the conquest into attack no matter what the odds, but it was the reverse of easy to order a retreat, because many of us were ready to take such an order as an affront.

"Caballeros, brothers," Orellana began, "in testing us so hard today, God is showing it to be His will that we continue serenely with our journey of exploration, which was none of our seeking, but His. That is why I have ordered Enríquez to fight a rearguard action, and the brigantines to be loaded. I value my own hide no more highly than that of the least among us, and I demand that each of you feel with me that the life of one is the life of all. We cannot go on with work like today's without losses so serious as to condemn the whole expedition. I have often said, and I repeat it now, that our duty is to get down this river. When we have to fight, we shall continue to do so with all our spirit and all our strength, and will succeed, amigos, as you have succeeded today. Then our Lord, perceiving how hard are our endeavours, will grant through His grace that we complete a memorable voyage of discovery. Only by combining good sense with boldness and by refusing to admit pain, fatigue, or hunger, will we at last strike through to some softer land where there are Christians. Then, lads, shall the rewards and recognition for our present hardships be splendidly forthcoming, and our deeds will burn in the memories of those who live today and of those who will be born of Castilian mothers. You are each of you earning an imperishable title to honour and a soldier's fame. . . . Get ready, gentlemen. My decision is to leave this place. . . . Ah, here is Enríquez himself. Well done, Enríquez!"

Then he led us from the white houses, our pace steady, our heads high, and our aspect sincerely menacing.

We had barely pushed out from the bank when the leaders of the Indian horde rushed onto it and subjected us to a rain of estoricas. Here we crossbowmen taught them a lesson, and the arquebusiers did almost equally well. The arquebus of Hernández the Unlucky was handled beautifully and with good fortune by Hernán Gutiérrez de Celis. Indian canoes attacked us again and again, the crews acting as though their lives were cheap in their joy at our withdrawal from their settlement. Our combined shooting contrived to upset three canoes, and we rejoiced to note that the blood in the water attracted fishes or alligators, so that many of the Indians died unpleasantly, as they deserved.

It was sundown, and the moaning of our wounded was loud in our ears. Loudest of all were the cries of the Captain's favourite, Hernández, who had several flesh wounds and had also lost much of his right hand in a blow-back from his arquebus. This was to be the end of his career as an arquebusier, and few of us regretted that, though we were sorry enough for him because in our profession the loss of a right hand is the worst that can befall a man with the exception of blindness or death itself.

There could be no argument about the day's doings; we had won no honour from them, but they entitled us to some rest and leisure to dress our wounds. Alas, there seemed little prospect of such rewards! Indian canoes harried us all night, and redoubled their efforts with the dawn. It was a hot dawn, being windless, and it showed us that we were toiling past many of the beehive settlements, all at least as big as the one where we had fought, and many twice that size. The hives of the Indians climbed the slopes in terraces. Around them were ridged plantations, and down by the river the vegetation, luxuriant yet controlled by man, looked like a strip of garden. Thousands of people danced on the bank, throwing dust and earth into the air round them. Most of us had seen the Indians do that in battle and had supposed that they did it to conceal from us the effects of our fire. But apparently among the peoples of the river it is a sign of excitement.

From that thickly peopled and prosperous shore, canoe after canoe put out filled with fresh warriors eager to prove that they could best us. They always paddled outside us and came at us from the port side, seeking to bundle us nearer and nearer to their own bank, but in this they did not succeed, though they managed to prevent us from crossing the river. Those who were tired of the disagreeable reception we continued to give them paddled to the bank, shaking their oily heads, yet always more paddled out to keep up the pressure, so that our running fight was continuous.

About noon Orellana, thinking that we must get some rest or none of us would be able soon either to hold his oar or to fight, put in to land on a big sandbank that formed a treeless island. The sand was clean and wholesome, here fretted in little waves, there smoothed in hills, valleys, and saddles. It was alive with herons, egrets, and duck, and round it dolphins sported.

The Indians let us land. They let us light driftwood fires. Then they came at us. Three fierce water attacks were beaten off before they decided to attack simultaneously by land and water. Half their canoes hurried round the sandbank and were beached on the far side. Caught between two forces with several hundred enemies in each, we might have found things awkward, so the Captain ordered us back into the brigantines and we pulled out, fighting our way through three lines of canoes with some hand-to-hand work. The Indians we had left on the sandbank rushed at our cooking fires and speared them to pieces.

The canoe attacks then appeared to become more concerted, as though we were now dealing with Machiparo's navy, whereas what had been done before had been the work of corsairs, of individualists. Among the enemy canoes we saw five sorcerers, whose bodies were painted white and who wore masks of feathers. They filled their mouths with fine ashes, and these they blew high into the still, hot air. They carried scoops with which they flung water about as their canoes circled us. When the circle was completed, the demented creatures called on their fighting men, who at once sounded trumpets, beat drums, and with one yell came at us, the foam hissing on their paddles, their heads bent so low that we did not see their faces. There was more close fighting, but it was encouraging because we found that the brigantines' extra stability and height gave us a great advantage over the canoes.

Crossbow bolts were running short, and I set some of our wounded to search for bales of them that we had stowed among the cargo when we had made them at Aparia. The Indians remained close around us and kept us busy with feint attacks from many angles. We were continually on the alert because their estoricas were always in the air, and they are hard things to stop if one cannot avoid them. To make things more difficult for me, we were so short-handed that Rebolloso was often called away to some other task, leaving me without a helper. Fortunately, however, the clever fellow had noted the excellency of the Machiparo sea-cow shields and had put a good many of them aboard the brigantine while we were ashore at the settlement. When Rebolloso was not there to look after me, I strapped one of the big shields to my shoulders, hanging down my back, and when I had to wind my bow, I turned my back on the enemy (very unusual behaviour) and felt the heavy estoricas thud on the protecting hide. Few of them penetrated at all, and if they did I wore a good chain surcoat over my thickly padded escaupile.

So busy were we defending ourselves (and we had been fighting for more than thirty hours on end) that we did not take stock of our position until it dawned on us that they had us in a trap. We saw, too late it seemed, that they had managed to hustle us out of the main stream, and a fast current was drawing us into a narrow, shoaling channel between two islands. Both islands were covered with hostile Indians. They waited for us both on land and standing in the shallow water, silent, but betraying all the eagerness of Roman lions and tigers who thought it time to eat another Christian.

We had thought until then that the trumpet's screechings, the thudding of base and the rataplan of treble drums, were done merely for the sake of noise. Now we understood that they were signals to which the Indians reacted, and that among them was a commander planning our downfall. There could be little doubt who and where he was. A tall and massive person, his head surmounted by waving white plumes, stood in the bows of the biggest war canoe and turned from time to time to give orders to his signallers. He now formed up his fleet in lines abreast with his own canoe in the centre of the foremost line, and directly astern of the *San Pedro*. Once more the sorcerers went through their rigmarole with ashes and water, and the paddles were all poised, waiting for the signal to spring the canoes forward in a charge that would give us the last jolt and enmesh us in the trap ahead.

At that perilous moment, by the grace of God and a steady hand, Hernán Gutiérrez de Celis brought off an arquebus-shot, the kind that marksmen dream of. He hit the splended cacique in the middle of the chest. The Indian flung out his long arms, jumped high in the air, and fell back into the crowded well of his canoe. Those of us who had the good fortune to be ready poured in a volley to confuse the enemy still more, and while they were in disarray we found new strength to row across the current. We lumbered through their left flank and reached the open river. Perhaps I should not say it, but we had been saved by the wounds of Hernández the Unlucky, who could never have accomplished such a shot. In Gutiérrez de Celis we had found an arquebusier of the highest class, which is more than even Orellana could claim for the arquebusier whom Gutiérrez de Celis had so brilliantly replaced. . . . There is another important thing to mention: just before we broke clear of the trap, two eagles flew low over us, bound east, and that was certainly a good omen.

When, you may ask, are those poor devils in the two brigantines going to get some rest? Human flesh can bear only so much wastage from effort before it must recuperate with sleep. My friends, you cannot ask the question more fervently than we were doing there in the brigantines. Yet the Indian assaults continued and did not slacken. Hard did my war-bow work, and well did the steel spring prove itself. For as soon as I had fired a bolt, I would crank again. We all took our turns at the oars—the Captain, the friars, even some of the badly wounded. When I had to row, I kept the crossbow ready to fire at my side, and if there was an attack, or a neat shot to be taken, I shipped my oar and did the work I was born to do. This helped me greatly to forget my aches and terrible weariness.

During those nights of fighting on the water, we lashed the two brigantines side by side for fear we should get separated and so that fewer of us would have to row. The enemy were always thick about us and too energetic for any of us to sleep. We were lucky in that none of those nights was entirely dark on the water; if it had been otherwise I should not be here, talking to you now.

I often envied those of the wounded who lay groaning under the roof of woven palm leaves, for they at least had the right to lie and do nothing but suffer their pains, and they were in another sense fortunate because Machiparo's men did not use bows and arrows but relied on their vicious estoricas, flinging them low across the water. Had they attacked us with high-flighted arrows, they would have killed all the compañeros lying in the wells.

The lands of Machiparo, and I can only describe the river frontage, stretched down the right bank for a good eighty leagues.* I declare that there was scarcely a crossbow-shot between any of the settlements, and some of these were huge places by any standards, even if they contained no buildings of any size or grandeur. We passed one settlement that seemed to go on for ever, and our seamen calculated its frontage at no less than five leagues.† Therefore Machiparo was a very powerful lord, and it seemed likely that King Ica, who, according to the excellent Aparia (how distant in time and scene Aparia now appeared to us,

* 290 miles. † 18 miles.

he and his friendly Indians!), owned a vast domain inland of Machiparo's, was of even greater power and wealth. It was a bitter grief that we were unable to land in those places.

We had come on the upper houses of Machiparo's territory on the morning of Sunday, May 7, and we had fought our way down to the end of the last village waterfront by noon on Wednesday, the 10th. Then the war canoes let us go on unmolested, content that they had harried us to the very end of their own waters.

Drifting as much as rowing, we covered another nine or ten leagues, becoming quickly flaccid and drowsy without the stimulant of danger that had been ours for so long. It was very hot, the biting flies were a torment, and a sorry thing had to be done. The friars had decided that Hernández the Unlucky must have his hand cut off because it was festering, but neither of them would do the cutting. Orellana thought it right that he should personally accept the responsibility. A pot of boiling resin was got ready forward. Hernández's right arm was bound tightly above the wrist. Orellana stunned his poor friend by hitting him on the temple with a stretcher padded with cloths. Then taking a sharp axe, he cut off the injured hand and dipped the stump of the arm in the hot resin. Both Hernández's arms were then bound securely to his body lest when he recovered consciousness he should do himself an injury.

Omagua's frontier village in no way resembled the pretty settlements of Machiparo. It was a dark place on a hillock with a palisade round all but the waterfront at the place where a small port was set. The port itself was protected with spiked stakes both in the water and out of it. Orellana, pale and irritable after his surgeon's work, called the *San Pedro* alongside and gave his orders. The village, he said, looked a good one for defence, once we had taken it. Since these Omaguans would be new enemies, we would have the advantage of surprise. If they showed fight we would attack and put the place to the sword until we had cleared it, and once we had done that, we should be able at last to feed ourselves and to sleep.

Sleep! We prepared to earn like men the reality for which we yearned so desperately. Several of the wounded revived, and

Cristóbal de Aguilar, with only half his handsome face showing through Father Vera's bandaging and his left arm bound to his chest, came crawling out from under the awning and adjusted the buckles of his harness with a bloodstained right hand.

Flank to flank, the brigantines lay ready at the entry to the little port while Orellana in his dirty armour began to parley from the *Victoria*'s bows. His answer was a shower of spears, so he told the oarsmen to hold steady while we marksmen cleared a landing-space. For once Mateo de Rebolloso was not beside me with his ready shield. I shouted for him, but got no answer, until Father Vera, taking up a shield, clumsily did his best to protect me so that I could concentrate on my shooting. Orellana, still in the bows, was the first to jump ashore. The swordsmen streamed after him, and crossbowmen and arquebusiers deployed to either flank. We drove the Indians up from the river, drove them through their huts. So thorough was our momentum that we drove them over their spiked palisade without a pause, and they left their frontier fort and all it contained in our hands.

When we began to unload the wounded, I learned with agony why my dear friend Mateo had failed me in our last engagement. We found him lying in the bilges, dead. Knowing that we were fighting and that every man was needed, he had not cared to worry anybody or even to ask one of the friars for his safe conduct to the next world. In death he lay gracefully as he had lived, poor little Valencian. We gave him a blanket of soft vicuña wool for his shroud. I mourned him, quiet, brave, and uncomplaining man, and I missed him as I have missed few others, though often when he was alive I had scarcely given him a thought unless I needed him. The loss of Mateo soured sleep that would otherwise have seemed perfect, having been truly earned and overlong delayed.

CHAPTER SIXTEEN

FOR THREE NIGHTS AND TWO DAYS WE STAYED IN OMAGUA'S frontier fort. Lieutenant Robles and his patrols reacted so violently against any Indians in the vicinity that at first we were left in peace that was sorely needed. Father Vera looked after our wounds, and most of us began to recover from the effects of our fight through Machiparo's waters. We crossbowmen spent one whole day making bolts. We thought we had made enough at Aparia to see us home to Spain, but Machiparo's men had shown us otherwise. We found a storehouse in the fort filled to the roof with hard biscuits made from a mixture of maize and yuca flours and strongly salted.

Orellana did not wear us out by ordering too many guard duties, but he had taken all proper measures, and on the Sunday after Ascension Day, when many Indian canoes and swimmers attacked the port in an attempt to cut out the brigantines, most of us were quickly at the waterfront and quickly drove them off, though we nearly lost Vayón the Pike, for he went deeper and deeper into the water in his enthusiasm for spearing swimmers until at length he stepped off the side of a ledge into deep water and disappeared. The Negroes were not there, and it was some time before the rest of us could pull him out. He wore so much steel about his person that he had sunk to the bottom like a stone.

Well-trodden paths led inland in several directions from the fort, and after the river attack Orellana said it was time to leave, as a hostile force must be gathering in the forest and he was surprised that they had left us alone for so long. The last hour was spent in gathering fruit outside the palisade.

As we of the *Victoria* began to row, Enríquez, who was for ever asking questions, asked Bermúdez, who was steering, how far he thought we had come from Imará. The answer was 340 leagues,* two hundred of them uninhabited.

We had not travelled another two leagues when we sighted the mouth of a great river that came in from the south. The tributary was of such a width that although three big islands were set in its mouth they in no way corked it. We named it Río de la Trinidad.† Our eyes were regaled by the sight of many shaded dwellings and gardens and fruit trees. But fighting men came out in canoes, their behaviour so truculent that we kept on downstream, only a crossbow-shot out from that agreeable bank. Orellana hailed some of the nearer canoes, and their occupants answered. The unusual thing was that although they answered in husky whispers, they had a trick of so directing the sound that we heard every syllable more clearly than if they had shouted. For once Orellana could not understand a single word. Those men were among the ugliest we had seen on the rivers. Their heads were flattened, like huge coins, and were of great length from chin to topknot. When they showed signs of moving nearer to try their throwing weapons, one arquebus-shot from Domínguez Miradero sent them off to a safer distance, whispering among themselves.

That evening when the parrots were beginning to take to the wing we came to another village of great charm. Its houses were set in clusters under high and graceful palm trees. The walls were white. The roofs came out to form shady verandas. There were many flowers, and children—until they saw us—were playing in turtle paddocks that were ringed with white fences. Vayón the Pike, completely recovered from his half-drowning, said with the usual complement of oaths that it reminded him, except that the water was yellow instead of blue, of small seaside villages in the Kingdom of Naples. The inhabitants, however, received us disagreeably. The men were smart fellows, quick-footed and stubborn. It took us an hour to teach them discretion, but we rattled them so quickly about the place that they had no time to make off with their stores, and we took some twenty prisoners.

* About 1,250 miles.

† River of the Trinity. Now the River Jurua.

During this fighting I killed no fewer than seven of the Indian spear-throwers, and recovered all seven bolts. When we had pacified the place, we were astonished to find that every house was a manufactory of china, and beautiful china at that. Some of the jars were made to hold as much as twenty-five arrobas,* and they were quite perfect, though equal pains and skill had been lavished on the smaller pieces—bowls, plates, and things shaped like candlesticks. They could not have been surpassed in workmanship by the best artists of Talavera or Placencia, and the lustre of the finish, the depth of colour, the ingenuity and variety of designs and embellishments, were a marvel. We named the place Pueblo de la Loza.†

Lorenzo Muñoz picked up an estorica inlaid with gold and silver, and someone else found a copper axe similar to those in Peru. Questioning the prisoners, Orellana understood that at no great distance inland there was a village whose inhabitants were all goldsmiths.

One of the houses was four times the size of any other; it contained a magnificent collection of china stored carefully on racks, and two idols guarded its entrance. We named them los Orejones.‡ They were made of interwoven palm leaves with silver disks on their arms and their legs. Their ears were stuffed with fresh flowers, red and white. Each idol was no bigger than a man, but somehow it looked bigger. For silly though they must sound to you when I speak of them, I can only say that among those neat white houses, with the ever-moving sharp shadows of the palm trees and the whisper of the river near by, their effect was monstrous and impressive.

When Orellana saw all this and heard the stories of gold, he said it was a tragedy that at El Barco we had not built ten brigantines instead of one, for here at last we had reached a suitable place to use as a centre for major explorations. The village obviously existed by selling its admirable china to rich communities inland. He would give one arm to be there with one hundred and fifty Spaniards and thirty horses; instead he found himself

* 100 gallons.
† Village of the China.
‡ The Big-Eared Ones.

with no horses, two friars, two Negroes, some parrots, and two boatfuls of wounded Spaniards. Nevertheless his curiosity was more than he could bear, and he took fifteen of us inland. When we had marched half a league, we found that our track joined another that was at least the width of a royal highway in Spain. Then, thinking of his brigantines and the wounded and the dangers that might lie ahead in a country that was evidently well developed, Orellana turned back.

While we were away, the others on his instructions had been taking from the brigantines the rough earthenware jars made for us by the women of Aparia and stowing away china ones in their places. Maldonado wanted to carry off one of los Orejones, but we could not encumber ourselves with large objects, so he contented himself with their silver armlets.

Orellana led us into the forest to spend that night. The brigantines, with strong guards on board, were anchored near us. There, among trees and ferns that rustled in the darkness, Pedro de Empudia died as a result of his wounds in the Machiparo fighting a week earlier. Nobody could reproach himself with Empudia's death. Rather was it a miracle of good nursing that he had lived so long. He had been one of the smallest eaters, yet one of the hardest workers among us, for he was of that stringy composition that seems best fitted to withstand heat, wounds, and exhaustion. In the early morning we buried him under the tall trees, and the leaf-mould where we laid him was so deep that we could not dig to the bottom of it.

Our supplies of food being as great as when we left Aparia, Orellana decided to give his many wounded a chance to recover before facing other enemies. We pulled out into the middle of the Marañón and travelled down without going near either bank for a distance of a hundred leagues.* If the wind came fresh upstream, as it often did about midday, we made fast our anchor warps to the biggest floating tree we could find upon the waters, and there were always plenty to choose from. One night was stormy, and in the darkness the *San Pedro* blundered into an island of floating weeds and grasses. Maldonado shouted to us that they were more comfortable there, so by major exertions at

* About 370 miles.

the oars we embedded the *Victoria* near them and felt secure although a sea had risen quickly on the open river, and we had been shipping water as well as spray. The tangle of greenstuff round us moved sinuously downstream, unaffected by the wind against it and by the waves that it smothered without effort.

We had brought two Indian prisoners from Pueblo de la Loza, and some of us said that their company was the reason why Orellana had decided to keep so long away from land—he wanted peace to work on his vocabularies and learn the Omaguan language. When it was time to get more food, we put in at the first settlement of another territory, which, according to the two Indians, was ruled over by one named Paguana. It was a place of great size; its waterfront stretched for two leagues.* As we were rowing in, ready for anything, Orellana asked our Loza Indians if we would have to fight. They laughed and told him not to worry—which annoyed him a little. He informed them that if there was no fighting he would give them a canoe and other presents and would let them go back upstream to their wives, but that if we did have to fight, he would hang them both. At this they laughed again, so we had no idea what to expect.

Our reception was astonishing. The inhabitants quietly watched us land among them. Even the women and children stood there with their mouths hanging open. As we stepped ashore, pushing them gently away from the brigantines, Maldonado asked in Castilian: "What's afoot? What manner of place is this?" Hearing his resonant voice, they thronged round him, goggling and snickering, so Maldonado cried: "It must be el Pueblo de los Bobos." †

They allowed us to wander at will in and out of their houses, and they did not follow us, but merely stood around like so many turkeys—plucked turkeys, for all of them were naked as they had been born. Orellana could understand their speech, but when he spoke to them they were either slow and stupid in answering or they gaped at him without answering at all. No cacique came forward to ask what we wanted or why we visited the settlement.

Some of the children led about great hairy spiders on strings.

* More than 7 miles. † The Village of the Half-Wits.

These repulsive brutes were their pets. We were all in high spirits, and Vayón the Pike thought it funny to stroke and make much of one spider, as though it were the prettiest kitten imaginable. But he at once regretted his foolery, because his hand began to itch, and it pained him greatly for three and a half days. Other children led parrots as big as turkeys, pale blue with white circles round their stony eyes. None of us put a hand near those birds, for we noticed them cracking palm nuts in their bills, which was more than we could do with axe or hammer.

In certain big huts we saw young women imprisoned in cages hung high up under the roofs, and fires smouldered under them so that they were enveloped in smoke. The flesh of their nakedness poked through the cane bars. Some of us were for releasing them, thinking that they were going to be sacrificed (and possibly thinking that smoked ham is a delicacy), but when the Captain learned that they were virgins undergoing purification rites before a communal marriage ceremony, he would not allow us to set them free or even to climb up for a closer look at them.

The two Loza Indians said that Paguana's people were rich in llamas and in silver. We did find a few scrawny llamas, and killed them to provide a change of diet, but there was no silver to be seen anywhere—so perhaps the Bobos were not as silly as they seemed. We took great quantities of fruit: pineapples, custard apples, plums, and pears, and several other fruits unknown to us but well worth eating. The maize bread in Pueblo de los Bobos was the best we had ever tasted anywhere, light and sweet. So we took all the maize we could pack into the brigantines, and we also carried off (though there was no force involved) five strong women to act as bakeresses to the expedition. Lastly, Orellana decided to take three Bobos boys, in the belief that they might be trained as oarsmen, servants, fishermen, and interpreters. We had much amusement trying to pick out three who looked a little more intelligent than their fellows.

Keeping his promise, Orellana gave the two Loza Indians a canoe and some beads. They showed no emotion at receiving their freedom, and they would doubtless have been equally calm had we hanged them. We were delighted to be rid of them. They were voracious eaters, lazy even for Indians, and they had a maddening habit of wetting us by splashing water about with their hands.

The Marañón had now grown so wide, having swallowed many tributaries that were themselves kings and queens among rivers, that from one bank we could no longer see the other. We rowed for two days down the right bank, then crossed over and rowed two days down the left. In one day's rowing and drifting we counted twenty Indian villages, all unmistakably hostile. Crossing once more to the right bank, we came near a fine settlement with houses set in spacious gardens and plantations which, when we rowed in closer, proved to be filled with well-tended bushes that carried dark beans on their fragile stems. There were so many inhabitants, all armed and hopping about, that Orellana decided against a landing. So canoes came out and followed us with much shouting. They appeared to suggest that we were curs and to beg us to try conclusions. There was nothing many of us would have liked better, for we were suffering from ennuis brought on by the heat, too much rowing, and a surfeit of our friends' close company. We envied those Indians their cool-looking bluish-white houses, and even their lack of clothing.

On May 29, a Monday, we came abreast a settlement that seemed to be divided into separate districts, each with its own small harbour. There must have been more than five hundred houses, all shaded by fruit trees. It looked peaceful, and even the Captain thought it a suitable place for a landing. Suddenly, however, the whole settlement began to buzz, and swarm upon swarm of dark warriors leaped out into the sunshine, their bearing leaving us in no doubt that they intended to defend their town most wholeheartedly and asked nothing better than an opportunity to do so.

"Pull on, lads," the Captain said.

Seeing that we were passing meekly by, several hundred of them jumped into canoes and came at us. Our fire was to theirs as the thunder is to the noise of a falling acorn. We were irritated with them, and gave them several volleys before they left us, carrying their dead with them. We named their pretty settlement Pueblo Vicioso.

That same evening during a sultry calm we landed at a smaller settlement where the Indians cleared off without so much as throwing a stone at us. We set our Bobas to baking bread while most of us gathered fruit and Robles and his foragers combed through the houses. These had clay walls painted white, and were thatched, not with the palm roofs to which we were now so well accustomed, but with a kind of coarse straw. From this we deduced that not far off, behind the river's implacable fringe of forest, there lay savannas where crops grew. It was a pleasant thought. For we still hoped as we went down that immense river that one day we would glide into a countryside gorgeous as the Plain of Granada, where the people would welcome us as interesting friends who had come a long way and a hard one, and therefore deserved consideration and cosseting.

In this settlement we did make one most exciting discovery—salt. It was packed away in a dry storehouse in the form of blocks that looked as though they had been hewn. It seemed to us the best thing we had ever tasted. A store of it was set aside, together with some sweet palm oil, to be used by the friars for dressing wounds. Robles also gathered there good quantities of partly roasted ducks and parrots. The parrots were a greater delicacy than the ducks. I have said it before, but it is worth repeating: parrot flesh is second to none, though the meat of certain monkeys runs it close.

This profitable halt was the last in Paguana's country, where our reception had been inconsistent, for in some places there had been no opposition at all, while in others the inhabitants had been eager to exterminate us.

Now we entered a more warlike province. Indians attacked us frequently, and as we made neither friends nor prisoners, and the Indians with us were idiots, we did not learn the name of the province or that of its cacique. Our enemies were of medium height, well built and muscular, and not pot-bellied like many of the other tribes. They used hardwood shields and were dextrous with their throwing-spears and small sticks loaded with stone, which they also threw. We could not but admire their bearing (which was nearly the equal of our own, and they, like Machiparo's men, should make good native auxiliaries once they have been pacified).

On Saturday, June 3, the friars began to plague the Captain, insisting that it was his duty to make port that evening because the next day was Trinity Sunday, and in their opinion things might go very ill for us if we did not spend a day of such religious import in the ordained manner. Somewhat ruffled by their importunities, Orellana answered that while no man was more grateful to our Lord than he, it was his right to choose where we should or should not land, and he was not going to be dictated to. However, that afternoon he steered us to a village of no great size. He had chosen ill, because we had to fight like demons to clear the place, and although our opponents were not many by Indian standards, they made up for that by darting about so that we could neither shoot them readily nor get at them with our steel. Also they were adept at taking cover behind their huts and suddenly letting fly at us with their throwing-sticks. Orellana took one blow on the ear that knocked him down and removed his helmet. He got up in a second, angrier than ever. Robles and his party lost no time in gathering together a quantity of food, and this included a few live fowls of, we thought, the Castilian breed. Did this mean that Spaniards had been there before us? . . .

We had no leisure to debate the point, because Orellana gave the order to re-embark at once. I suppose he judged the village unsuitable for defence against a night attack, but he gave no reason for his decision. Father Carvajal spoke out against it, asking if all our trouble and fighting there was to go for no greater reward than a few fowls and some maize and pineapples. He drew no response from the Captain.

Soon we saw a great gap in the left bank, and this proved to be the mouth of a river that surely must seep out of swamps of such extent as to constitute a swampy sea. Its waters were black as a black horse, and they came a long way into the yellow Marañón until there was a dividing line between the two kinds of water, and here and there beyond that line a patch of crystalline black writhing in the yellow and gradually losing its clarity. We drank some of the dark water, which had a reddish tinge in our gourds, and we found it to be sweet and good. Orellana named that river, which must be one of the earth's biggest, the Río Negro.* We saw a few villages on its eastern bank near the confluence.

To show you how the Marañón grows in power from the swallowing of its tributaries, Diego Bermúdez had been taking depths in the main channel, and he had found from eight to twenty brazas † above the mouth of the Río Negro, but below it he never found less than thirty, and often more than forty.‡

That night was spent on the river, and the current took us close to the left bank. As dawn came damp and cool, it showed us some fishermen's sheds and huts close at hand, and we at once landed there and disposed ourselves comfortably in the empty huts while our Bobas bakeresses lit fires. There was an impressive store of fish in the place, both fresh and either smoked or salted, and there were many well-made canoes. Truly the life of those Indians was easy. They did not have to fell and haul trees to make their fishing craft; they merely allowed the river to bring an ample selection to their doors, and they tethered the more suitable ones by the bank. But while they are lazy, they are also ingenious, and if you had seen the boat-builders' tools as we did, you would agree with what I say. Axes there were, made from the breast shells of turtles, cured, sharpened, and burned into wooden handles, and adzes—blades of the same shell bound into the jawbones of sea-cows. Their gouges and chisels and boring tools were made from the teeth of different animals, sharpened on stone, and cleverly fitted to neat handles pleasant to the touch.

When we had taken part in the religious ceremonies proper to the day, with nothing skimped, we sat down to a copious breakfast. The insects were less plaguesome than usual. Our thanks to God and to the Captain were the more sincere because of our comforts.

Thus it happened that we passed Trinity Sunday in a seemly manner except that some men are always seeking excitement in

* This, perhaps the most obvious of the names given by Orellana's party to geographical features, is almost the only one that survives to this day.

† Fathoms.

‡ 40 fathoms: 240 feet.

one form or another, and our sentries reported movement in a small fortified village on an eminence, some three crossbow-shots above us. In times of peace, it would seem, the people used the fishing centre where we were established, and they withdrew behind their palisade up above there when they were threatened. Robles suggested that it would be unwise to leave the upper village alone, since the men in it might choose their own moment to come at us, and the slope would be in their favour. The Lieutenant, taking ten Spaniards with him, therefore climbed the hill. He marched straight to the gateway that afforded the only entrance, and seeing so few, the Indians did not trouble to close the gates. Robles went in, and we assumed it was to be peace. But the stupid Indians took up their arms. Robles and his men fought their way back to the gateway. There they formed up, in full view of us, and refused to be budged.

Young Enríquez led us up the hill at a run. We halted for a few seconds near the top to get our breath. Robles fought with the burly Maldonado on his right hand and Papa Illanes on his left, and the three of them were having an argument about their swordsmanship.

"Do you think you are mowing hay?" we heard Robles say to Maldonado. "Look now. I lunge at the throat, like this . . . or flick open his belly, thus. . . ."

Then we advanced, and Robles and the others stepped aside to let fresh men have the play. We fell upon them with such zest that soon we did what we liked with them. We could have taken fifty prisoners had we so desired, but we let them scale their own walls and fly. We found stores of food and drink as though to withstand a siege, and after making several journeys up and down the hill we had once more stocked the brigantines in a most thorough manner. All the china jars from Loza that were lashed under the thwarts and along the sides of the *Victoria* were filled to the brim with meat, fish, maize, yuca, and salt. Orellana was angered if he thought we handled the jars too roughly, and when Father Vera, getting out some salt, chipped one of them, he felt the sharp edge of the Captain's tongue. For the jars were numbered in the collection of objects that Orellana intended taking with him to Spain. The same system of stowage in jars was not so successful on the *San Pedro,* whose lines were less full and whose buoyancy was greatly inferior.

Next day, Monday, June 6, we woke to find a light breeze travelling downstream, an unusual and most welcome quirk of the weather. So we tumbled aboard without waiting for anything. Each brigantine set its square-sail, and with wind and current of the same persuasion we made wonderful progress, passing many settlements. We cooked our breakfasts on the charcoal fires set in the bows. Our breeze, after serving us royally, dropped to nothing when we were passing a village in which we saw a large and unusual idol, and we landed to investigate. The inhabitants fled at once, with us giving chase in several directions. Gines Fernández, who could run like a deer—though I never heard of him running in the wrong direction, away from an enemy—caught a man with whom the Captain could talk. He first tried the three Bobos boys, but as they were too stupid and lazy to be of the slightest assistance, he fell back on his own wits and made good progress. At the same time he determined to have done with the boys, who were good for nothing but eating and drinking, and who besides were always attempting to tamper with our invaluable bakeresses.

The "idol" that had attracted us to that place was more like an altar. It had been carved out of a single tree trunk of immense girth. Two lions in half-relief sat on their haunches with their heads turned so that they looked into each other's eyes. Between their paws they held a walled city, and at the city gates were two towers, each with a door. Through the main gateway was a channel into which the Indians evidently poured offerings of chicha. The baked earth around was worn smooth as marble, and there was blood on the altar, though whether human or not our prisoner would not say. This apparently ancient thing, giving evidence as it did of proper buildings, or at least some signs of more advanced civilization than any we had seen since Peru, greatly fascinated us. And while we were crowded round it we heard shouts of astonishment from others who were searching the settlement. These led us to a building, large by Indian standards. It had low walls, less than the height of a man, but its pitched roof was immense, and was cunningly supported on a system of scaffolding, all the slender poles of which were painted in bright colours. The only light that entered came through the single doorway, and the interior was a wonder to behold, for it was thickly festooned, even high up in the air, with ceremonial robes made of cotton cloth upon which were fastened soft feathers of all colours, layer upon layer of them. We could recognize the plumage of parrots, toucans, eagles, duck, kingfishers, egrets, herons.

The Indian prisoner was brought to that place, and he entered hanging his head as though in shame at being there with us. He told Orellana that his tribe made feathered clothing for the race of warrior women who lived farther east, the subjects of that same Queen Coñorí of whom both Aparias and many other Indians of high as well as low degree had spoken to us. When Orellana put more questions about the women, the fellow became surly and said that if we continued downstream we would soon know all about them, for they would kill us. To such harmless questions as "Are they fat or thin?" or "Are they rich?" or "Do they wear dresses under these feather cloaks?" he hung his head and sulked. But instead of slitting his tongue, Orellana gave him a generous handful of beads and told him to be off to the ladies downstream just as fast as he could paddle, and to tell them he was the bearer of great news, for they were about to meet men of an interest, charm, and quality, quite new to them, who had only known the peoples of the river. He was also to tell the ladies that we did not fight with their sex, and furthermore that we meant nobody on the river any harm, and although we had powerful means of defending ourselves, all we asked was to be allowed to pass on our way in good fellowship. Orellana also told the Indian that he intended to leave the three Bobos boys as a gift to the village of the altar, and he added suggestively that the boys were so intelligent and industrious as to be worth their weight in gold. But the Indian did not offer to pay for them at all. He looked at them and gave a sniff.

Later that day we landed at another village, a bigger one, where the Indians came at us in proper fashion, very ardent and bloodthirsty. Once formed up on shore, we were able to fight our way about those parts of the village near the brigantines, where we secured some maize and fowls. But the Indians would not slacken their efforts, and we were collecting too many wounds for Orellana's liking, or anybody else's. There was an altar in that village too. We cut a way through them to have a look at it, but they re-formed and fought so bitterly that the price of curiosity seemed on the high side, so by fighting a classical crossbowman's defence, the crossbowmen and their shieldsmen holding the beach until the brigantines had cast off, we embarked without loss and left that place wishing we had been numerous enough to teach its inhabitants the law of courtesy to courteous strangers.

We now passed a number of villages similar to the last both in general appearance and in the fierce temper of the men, who pranced on the bank and yelled at us to come and fight them. Orellana did not allow that, but now and then, to show them we were not harmless, we shot some of them. Not understanding the range and accuracy of our weapons, they remained in lines silhouetted on the bank, and the shooting was so unusually good, its results so easy to observe, that I gave the crossbow in turn to each of my understudies, Gonzalo Carillo and Cristóbal de Palacios, criticizing their performances where criticism was useful. I never saw a more obliging or interesting set of targets.

Our five Bobas bakeresses, sitting scratching themselves in the bows, were dimly amused by our shooting and did not seem in the least to disapprove of it; on the contrary, they were pleased by any spectacular shot. But then they were females, and therefore inconsistent. I say this because that same day a school of pink porpoises had played round us, and Márquez the Silent shot one. Then what a howling and bawling from the bakeresses. The vast river was full of porpoises. There were indeed far too many, for they consume the smaller fishes. Yet it would seem that the Indians—at any rate the Bobos tribe—revere pink porpoises, and perhaps the ordinary ones too.

We did not land again until Wednesday, the day before Corpus Christi, when we came abreast of a fishing village where the cooking fires beckoned us. And if the women round the fires did not beckon, they showed no signs of running away. It therefore seemed an ideal place in which to celebrate Corpus Christi, the most splendid festival of our splendid Church; and as in addition all of us were weary and some were sick, while others were wounded, we asked Orellana to consent to a halt there of a few days' duration. He refused. When pressed to give his reasons, he said that the country was populous and warlike, that the village was a hopeless one to defend against numbers, and that the women's husbands were away fighting or fishing, but no doubt they would return in the evening. We would do much better, he insisted, to row away when we had taken anything we wanted from the village, and spend the night upon a thickly wooded part of the bank where we could sling our hammocks and rest in security.

So many arguments and so much grumbling followed this unpopular decision that at last, most reluctantly, he agreed to let us have our way. I hardly like to say it, but in some ways it is only fair to Orellana if I do say that he had no option in making this concession to the general opinion. He went so far as to call us a mutinous and idle lot of dogs, and he repeated often and in the strongest terms that he was sure he was in the right, and that the rest of us were behaving like weaklings. The two friars, thinking of their Corpus Christi, supported the rest of us against the Captain. Even Robles did not speak up on Orellana's side. As for Maldonado, he swaggered about the village saying that we would never get down that river if we persisted in fearing what the Indians might do to us; if *he* were in command, he implied, a very different policy would operate.

All was quiet, peaceful, and agreeable until dusk, when the Indian women made their huts uncomfortable by lighting lamps filled with sea-cow oil, which emitted a suffocating and evil-smelling black smoke. We were willing to tolerate even that, but about eight o'clock, as Orellana had foreseen, the Indian fishermen returned to their homes. Finding us there, and their wives also, they made a tremendous hullabaloo round the village, shouting at us to clear out. Some of us found the situation vastly amusing.

An attack came while we were having supper, an attack mounted on anger and outraged dignity rather than on strength. Juan de Alcántara, Alonso de Cabrera, and two others held them until we had swallowed a last mouthful, and then we set about them so thoroughly that they were driven into the river and had to swim away from us. This happened so quickly that when Orellana, wiping his mouth, came out from the supper spread, not an enemy was to be seen. He was still in a bad humour, some of which he vented by posting extra sentries.

In the midnight stillness the moon slipped out over the wide waters, and Indians fell on us from three sides after approaching the village as silently as owls. Their first onrush carried them clean through the cordon of sentries, and they were right in among us for some time. The fighting was extremely confused and difficult. Many of us were saved by our armour and by nothing else.

Then Orellana emerged calmly from the hut where he had been sleeping and cried to us, who scarcely knew where to strike, or which shadowy figure in the moonlight was Spaniard, which foe: "Shame, shame, caballeros! They are nobody. Have at them!"

So we all gathered close round him and at once began to make progress instead of each scratching about for himself like so many half-doited chickens. The throwing-sticks flew at us, and in the dim light it was difficult to avoid them. Some of us were knocked down, and I was not the only one to have his nose broken, which is a disagreeable occurrence. It was uncomfortable fighting, and tempers were lost. When the enemy began to have enough, Orellana ordered us to take prisoners, and this we did, though we could not hold the slippery brutes unless we first stunned them with the flats of our swords. They made off, the rest of them, and all of us stood to arms until morning, with two ambushes ready at the outer entries to the village. A steely hush pervaded the place. I had to guard the *Victoria,* and I sat in it watching the water slide through the reflected moon. I was irritated by my nose (which never recovered its original symmetry, as you may observe) and I also found it hard to breathe and swallow. Such a knock did not, of course, rate as a wound, though it was equally painful, and more undignified.

At dawn we saw that Orellana was in no better temper, for the veins were swollen on his forehead and his throat, and it was plain, although he did not say so, that he blamed all of us for the night's upheavals. One of our prisoners was most terribly, though superficially, wounded. His back was laid open, with a sword-cut running from the roots of the neck to the rump. Him we turned loose to go after his friends as a messenger of good will, and to remind them that when they came to call us out, they did not have to do with cherubs. When the brigantines were loaded and ready, the Captain ordered the remainder of our prisoners, some fifteen in number, to be hanged in different places about the village. Then we set every hut on fire. And as we left in chaos and bitterness the place that twelve hours earlier we had named the Village of Corpus Christi, the vultures descended into the smoke to take possession.

Although we were shadowed by Indian canoes, we ran into a creek at midday, hoping to have a siesta, and when the Captain had watched us hack a clearing in which to cook and rest, he spoke to us bitterly:

"From this day on, the tactics shall be mine and shall be dictated by reason, not by the lusts of a majority for the comforts of the moment. For we did not come here, Spaniards, to seek repose. In general our policy will be this: we will make our landings during the day and will take what food may be available, for during the day there is always a chance that the men will be away from their villages working in the fields or on the river; and at nights (unless I decide otherwise) we will avoid villages and will sleep in the forest or in the boats. It remains my policy to let the Indians attack us first. Otherwise we may alienate some who might prove friendly. Remember, it is cheaper to barter with them than to fight them."

Orellana's next words surprised many of us, myself among them, but doubtless he knew what he was talking about. He began with the proverb: "To the worthless sheep the wool seems heavy," and went on to say that some of our party were so tired of our continuing hardships, and particularly of the constant work at the oars, that they were plotting to desert at the next village where the Indians seemed prosperous and friendly. He knew the names of the plotters, he said, and need hardly emphasize that he would watch them and would leave no *living* Spaniard behind him as he led the rest of us downstream on the path of duty and honour. Those who felt themselves weakening must take heart from the example of their betters. He would close so painful a subject, he hoped once and for all, by saying that on the whole, in spite of all our imperfections and waywardnesses, he was proud of us and was prepared to lead us through the chambers of hell if necessary, though our case was not yet as dismal as that, for at any turn of the river things might well improve.

He then announced that he had decided on certain changes in the crews of the brigantines and in the foraging party of Lieutenant Robles, though none of the commands would be changed.

While Orellana and Robles conferred together, the rest of us ate, each wondering uncomfortably what his neighbours had been up to. As always when we had nothing else to say, we asked the seamen to compute distances. They said that from El Barco, where we had first taken to the water, counting the twists of the rivers and our crossings and recrossings, we had navigated one thousand leagues.* Long, perhaps incredibly so, as one thousand leagues down rivers may seem to you, I assure you that it seemed longer still to us who had done it—and we had no idea how many more thousands were still to be done. I know the sea was in my dreams as in my waking thoughts, restless old sea, rolling and sighing and smelling as does a Biscayan net.

* About 3,670 miles.

CHAPTER SEVENTEEN

WE KNEW WHEN ORDERS WERE GIVEN OUT DURING THE mists of first light that Orellana had gone to some pains to split up those small cliques, each with its own secrets, jokes, and dislikes, which will form with time in any body of men, military or other. I never learned precisely why he made this reorganization, though I suspect that he weeded out from Maldonado's crew certain men whom he mistrusted, perhaps with reason. I could give you their names, but it would be wrong to make known to you what at the most were only surmises on my part. Orellana also made several changes in the party led by Robles, but the chief cause for most of them was the number of wounds Robles's men had picked up.

Father Vera was informed that from then on he must travel in the *San Pedro*. This was common sense, for it had been wrong to have two friars in one brigantine and none in the other. I will not deny, though, that there was some personal bias in the Captain's order. The friars were importunate, even dictatorial, at times. Orellana could bear this from Father Carvajal, whom he liked and esteemed; he could not bear it from Father Vera, whom he only esteemed. Those who said Father Vera did not want to leave the *Victoria* because he would have less comfort and more work in the *San Pedro* certainly did him an injustice, although it was true that his skeletonic frame felt discomfort more keenly than would that of a well-fleshed man; and he was very attached to a padded nest he had made for himself in the bows of our *Victoria*. The friar was also loath to go to the *San Pedro* because he disliked Maldonado, failing to understand his bluster.

You may remember that after the lamented death of Rebolloso, Father Vera had been my shieldsman. I was now granted an even stranger substitute than the lugubrious and gangling friar, none other than Hernández the Unlucky. Orellana knew that I had never taken kindly to the Portuguese arquebusier, so before making known the appointment, he had a talk with me. He pointed out that Hernández had been greatly depressed and weakened in health by the loss of his right hand (and therefore of his arquebus, now carried with brilliance by Hernán Gutiérrez de Celis), and it seemed to the Captain wise and just to give him some position of which he could be proud. Orellana said he relied on me to make the unfortunate fellow welcome as my assistant. It went against the grain, but I did it. As soon as the new arrangements had been announced I stepped across to Hernández and, putting my arm round his shoulders, I said loudly how pleased and honoured I felt that we were to work as a pair, that it would be the first time I had had a marksman to shield me, and that I looked forward to having his help and advice in picking out our targets. . . . But he seemed embarrassed by my hearty efforts to be friendly. He merely answered gruffly that he would do his best.

This was June 13 and, still worse, it was a Tuesday, a day unpropitious for marriages or mariners, but we were soon afloat. With so many changes in the crews, there was much stowing and arranging to be done in each of the boats, and for some days, until the new men had settled down and knew how to find their few belongings, there seemed to be no room, and we were always tripping over each other's feet.

We had not gone more than four leagues when we saw to starboard a tributary of such a size that we named it the Río Grande. It was a most dangerous stream, for it carried a great press of timber on its surface, log grinding upon log.* The column of floating trees and grass islands fought its way out into the Marañón, but gradually its surge was deflected, and long before it had reached midstream it was breaking up and spreading, mastered by the monster river to whose swing and thrust each tree and each floating island now paid heed.

That night had been almost fresh, with few mosquitoes. It seemed that we were entering a more temperate region, and that

* Now named, because of the "press of timber," the River Madeira.

the land was beginning to assume a new character, for there were more heights, at any rate to port, and they were reddish in colour, with cliffs that were pitted everywhere with the holes of kingfishers. Orellana steered the *Victoria* to within twenty paces of the landing stages of a prosperous settlement. All the roadways were empty save for a few tame monkeys and some fowls that pecked the dirt. The fires still smoked, but not an Indian was to be seen. We hung there, backing water, with Orellana peering into every corner of shadow.

"Perucho!" he said.

"Captain?"

"Shoot me one of those monkeys."

Perucho did, and at the noise of his piece, squadron upon squadron of greased warriors jumped from their hiding-places, yelling and knocking their spears rhythmically on their shields. You may not credit it, but they made a noise that seemed to shake the river under us. We rowed on and soon came abreast of another fine village or town (I scarcely know what to call such places, since they were immensely bigger than our villages at home, yet not sufficiently developed to be called towns; after all, the word "town" brings a picture at least of a market and probably a cathedral, so to call a place a town is—I may be wrong—a compliment that those did not deserve). The houses were taller than any others we had seen by the river, and were roofed with straw. Dotted about in the streets we counted seven high gibbets, each holding a human head. The sight brought memories of Popayán, where the Indians have the same charming custom, and where the impaled heads have not infrequently been Spanish. Although, as I have said, it was a day of ill luck, we were all disposed to visit the place, which we took to be the capital of some overlord. But the oarsmen had not yet found cohesion in their new order. Off the entrance to the port the *Victoria* ran on a shoal. We had to ask those in the *San Pedro* to tow us off. Then both brigantines became entangled in a floating island of weed, and the weed was alive with red ants that bit us unmercifully. By the time we had extricated ourselves we were far downstream. We looked back regretfully at the settlement, remarking on its fruit gardens, its spacious turtle paddocks, the tame monkeys in the streets wearing collars that glistened like silver (though possibly only made of shells), and the peaceable men, women, and children, who stood about watching us. Blas de Medina, whom we could never believe because he was imaginative, swore that he saw three women with skirts on. But thinking the gibbets more impressive than the skirts (which only Medina had seen) we named that the Provincia de las Picotas.*

Among the few disagreeable sights in that town were bows, very serviceable-looking ones of a fair length, and all the men carried them.

Next day when we landed at a much smaller place, the men, having sent their families into their round huts, greeted us with a volley of arrows and then charged and shot alternately. Hernández was clumsy with the shield, being quite untrained to the work and I had occasion to curse him heartily. Then the fool tripped and fell just as I was aiming, and although I made my shot and killed a fat Indian, I was struck by five arrows, four of them on protected places; but the fifth grazed my cheek and might have cost me an eye. Hernández jumped to his feet and was so humble that I had not the heart to scold him. He wept when he saw the blood on my face and running off my beard, thinking the wound serious, whereas it was nothing.

Some of the Indians now fled, but the majority barricaded themselves in the round huts, which were strongly walled and had firing-slits. After calling for surrender and getting only arrows in reply, the Captain asked us crossbowmen to smoke out the Indians. We sent fire-bolts into the thatch of each occupied hut, and as the Indians came forth choking, we took many prisoners. One of the huts burned for a long time before we discovered that it was still full of men, women, and children. Rather than come out to face us, those stubborn people, some forty or fifty of them, had died most horribly; so we named their village el Pueblo de los Quemados.† The sight of the charred bodies disagreed with us, and we were eager to get away. So all our prisoners were set free with the exception of a comely and intelligent Indian wench with whom the Captain could talk. While we fought, the forag-

* The Province of the Gibbets.

† The Village of the Burned Ones.

ers had done unusually well, finding turtles, parrots, turkeys, ducks, chickens, and maize.

As soon as the brigantines were loaded we embarked and rowed on until we came to an island where we pulled into a pleasant strip of shadow under some tall trees. Camp was made on the bank after some of us had been sent to investigate what were taken to be important Indian fortifications in the shape of trenched earthworks. These, however, had been thrown up by a tribe of ants. On being disturbed, they came out at us in admirably bold columns. Where they bit they were almost impossible to dislodge. But when we retreated from their earthworks, they had the sense not to follow us.

Orellana asked our new prisoner why she showed no fear of us and why her people had not seemed to be at all astonished by our appearance, though the crossbows and arquebuses had made them blench. She answered that—although she had never seen them—she had heard of men like ourselves, pale-skinned and bearded, who lived with a tribe in the interior. She added that two of the bearded men had white wives, and the remainder had married Indian women, by whom they had many children. Orellana did not pass on this information to any but myself, Robles, and Father Carvajal. He said that he thought the young woman was speaking the truth. If so, those few Christians were possibly survivors of the expedition of Diego de Ordaz.

Ordaz had sailed from Seville in 1531 to investigate the mouths of the Marañón, but when he came to them he found himself in difficulties owing to calms, shoals, squalls, and the current. By setting all sail and navigating with both skill and good luck, Ordaz got clear with his own vessel. But his Lieutenant General, Juan Cornejo, who commanded the second ship with three hundred souls aboard, was less fortunate. They were wrecked, and as nothing had ever been heard of any survivors, it was assumed that any who gained the land had been cut down by Indians. However, as Orellana said, what could be more likely than that some at any rate had been assimilated into Indian tribes or had been passed up the river from tribe to tribe, being bartered as slaves or curiosities. Since they were Castilians, it was probable that the Indians would soon recognize them as men fit to be warriors and to breed warriors. It was also known that there had been Castilian women on board Cornejo's ship.

When we had eaten, we lay on our backs and rested, enjoying the cool easterly breeze that rustled the foliage overhead—until Vayón the Pike came to us with a long face. He brought with him some of the Indian arrows that had lodged in the sides of the brigantines during that day's fight, and he showed us that the arrowheads were smeared with a brown, sticky paste. Immediately those of us who had been scratched began to itch and to worry. The Indian wench was questioned by Orellana. She readily admitted that her people always used poison on their arrows, when they could get it. But she maintained that they had not been able to get any for some time, and that to be effective their poison had to be freshly made. So the Captain proposed that she should prove the truth of her words by having some of the brown stuff rubbed into a vein in her arm. She agreed to this without the least sign of discomposure. Several of the compañeros now suggested that as the Indian girl was handsome and gay, and all the bakeresses were worse than ugly by comparison, it would be wiser to experiment on one of them. But Father Vera (himself no beauty) insisted that the Bobas bakeresses had shown themselves to be in every way docile and that they made us better maize bread than any we saw in the villages. It would be wicked, he said, to make one of them suffer for something that was none of her doing, or even that of her tribe. Accordingly a cut was made in the pretty one's arm, and plenty of the stuff was smeared on the place.

The distress of Antonio Hernández was extraordinary. He kept insisting that my wound was his responsibility, and that if I died he would take his own life (which in no way reconciled *me* to dying). He kept coming to me with titbits of food and fruit, and he made me go to bed with a puddingy bandage filled with warm maize bread set over the wound on my face. I woke several times during the night, and on three occasions he was gibbering prayers over me.

Next morning the Indian wench was as bright as ever—far brighter, indeed, than any of the rest of us—and as the hours passed, we who had arrow scratches were relieved of our worries and all were glad (including the young woman). Quite the last to be reassured was Hernández, who kept saying with all solemnity, and he was a solemn cove: "Bachelor of Arts, you are pale this morning, and your eye is inflamed. You look ill. I know you will die, and I shall be your murderer, clumsy oaf that I was to fall down like that! Holy Mary, Mother of God, look down upon us I humbly beseech Thee, and spare this the life of Francisco de Isásaga, Thy servant and adorer. . . ." Tedious though this was, there was evidence of a good heart in it.

Near the end of the Provincia de las Picotas we saw an important settlement with more and higher gibbets than any of its neighbours, and the Indian girl told Orellana to make a landing there if he wished to find the white men and women who lived in the forest. This Orellana had no intention of doing. For if we extricated ourselves from the Marañón, those Christians of whom she spoke (if indeed they still lived, as she maintained) would in due course be rescued by the soldiers His Majesty would send to exploit our discoveries; whereas if we searched for those unfortunates, even if we managed to find them, far from the river and our brigantines, we should be in as pretty a fix as they and would be doomed like them to spend the rest of our lives as servants of the heathen. But he did not trouble to explain this to her.

As though to confirm her story, two unarmed Indians came out in a canoe to intercept the brigantines. They made signs, pointing inland. Those few among us who knew what the Captain had learned realized that the pair were trying to tell us that in the hinterland we would find white men like ourselves. They refused to accept any presents from Orellana, and we left them astern, still tugging at imaginary beards sprouting from their hairless faces, and pointing until their arms must have ached.

From then on we enjoyed some very fine toucan-shooting, for either there were more of the birds, and fatter, and tamer, or they change their habits and come down off the high branches at the beginning of the summer. They were tender, and well worth a bolt apiece. Orellana took some of their beaks and also their brilliant feathers and added them to his collection of curiosities. We also had very pretty skirmishes with Indians who delighted in fighting and who were good hands with the bow and arrow. They were expert canoemen, and were difficult targets on the water, since they used small, light, and speedy canoes. For this reason we did not mind them getting close to the solid brigantines, and those who did lost their lives.

Hernández now had practice to make him handier at intercepting the arrows without interfering too much with my shooting, though a century of practice would not have made him equal in skill to my dear lost Rebolloso. Although I always doubted the Portuguese's judgement, I never had any doubt of his courage. But he was an ugly man and an ugly mover. To be perfect, any movement in battle should be elegant. It ought to flow, to be a complete thing in itself, though born of what went before it and inspiring what comes after. In all my years of service I never had so much practice at war targets, and I believe that I never shot so well before. My skill was a blessing to us all, and was so outstanding that we attributed it to a special dispensation of our Lord. If Orellana was also, for reasons of his own, inclined to give some of the credit to my one-handed shieldsman, I was not small-hearted enough to feel annoyance, knowing that none of the compañeros would believe the Captain save only Hernández himself, who came to take extravagant joy in my success, and always shouted my score at the top of his grating voice, which cheered the swordsmen and made the other crossbowmen gnash their teeth in envy.

On Saturday, June 17, and again on the following Monday, Hernández and I were landed to guard the flank of Robles's foragers at villages where there was sporadic resistance. Truly it was a joy to see them at work, darting between the huts, gathering unbidden to quell any suspected opposition, making heaps of all they thought worth carrying off, and returning in groups to load the brigantines. In both villages we took supplies of corn, and bread made from a mixture of corn and maize, and in the second we found a big still with which the Indians made from corn a drink of very great potency. We took several jars of this fiery stuff and in the same storehouse helped ourselves to some things well made of cotton, not only hammocks and sheets, but long robes and loincloths as well. They were to come in useful as bandages. This was evidently a trading village, and although the inhabitants had not shown much spirit against us, their temple was hung with military wear, leather cuirasses, and other pieces to fit all parts of the body. There were also some tall ceremonial hats somewhat resembling bishops' mitres. Orellana took a few of those things to add to his store—the King's store, as he called it.

When we left the village to camp in the woods, we were followed by Indian canoes, but some good long-range arquebus-shots by Robles, Gutiérrez de Celis, and Orellana himself sent them packing. What a blessing were the stores of Gonzalo Pizarro! And where would we have ended our journey had we not had unlimited supplies of powder, lead, and bolt-heads?

The following day (another Tuesday) an east wind fought the current, raising an uncomfortable sea. We would have made no progress all day but for two objects known until then as Bermúdez's fantasies. Diego Bermúdez had asked Mexía to make him two strong wooden hoops, and to the hoops the seaman from Palos had sewn great bags of cotton, many thicknesses, and all reinforced with careful stitches. That Tuesday when we found ourselves in difficulties and could see no floating tree that might tow us, Bermúdez let out both his contraptions, each on a long warp. The current carried them on, and when they took the strain of the warps they opened like kites, or huge cotton buckets. As Bermúdez had fitted them with both floats and weights, and had left a small round hole in each apex, the water kites, or drogues as he called them, remained steady in the current and pulled us on like two horses. The *San Pedro* oarsmen, who usually thought they had the heels of us in the heavier *Victoria*, were pulling their hearts out, and although we were half-resting on our oars and were keeping much drier than they, we left them astern. Having done with laughing at their astonishment, we threw them a line, and so both brigantines moved on into the weather. Many of the compañeros were sick, for the movement was livelier than anything we had known, and we had to bail all day. The right bank was hidden in a haze, but to port we saw inhabited country, with white houses shimmering above the curling wave tops.

On Wednesday we rowed up an inlet to get some rest from the uneasy conditions on the river, and here we came upon a village whose houses were built at regular intervals along a single straight roadway, with a small plaza set precisely in the middle of its length. Some of us called the place El Pueblo Escondido * and others El Pueblo de la Calle.† Unfortunately we got little there in the way of stores—some cassava bread much the same as they make in Cuba, a few parrots, and fewer ducks. Our methods of cooking were wasteful and we needed a great deal of food to satisfy our appetites even for one day, now that the river was so wide and the air fresher. Also our supplies were dwindling at a time when we wanted to build them up in order to feast the coming Saturday, the day of St. John the Baptist, the glorious herald of Jesus Christ. That evening the east wind dropped, and the relentless current at once smoothed the waves, as a cloth rubs chalk marks from a slate.

Robles twice led his foragers ashore on the Thursday, and got nothing more than a little maize. Friday was a blank day, though we searched several fishing villages from end to end. That night, when we thought we would sling our hammocks on a wooded island, we found the banks to be all sodden, and a serpent longer than the *Victoria* and thicker than a man in its middle parts but tapering to either end, slid from the bushes into the water and swiftly hid itself in a dark hole under the bank. So we decided not to land, and we spent that night on the river, doing our cooking in the brigantines. Once or twice canoes came near to investigate our charcoal fires, but they did not attack. The shoreline was dark.

In the morning, while the brigantines lay side by side, rolling slightly, Father Carvajal said Mass and then spoke to us about Saint John. Then we took to the oars and, rounding the next bend in the shoreline, stopped rowing to see to our weapons and adjust our armour.

A fine village lay on the port bow, and pressing us in toward the village was a swarm of canoes many hundreds strong. It seemed the right moment for Orellana to talk peace as he had done so successfully at Aparia. He stood up in the bows. The canoes came closer with many shouts. We saw him frown and step back. As he went aft to the steering oar he told us that the order of those savages was that we were to keep moving because

* The Hidden Village. † The Village of the Street.

farther downstream were those waiting who would kill us and give our severed heads to their queen. Orellana asked for a shoot with all weapons. We did them damage, but they hung on our starboard flank, continuing to shout threats. Orellana steered for the village, which was farther off than we had thought, since the effect of the immensity of that river is to make all distances seem shorter than they are until the journey is undertaken, when they seem longer than they are. As we slowly closed the place, we saw hundreds of Indians moving into it. They trotted through the trees on the riverbank, shaking their bows at us and twisting their bodies into ridiculous attitudes. We supposed that they had been fortifying themselves for the conflict by drinking (a preliminary that they regard as manly and dignified, we as the reverse). So they massed on the waterfront to meet us, inflamed and as yet untouched by fear of us.

Our oarsmen rose from their thwarts, and fixing the buckles of their harness and such things as chin guards and steel gloves between strokes, they stood behind their oars, facing forward, because no man likes to have an arrow lodge in the back of his neck. The arquebusiers loaded with small shot, it being policy in such a crowd for them to hit as many as possible with each explosion. Looking for a target as we lay fifty paces off shore, I killed a big and very boisterous bowman, and thought I had done well, but Orellana tapped me on the shoulder and asked me to aim for the women.

Then for the first time I saw them among all that press. There were ten or a dozen of them, tall, fine-looking women with braided hair and rather pale skins. None of them wore any clothing beyond a small clout over her privy parts. Each carried a long bow and a quiverful of arrows. These were tipped with metal, because as I was winding my crossbow one of the women drove her arrow at least a span into the hardwood gunwale of the *Victoria*.

Orellana had detailed two of us crossbowmen and two of the arquebusiers to try to pick off all the women. It was not easy in that churning mob and under a very hot fire from the shore. The women saw quite well what we were about, and sometimes when we would have hit one of them she would save herself by pulling an Indian in front of her. When two of them had been killed, we seemed to be making some impression, and the Indians drew back a little from the landing-place. The women used their bows as staves to belabour those who quailed before the roars of the arquebuses.

At last the order was given to advance and beach the brigantines. The flights of arrows were so thick that every man among us had to look to his face, and as a result the rowing was weak. This was a very bad moment. Five of our people were gravely wounded, including Father Carvajal. An arrow hit him in the side and went through his ribs until its head reached the inner cavity of his body. A thumb's width deeper, and he was a dead friar. The thickness of his clothes saved him. Orellana himself was toiling at an oar all the way in, for he saw that we must make haste to get among them with our steel or the landing would be a shambles.

Before the bow grated, Robles was in the water, up to his chest in it, and he was followed by Alonso Estéban and the others. Soon they were joined by Maldonado and most of his men from the *San Pedro*. So our main body formed up round the Lieutenant and slowly fought its way across the landing-place. We marksmen were kept shooting from the extra height afforded by the brigantines, and in order to wind our crossbows we would shelter behind the bulwarks. I shot one of the women who had nearly been the death of me. Her arrow hit the foot of my steel barbote and was deflected into my chest, where it pierced my surcoat of mail and the thick cotton escaupile. When I saw the woman drop, I had to pull her arrow out. The head was made of copper.

Soon the Indians, thrust on by their queens, outflanked our swordsmen and attacked the brigantines. There was fierce fighting for every man of us. Hernández did surprisingly well with his sword in his left hand. The Negro Panama had been wounded in the head as we approached the beach, and his friend Number Five, though he was generally averse from fighting, took up a pike and with it manfully impaled an Indian who came at him. As this Indian fell, the Negro took the hardwood club from him. Then dropping the pike, Number Five wielded the long club as lightly as though it were an inflated bladder, and he skipped about like a madman, doing a great deal in defence of the *Victoria* and of his wounded friend.

Our swordsmen under Robles never left us long under pressure, for their part of the fight would come swaying back to us, and then, when they had cleared all the enemy from round our boats, they would hack their way into them once more. So at intervals we were free to shoot, while at other times we were defending ourselves with our swords. It was a precarious action, and there was more blood to it than is usually seen. Time and again our swordsmen led by Robles tried to cut their way through to one or other of the women leaders. But these were spaced out in the press of Indians, and however many Indians were killed, fresh ones rushed in to fill the gaps. The women saw to it that their henchmen had no time to savour their losses.

For an hour and more the fight swung to and fro over the beach, and had the women put more movement into it and varied their tactics with showers of arrows, that fight would very likely have been the uncomfortable end of our voyage. I suppose they were too proud to order even a feint withdrawal. Or perhaps they had more difficulty than we supposed in holding their men together.

Not until we marksmen had killed seven of the women did the Indians lose heart and our swordsmen, redoubling their efforts, roll them back. The few remaining women were doing wonders, drubbing their male warriors with their bows and haranguing them. Their treatment began to take effect. The Indians were jumping and dancing again, and were turning toward us. A young trumpeter ran forward, sounding his wooden instrument, and Orellana cried: "Gentlemen! Which of you will get me that trumpeter alive?"

The light-footed Ginés Fernández sprang from our ranks followed by Cristóbal Enríquez. They tripped the youth, gave him a crack on the head, and dragged him back to us.

We had had enough, and we saw that the enemy were preparing to come at us from the water in canoes. On that occasion none of us needed any explanatory oration from the Captain. Somehow we got the brigantines out from the shore and burst through the ring of canoes. They did not pursue us. All of them seemed to be staring at the seven dead women who lay on the beach. We drifted downstream slumped over our oars.

I looked to port at the shoreline. Reinforcements were still hurrying to the place where we had fought. A good country and well cultivated. Although it was only June, the Indians were burning over their fields, having taken the harvest and being eager for the next. You might imagine that everything green in those places would be shrivelled by the sun's heat; not so, because it rains nearly every day. It looked a country where wheat would do well, or any of our Spanish crops. The woods too were pleasant, as though they were kept under control. They lacked the fierceness of the all-devouring forest. I was very tired, and may have been "seeing things," but two leagues back from the river I thought I saw the walls, towers, and temples of a city that gleamed as white as Valladolid.

Still we drifted, though a few of us were beginning to row. Had we given the enemy so severe a drubbing that he did not care to follow us? Or had the Indians' drink turned sour in them? Or were they all obsessed by the sight of the dead women? I do not know how we would have fared had there been any pursuit, but I suppose it would have acted as a stimulant.

When we came near a settlement that seemed deserted, the compañeros asked Orellana to land there because our wounded were suffering in the heat and the cramped confines of the boats. Father Carvajal had been laid on the cargo under the roof of palm thatch, and to protect him against further wounds Hernández had covered him with two of the big Machiparo shields. Now the Dominican crawled out gasping. He said he could not breathe under the awning and would sooner scorch in the sun. Orellana answered gently that while he would do anything in reason to help the sufferings of the wounded, and most particularly of his friend Father Carvajal, who had had the cruel misfortune to be wounded on St. John's Day, he would not be doing his duty by us if he agreed to land there. The place was bound to be hostile, and it was better to go where Indians waited in the open than where they were lying in ambush. But Father Carvajal again complained, and the Captain could no longer refuse him what he asked.

Time had been lost in argument. We had drifted below the settlement and had to put about and row upstream close inshore to avoid the worst of the current. For a time we crawled up the shoreline unmolested, and then arrows poured down on us like rain. We could do little in reply because the Indian archers remained hidden in the thickets on the bank. Orelana would have moved out into the stream and left that settlement alone, but Maldonado in the *San Pedro* had hastened on, shouting at his men for greater efforts and more speed. He was making so much noise that Orellana could not call him back, so we had to follow through arrow fire that grew thicker. Father Carvajal was terribly wounded for the second time that day. An arrow entered one of his eyes, and the point emerged behind his ear. Hernández left my side, where he had little enough to do because I had nothing to shoot at, and he dragged the friar under the awning again, covering him carefully with the shields. We supposed that he was dead.

Maldonado, bold fool, was the first to jump ashore. He was followed by all but a few wounded, who stayed to guard the *San Pedro*. We continued to hear Maldonado's joyful shouts, but we could not see him or his men, for they were engulfed in a horde of Indians. Orellana led our people ashore and carved his way through the Indians. He was greatly heated, and his annoyance with Maldonado had been swallowed up by his anger with the Indians, because he had seen Father Carvajal wounded again. With Robles fighting on Orellana's right, and Estéban, almost supernaturally fierce and skilful, on his left, they were soon deep among the enemy and came face to face with Maldonado. But the Captain's coolness soon reasserted itself, and realizing that the Indians were too many for us, he ordered a withdrawal to the brigantines.

So the tangle of Spaniards and Indians came seething back to us. Right in front of the boats, while the others climbed on board and we marksmen fired as fast as we could load, the hidalgos formed a crescent and held the enemy. It was a pretty sight. Orellana was in the centre, tall and very correct in his swordsmanship, with the burly Maldonado on his right, and Robles on his left. Alonso de Cabrera was there, sweeping his two-handed sword, brave Juan de Alcántara, fearless yet polished, Papa Illanes, who fought with more of a crouch than the rest, young Cristóbal Enríquez, all strings and tapes as usual, but one of the most daring because half his mind was on his work while the other half dwelt in rapture on the glory and honour of such an action; and holding either wing were the two finest swordsmen, Cristóbal de Aguilar, he of the Indian mother, and the hawklike Alonso Estéban from Moguer. When we were ready, the hidalgos got into the brigantines, one by one, until only Orellana, Aguilar, and Estéban, were left fighting, with the water up to their waists. We hauled them over the gunwales and quickly thrust out to the main stream.

There we were, once more carried on the current, most sorely battered, and each brigantine a mass of debris and arrows and slippery with blood. We made the sad discovery that all our bakeresses from El Pueblo de los Bobos had been killed, and so had the comely young Indian woman. They had taken refuge in the well of the *Victoria,* but the thatch above them had been pierced by scores of arrows. We slid their bodies overboard before all the cargo should be ruined by their bleeding. Father Vera had come back to the *Victoria* so that he could attend to his sorely damaged brother friar, and when we had cleared a small space below the awning he laid out Father Carvajal and carefully washed him. One of us cut off the head of the arrow, and then the shaft was drawn from Father Carvajal's eye. Father Vera treated the wound with salt, and plugged it with oiled cotton. When he came out to wash his hands over the side, he looked like a pale ghost of himself (though he was never florid), and none dared ask him for news, for he was weeping.

Meanwhile Robles had been tugging at the arrows embedded in the *Victoria*'s sides, and indeed everywhere, and he showed us that the copper heads were clean, with no trace of poison on them. The arrow of the woman warrior that had lodged near me in the gunwale would not come out, so Robles hacked through the shaft, leaving the head in. When our *Victoria* rots and sinks, she will carry that arrowhead with her to the bottom.

We were about half a league from the left bank, the pretty left bank with its savannas and its polite woods. We saw canoes patrolling inshore. Night was approaching, and we had to tie up somewhere to rest, but where? All the left bank was certainly under arms and waiting for us. Orellana said we must make a long pull to the other side of the river in the hope that it would be friendly or, almost equally good, uninhabited. So saying, he told those who were worst wounded to rest and clean their wounds, and he took off most of his armour, caught hold of an oar, and set to work.

It was dark when, thoroughly exhausted, we tied up to trees that overhung the river. We had seen a few lights moving on that bank, and Orellana decided that nobody might land to sling his hammock, and that if we spoke, it must be in the lowest of whispers. He remembered the aguardiente we had found in the village with the still. The drink helped us to sleep, which was as well, for the night was damp and chilly, there was no room to lie down, and we were stiff with wounds.

Thus ended our St. John's Day of the year 1542, without feasting, celebrations, repose, or even prayers.

CHAPTER EIGHTEEN

IN THE DARKNESS I WAS SUMMONING THE NECESSARY EN-ergy to rub salt into a gash in my arm when Orellana asked me where the Indian trumpeter was. I supposed him to be dead, for after tying his wrists and ankles Enríquez and Fernández had thrown him into the bilges along with the Indian women. When the Captain had groped about with me we found the Indian, who had rolled himself to the side of the hull, had burrowed in among the china jars, and had been protected from the arrow storm by our bodies above him and by the thwarts. Would you believe it? The rogue was comfortably asleep, and was not even scratched—in which he was luckier than any of the rest of us.

Squatting beside the prisoner, the Captain undid his bonds, and asked me to find fish and aguardiente. When the Indian had eaten the fish, he diluted the corn alcohol with water and drank enough of it to satisfy a bullock. Before he could go to sleep again, as was his evident intention, the Captain began whispering to him, and occasionally giving him a pinch to keep him awake. At first they could not understand each other. Orellana continued to whisper and demand answers. He was building a vocabulary, word by word. When he had found and verified a word, he repeated it endlessly, asking the Indian to correct his pronunciation. In the morning he would make a list of new words in his primer. I slept. Their whispering, together with the moans and howls of the wounded, affected my dreams, which were uneasy, being disturbed also by tall women who were implacable even in dreams.

When daylight awoke me I looked at the Spaniard who sat next me. It was Juan de Alcántara, he who had first commanded the *San Pedro* at the time when I had command of a canoe. His face, grey and twitching, was slimy with sweat. Knowing that he had taken a spear-thrust in the side in the last action, when the hidalgos were holding off the Indians, I asked him if his wounds pained him, and if I could get him anything. He could not answer. Somebody else attracted my attention, and when I turned back to Alcántara, that bold and generous caballero was dead. He was one of the best among us. We had left Gonzalo Pizarro, you may remember, taking with us two men named Juan de Alcántara, who resembled each other in name alone. Now we had lost both, so the name must be as unlucky as it is musical on the ear.

Our bony friar, beside himself with worry, was laying damp cloths on Father Carvajal's grotesquely swollen head. Orellana called Father Vera away from his worthy administrations, and when we had heard Mass, the Captain sent us all ashore for ten minutes. Then we went downstream, some rowing and some clearing all the stowage space and washing out the bilges with water and soap, for they smelled like a slaughterhouse. Meanwhile Orellana was talking again with his Indian trumpeter, and was writing in his primer as busily as though he was describing history, instead of making it.

We floated past a succession of shady islands so placid and lovely with the feathery palms pluming the thick web of the treetops that our spirits rose at the sight. However, Indian canoes came threading their way out of the island channels until we could count as many as two hundred, and the Captain, reluctantly setting aside his studies, observed that they were different from any craft we had seen on the rivers. He called them piraguas because they resembled the canoes so named that he had known on the coastline by Nombre de Dios. Each canoe, gaudily coloured, with a long snout and a steering platform like a ship's poop, held from thirty to fifty men. And as each of them, like ordinary Indian canoes, was made from the hollowed trunk of a single tree, you can imagine the size of some of the trees in those forests. The piraguas must have measured twenty-four paces from end to end, for they were more than double the *Victoria*'s length. Each piragua had its own orchestra—drums, pipes, trumpets, and three-stringed instruments shaped like rebecks.* Those Indians who carried no instrument drummed on their shields with their spears.

* Or mandolins.

They refused to hush their silly noise when Orellana attempted to suggest peace. So as they closed round us he decided to let them hear *our* music. Not liking the bass song of the arquebus or the hissing salute of the war crossbow, they drew off.

The biggest of those most beautiful islands was six leagues * in length. From its lower end more piraguas put out to intercept us. This time when he went to the bows to speak with the strangers, Orellana took our prisoner the trumpeter with him. As the piraguas came near he told the trumpeter to sound a call. This came out like the braying of a donkey, but louder, and we laughed until our wounds opened. The Indians paid no heed. Maldonado cried from the *San Pedro* that his marksmen were offered tempting targets. Begging them to hold their fire until he had tried a new stratagem, Orellana half-filled a big gourd with chaquira consisting of beads and bells. We rowed on a little, then rested on the oars to watch the first piragua come up with the floating gourd. They picked it out of the water, and what followed was as disconcerting as it was new in our long experience of Indians. They scorned the chaquira (as we might have done ourselves), knowing it to be composed of objects of no value. They seemed to find it ridiculous, even insulting, that we should seek their friendship with gifts so paltry—as though any gift is meaningless when it is offered from a good heart and with a pure motive.

They followed us, making more noise than before, and from time to time we shot at them. They were good bowmen, and swift on the water. We had to keep them away from us, since with craft as big as theirs we would not have enjoyed our usual advantages in a hand-to-hand struggle. They kept us so busy that we had few chances to observe the land, nor dared we approach any of the fine villages of those people. But in the evening—and glad we were to see it—the piraguas put about and paddled away upstream, breasting the current easily and leaving behind them a fading trail of ugly music.

Orellana chose an agreeable camping site in a grove of trees set in a small savanna. In the grove there was a smooth depression like a dewpond. We lit a fire at the bottom, judging it would not

* 22 miles.

be seen, and slung our hammocks from the trees on the rim of the depression. Sentries were posted on the outer edges of the grove. The air was cool and smelled of dying vegetation as well as living. It was a snug billet. After supper Orellana called me to his side. He said he intended to question the Indian trumpeter about the warrior women, and he wanted me to write down questions and answers, using the firelight as my candle. Most of the compañeros gathered round the three of us because ever since Imará village we had all been curious about that tribe of women who were so famous as to be a legend of the Marañón and of its tributaries.

Orellana first required the trumpeter to say who he was, warning him that although we meant him no harm, we would know at once if he lied, and would then feel it our duty to cut his tongue out, since we considered lying (so he told the trumpeter) one of the vilest of sins.

The Indian said that when he was a young boy he had been captured from his own tribe and taken to the place where we fought the first of our two fights on St. John's Day. The cacique there was a powerful one known as Couynco, whose sovereignty extended along the left bank and among the islands for a distance Orellana calculated to be one hundred and fifty leagues.* Powerful though he was (the Indian said), Couynco had to pay tribute to Queen Coñorí, and had to allow her female taxgatherers, organizers, and spies to live when and where they wished in his domain. The tribal region of Queen Coñorí and her women was four or five days march from the Marañón up the banks of a tributary.†

"Do the women have husbands?" Orellana asked.

"No," was the answer. The Indian then talked so rapidly and for so long that Orellana had to stop him, making him repeat various things he had said.

He claimed that he had often been to the women's country, having gone there as a porter carrying tribute from Couynco. The women tried to keep their manner of living secret from their neighbouring tribes, over whom they held a complete ascendancy, but he had been able to see with his own eyes a good deal of their

* 550 miles. † The River Trombetas.

behaviour and of what went on in their country. In battle (as we had observed) they went all but naked. At ordinary times, however, they wore cotton robes wrapped closely round their bodies from below the breasts down to the ankles. They also had woollen cloaks, which they wore over their shoulders, securing them by a pair of cords at the neck.

"Are there many of the women?"

"Very many," he answered, naming their villages one after another until he was stopped because the names were gibberish to Orellana. The trumpeter then named the villages slowly, setting apart one acorn for each name. Thus we found that he claimed to know the names of seventy such villages. The houses, he said, were built of stone and had wooden doors, and in the town where Queen Coñorí lived there were five big temples dedicated to sun-worship. They called the sun Caranain. Inside the temples, from the ground to the height of a man's chest, the walls were studded with silver plaques, and from that height the wide roofs sprang, supported on painted poles. There were idols in the temples, all in the female form, and cast in gold or silver. The whole of the women's province was ruthlessly ordered and policed. No stranger might enter the province without paying tribute at the frontier guard post, and none might leave without permission to do so. The roads of the province were, he said, as smooth as eggshells. Every road was walled on either side, and those walls were spanned at intervals by stone gateways in which were guardrooms and toll offices.

"Do those women bear children?" he was asked.

They did, he replied. Now and then an army of the women marched on a province belonging to one whom he called the White King, a province whose people were tall, shapely, and almost white-skinned. The women took only male prisoners, and these they carried home with them. When they found themselves to be pregnant, they sent their prisoners away, and when they conceived they rid themselves of the boy babies, though whether they killed them or whether they sent them to their fathers, he did not know. The girls were reared with great care and ceremony in places reserved for that purpose. They were well fed to make them beautiful and strong, and they had constant lessons in the use of weapons, particularly the bow and arrow. No sign of weakness was permitted in them, and they were encouraged to be cruel and overbearing.

Yes, the trumpeter said in answer to another question, there were degrees of wealth and importance among the women. Some were much better clothed than others. Some wore gold crowns in their long hair, which they braided up only for battle; otherwise they allowed it to hang loose over their shoulders. And some ate off gold dishes, while others used wooden or clay platters. They wove the best of their cloth themselves from the wool of an animal that seemed from his description to be the Peruvian llama, or at least to resemble it. And they took pleasure in dressing themselves in robes covered entirely with bright feathers. Orellana also understood him to say that the women had animals resembling camels, and that they rode them and also worked them, as we at home worked oxen. The trumpeter described other animals about the size of horses that had hair on them as long as the span from thumb to forefinger, and had cloven hoofs; those animals, he said, were kept tied up, and there were not many of them.

He said that the women's province had a "cold" climate, and that they had not enough firewood to keep their stone houses warm. They were rich in food of all kinds, and enjoyed the blessing of two salt-water lakes, on the shores of which they cast salt in blocks, and some of this salt they traded with other tribes.

All this the trumpeter told Orellana that night, and as the Captain translated to me, the compañeros crowded ever closer, forgetting that it was past time to go to sleep. We believed the Indian. Why not? All the way down the Marañón, and even upon the head waters before we came to the greatest of all rivers on St. Eulalia's Day, we had heard the same story volunteered by Indians who were under no compulsion to speak of that or any other strange subject.

Vayón the Pike, who had the keenest of noses for treasure, had noticed that while the trumpeter spoke with Orellana he often slid his hand over a pouch of monkey-skin that hung at his waist. When the questioning seemed to be done, Vayón, despite the Indian's protests, opened the pouch and took from it a green stone about the size of a big apple and most beautifully carved in the shape of a baby sea-cow. The stone was so hard that none of our steel could make even the slightest scratch on it. How then had it been so well carved and smoothed and polished? The trumpeter told Orellana that in the women's country such stones were common, and that all the peoples of the river held them in reverence, believing them to be powerful magic. When Orellana took the stone to add it to the King's store, and the Indian saw that he had lost it and that he could do or say nothing to get it back, he became sullen and would not open his mouth again that night.

Among ourselves we gave the women the name Amazons—though inaccurately, as Father Vera (who seemed averse to women in any shape, though the uglier the better) was not slow in pointing out. He said that the word "amazon" in the Greek language meant "having no breast," because the Amazons known to the Greeks had cut off or burned their breasts so that they might draw stronger bows. The women who had fought us certainly had both breasts undamaged; and wonderful bows they drew, despite those natural and picturesque encumbrances.

Next day, after Father Vera had said Mass, we left the grove, relieved to understand that if what the trumpeter had said was true, and we had no reason to doubt him, we were unlikely to see any more of the fighting women. We saw splendid country to port, cultivated uplands and populated valleys. Although we were far out on the river, piraguas sped from the bank toward us, and the trumpeter warned us to have a care.

He said that beyond the uplands we saw, there lay a great lake which, with all the land down to the Marañón and far along its banks, belonged to a cacique named Arripuna, a noted man of war. According to the trumpeter, Arripuna's people were cannibals, and it was they who held most of the Christians of whom the young woman had told us, farther upstream. He even said he had seen some of the Christians, but we did not believe it.

The cannibals (if such they were) thrived on their diet, for they were heavily built specimens, as big as Germans or even bigger. They wore their hair clipped short to the skull, and stained their bodies and faces black. We would not let such customers near enough to do us any damage, but we could, and did, damage them. Several of them must have wished for the rest of their lives that they had never put out from the bank that day, while others were for ever beyond wishing when we had done with our shooting. We were loudly encouraged by Father Vera, who, when he heard that those men ate human flesh, wanted us to pursue them and kill them all. Orellana did not agree.

Because of the stain on those muscular enemies we named their country Provincia de los Negros. The trumpeter insisted (he already seemed to be aware of our likes and dislikes) that Arripuna's people were immensely rich in silver, but Orellana would not hear of making a landing there, and, though we lacked supplies, having little but bread and maize left in the brigantines, we all acknowledged that we needed a rest from serious fighting even more than we needed food.

So we went on down the river, which now was falling and baring many sandbanks, on which the waterfowl preened themselves, and not a few of them were claimed by us crossbowmen for the pot. Two days later we made a landing. The Indians were hostile, but Robles and his party cleared the village without our help. It was a poor place, and they found little. At the next village, where we got some maize, the inhabitants acquitted themselves properly, and it was only after thirty minutes of scrappy but hard fighting that we routed them. Most of us were set to carrying maize from the storehouse to the brigantines, and as our reward for this work we had very dismal news. Antonio de Carranza from Frías in the province of Burgos had been wounded by an arrow. It was only a scratch across the top of his foot, yet he was in agony. When we examined the Indian arrows lying about we saw that many of the heads were smeared with paste, and we knew what that meant. Unfortunately we had not troubled to take prisoners, so no punishment could be exacted apart from setting fire to the huts.

Carranza's boot was taken off in the brigantine. His toes were already black, and the poison was bubbling in his leg. Parts of him were cold, and others very hot. His bloated tongue filled his mouth so that he could not drink although he craved water. Some of us thought that his life might be saved by cutting off his leg. But none would take it upon himself to inflict further suffering upon a friend in such straits, and the more cautious among us said that supposing the leg were cut off and Carranza recovered, he would soon turn against the surgeon, saying that his leg had been needlessly stolen from him—for such is human nature. At this the Portuguese, Hernández, asked if *he* had ever been anything but grateful to Captain Orellana, who had removed his right hand and thereby saved his life? And Hernández took an axe in his left hand, but when he stood by the unfortunate sufferer he could no more make the first blow than could any of the rest of us. A leg is a big thing, and there can be times when it seems bigger than it is. We tried to head the poison off with red-hot metal, by making incisions near the wound, and by other methods, including (so I was told) the charm. But the evil would not be stayed, and Carranza was glad to make such shift as he could to confess his sins to Father Vera, and gladder still, I suppose, when his last tortured moments came to an end. On such an occasion the brigantine *Victoria* seemed uncomfortably small, and the cries and convulsions of the dying compañero did nothing to calm us as we rowed on, hoping to come on more decent enemies in the future. Carranza, when he had gone, was consigned to the great river with all speed, for he was terrible to look at, and may his poor bones rest in peace, though I suppose they have long ago been ground along the river bed and pushed far out into the Northern Sea. Maybe one day in the shape of curly seashells fit to decorate the smooth hair of Castilian maidens they will show up on the beaches of the Bay of Bilbao, which is about as near Burgos as they will get.

While we continued on our way, Orellana asked me, as his leading crossbowman and a sportsman who might reasonably be expected to know all about such things, how arrow poisons might be made. I answered that I had been taught as a boy how to make the best of our hunting poisons, and I had seen it used to bring down deer, wild boars, wolves, and bears. Let the hunter but treat his bolts with it in the proper manner and, using only the lightest of hunting crossbows, he can bring down the most powerful of beasts.

The "crossbowman's herb" is the white hellebore, which grows to perfection in the Guadarrama. The roots of the hellebore are used. The fat, glossy ones are inferior, and you should choose the yellowest, meanest, scraggiest, hairiest ones, and should gather them in August. Wash them well and squeeze out their juice in a press used for no other purpose. Strain the juice and put it in a pot to boil. Strain it, skim it, and put it in the summer sunlight from ten in the morning until dusk. Repeat this, standing it in the sun for a period varying from three to six days. Each morning the juice must be strained again and any scum taken off, and each morning after the third you should test it by dipping in a twig. When it is ripe for use, it will make you sneeze when you hold the twig under your nose, and it will be thick and tacky enough to stick to your bolts. Smear the bolts from the head down the shaft for a hand's breadth and then wrap a strip of thin linen over the paste, which grips the linen and seeps into and through it.

I told them I once saw a splendid stag die of that poison though he had only been scratched above the foot, on the coronet. He made some thirty bounds before he coughed, vomited, and fell dead. And I could have told many more stories of the same kind, but Orellana bade me stop talking about the effects and say rather whether I knew of any remedies for such poison. I said I did not, for it was we who shot the deer with bolts so treated, and not they us.

Our attitude to the shore was quite altered by the fate of Carranza. It was remarkable to witness how assiduous those resting from the oars were in stitching at their cotton-stuffed escaupiles and digging out from among the cargo old chin guards and leg pieces, boots and jointed gloves that they had long ago discarded as being too cumbersome or uncomfortable. I have probably told you enough to satisfy you, Señores, that until that day we had most readily faced very heavy odds, and that no Indian squadrons either afloat or on land had had the power to daunt us. Yet now we flinched at the sight of a single naked Indian in his slender fishing canoe.

After consultation with Diego Mexía, Orellana told us all to keep a lookout for any grove of hardwood trees by the river, like that in which we had recently passed a comfortable night. One afternoon such a grove was sighted on an island at the mouth of a big tributary. When I say that the tributary was big, I am using

Marañón standards; at its mouth it was at least a league wide.* We saw some Indian huts at the mouth, but we hoped to be left in peace in the grove, which was on the outer side of the island.

As soon as we had landed, Orellana made known his plan, which was to alter both brigantines to give us more protection against arrows. The brigantines were unloaded to get at the spare nails and timbers that had providently been brought from Aparia. Having completed his measuring and calculating, Mexía, who for once was as keen as anybody to do the work, told Orellana what wood he needed and how it should be cut. Some of those who were too weak for such work were set to fishing, and we crossbowmen were told to hunt (which was better than a holiday), but not to show ourselves on the landward side of the island. I had some sport the first day, shooting three iguanas, a dozen big herons, and a swimming sloth that stewed well. The other crossbowmen all killed this or that. Hernández the Unlucky, whose bad luck had perhaps left him with the loss of his right hand, using the net made by Sebastián de Fuenterrabía, brought in more fish than all the rest put together. So we had something to eat, if not overmuch among so many—though our numbers were by this time reduced to forty-four fighting men, two friars, two Negroes, and the Indian trumpeter.

In thirty-six hours the work was done. The bulwarks were raised so that each oar went through an aperture. Mexía had refused to put much thickness or weight in the structures, as he feared to give the brigantines—especially the *San Pedro*—such top-hamper that they might overturn in bad weather. To make them more arrowproof, the bulwarks were padded with Peruvian blankets stuffed with cotton. Our two craft now presented an odd and ungainly appearance—but we were not preparing them for a royal review. Seated on the thwarts we were concealed from any enemy, and when we stood upright we were protected as high as our chests. By increasing the windage, the new bulwark made the brigantines harder to row and manœuvre, and they had another serious disadvantage: it was almost an acrobatic feat to get in and out.

During our second evening in the oak grove, Márquez the

* This was probably the River Tapajoz.

Silent and myself, concealed in the rushes, shot twenty-three out of a large number of duck swimming in an almost landlocked bay. Domínguez Miradero had noted a similar bay frequented by duck on the other side of the island. He also hid himself. But he killed only one, his first shot scaring the others away. For this reason I say that firearms will never be satisfactory weapons until they are made silent.

When we returned to the camp and settled down for the night, we were visited by a bird whose shape we never knew, but with whose piercing and recognizable cry we were all familiar. Once again we could not see it as it perched somewhere in the leafy world above us. We disagreed about its cry, some maintaining that it said "*Huí, huí, huí,*" others "*Huir, huir, huir,*" * and others that it was trying to utter an Indian word for a hut, "*Buhío, buhío, buhío.*" One thing was certain: this bird always brought us luck, and soon after he had serenaded us we had always come upon stores of food.

Next morning five big canoes slid past the grove. We knew that the Indians must have seen us, but they pretended not to and went slowly on. When we were ready we followed in the same direction. The five canoes had vanished, but soon after we left the island astern, one of them came out of a creek and travelled swiftly to the right bank, where drum signals began, and fires were lit that sent up a great deal of smoke. Orellana ordered us to row for the other side of the river, and we did so with a will. Despite the visitation of the lucky bird, most of us had a presentiment of evil. Orellana allowed nobody ashore. There were to be no fires, no talking. It proved to be an anxious night. Indians came searching for us in a great fleet of canoes. Drawn well into the black shadows, gripping our swords, we watched them pass on the river so near that we heard every drop of water that fell from the round paddle blades. There were also Indians moving near us on land. We sometimes heard them talking. The clumsy toucans, stumbling on their perches overhead, made our hearts turn somersaults. Hiding from an enemy is much more frightening than facing him, and suits our temperament less well.

* Both meaning presumably "fly," or "escape," or "move on."

In the morning Father Carvajal ventured to say in his now thin and trembling voice that our Lord had blinded the Indians who hunted for us and had stopped their ears. That may have been so; but the truth was that those of us who were too much on edge to sleep a wink had assisted our Lord in the matter, for we had been quick to prod into wakefulness any who showed a tendency to snore or whistle or click, and one of us had been alongside Father Carvajal all night with a big gag stuffed with feathers, because although the good Dominican now had control of himself during the daytime—which said much for his strength and fortitude, and indeed was as good as a miracle—he was still inclined to groan and yelp in his sleep.

Father Vera was about to say Mass when there was a great cry from Diego Bermúdez: "Hombres! We are saved!"

Saved? We looked down the vast flood, expecting to see the emblazoned sails of a fleet from Cádiz or Seville. We saw only the tawny wavelets, the parrots flying over two by two, the dolphins rolling and turning. Saved?

"The tide!" Bermúdez shouted. "The Northern Sea pushes up as far as this place."

Then looking at the bank against which the brigantines had lain so closely, we saw the marks of a regular rise and fall, and some of us remembered to have rejected during the night the sensation that the river was rising under us. Father Vera gave special thanks to God, and then we laid on to the oars with good will, while Gonzalo Díaz, whose father was ferryman on the Tagus somewhere between Talavera and Toledo, sang:

Callen todas las galanas
Con las damas toledanas.
Las doncellas de Sevilla
Lindas son á maravilla,
Pero no son su servilla
De las damas toledanas.

Orellana said he was the last to wish to damp good spirits, but he must warn against unthinking elation, since that way comes the despair that sprouts readily in a soil of broken hopes. With such a huge river as the Marañón, he pointed out, the tide might be expected to run up a distance of several hundreds of leagues. . . . But to his words of caution he added others of a spirited nature, words likely to draw ringing echoes from bold hearts; and listening to the Castilian on his lips, we felt that great Spain was round us again with her flocks, her horses, her gardens, her churches, her spirit, and her blessed and noble women. Díaz continued with his song:

Son sus gracias singulares,
Sus gestos angelicales,
Y sus trages tan reales
Que son más que cortesanas.
Callen todas las galanas
Con las damas toledanas.

But in any company there will be some who see disaster ahead, and such a one in this case was Alonso de Tapia, who said that a more suitable melody for the occasion as he saw it would be:

Pásame por Dios, barquero,
D'aquesa parte del río.
Duélete del dolor mío.

And Tapia said that the "tide," as Bermúdez called it, should now be rising, yet the current still ran *down* as swiftly as ever.

What he said was true. But our earringed sailor from Palos argued stoutly that the Marañón had such power in it as to overcome even the sea, and very likely the tide at no point flowed up the river, though with the rise and fall of the sea's level—which would have the same effect as damming the estuary—the level of the Marañón would also rise and fall within a certain distance of the sea. Orellana and Robles agreed that this seemed to make sense. So did Father Carvajal, an intelligent person. So did young Enríquez, because he considered it the duty of a young officer, particularly one of impeccable birth, to be a consistent optimist; also he always agreed with everything that Orellana said. Papa Illanes began, as usual, to make a rambling discourse that none could grasp, including himself. But this was stopped in summary fashion by a flotilla of piraguas. The Indians came straight for us, yelling and whistling, their drums throbbing.

They were so set on finishing us that we supposed them to be those same ruffians who had persistently hunted for us all night. They attacked from both sides at once while we moved bow to stern, the *Victoria* in the lead. As we marksmen could not shoot fast enough to hold them off, there was hand-to-hand fighting, with the swordsmen and pikemen prodding and slashing across our new bulwarks. Time and again it was a near thing.

This water battle moved downriver close to a shore lined with immense crowds of Indians who danced and waved palm leaves, madly excited by the guazabara, which must have provided the most entertaining of spectacles—though I dare say their enjoyment would have been even greater had we shown more signs of allowing ourselves to be bested.

We fought them off for three hours, from seven in the morning until ten, and the action ended with two remarkable shots, both fired from the *Victoria* at the most dangerous of all the enemy's piraguas, a craft that constantly led the attack and had three times grappled with us. The first shot, fired by Alonso de Robles, went through one Indian's throat and hit another between the eyes, killing both outright. At the same moment Biscayan Perucho went one better. He was loaded with shot, and at close range he knocked over three warriors and wounded several others. The Indians could not hold their craft steady, and they capsized, a most unusual sight, and a most unfortunate one—for them. Both brigantines bore down on the swimmers. Dive though they might, and eels were not more at home in the water, we slaughtered thirteen of them with pikes.

But the engagement, although a victory over odds, ended sadly for us. A high-flighted arrow had nicked García de Soria's thigh as he sat rowing. So nearly spent was it when it had pierced his padded leg guard that it fell from the wound. The poison on it, however, soon did its awful work. Once again we had to witness the death agonies of a friend. But for our raised bulwarks, our Machiparo shields, and the care we now all took with every detail of our protective harness, we could only suppose that many of us would have shared those agonies.

Orellana steered us away from the right bank and across the

river to the other side, where we saw a line of blue hills cut off as squarely on the tops as slabs of *carne de membrillo* * and divided each from the other as with a saw cut, the sides all looking as straight as the tops, on which some fortified villages stood. Down by the river there were no villages, and this vexed us, for we needed food. We buried poor Soria on a bank among oak trees, or at any rate trees resembling the white, cork, and evergreen oaks of Spain.

The night was without alarms or alerts, and the place seemed so healthy from every point of view that Orellana decided to stop there two days. He set some of us crossbowmen and all the fishermen to looking for food, and sent Lieutenant Robles with all his foragers and two crossbowmen on a scouting foray. We had no great luck in our hunting by the river, but Márquez the Silent and Mexía, who marched with Robles, had shooting in plenty. They went through a country of woodlands and savannas, with game everywhere. They were constantly finding traces of Indian hunters, fires and leafy shelters, pits to trap big animals, feathers and skins. At length Robles turned back, not wishing to exceed his orders or to bring trouble on our camp, and when he returned, with no news but a good deal to eat, the Captain praised him warmly for his prudence.

At that time I was kept busy writing, and it was the fault of Cristóbal Enríquez. Enríquez (always the zealous young officer) had been pestering Orellana for instruction in the business of war, and having plenty of time on his hands for once, Orellana said he would dictate to me certain rules for the successful leader of Spanish soldiers. I have them here, and they are as follows:

1. Seek to know several languages, and particularly those of your likely enemies. This was a habit of the Romans, and it was one of their greatest strengths.

* *Carne de membrillo:* an excellent sweetmeat—not too sweet—made from pounded quinces, which in Spain is much eaten to this day. The flat-topped hills are now known as the Serra de Almeirim. Von Martius estimated their height above river level at 800 feet. They extend for some 90 miles along the northern bank.

2. Eloquence is perhaps an officer's most useful gift, and it is available to all, for a man is born a poet, but he becomes an orator.

3. Vis-à-vis your own men, try to make yourself loved rather than feared. But respect there must *be, and a small fear is therefore healthy. Respect is gained by integrity. From over-severity will spring a big fear that is dangerous to you. Enemies, on the other hand, must be made to know fear first, then respect, then love—if it will come.*

4. When punish you must, try to leave punishment in the hands of subordinates. You yourself should appear as a moderating influence.

5. Always indoctrinate love for the King. It is your duty, and it pays.

6. It is wise to have favourites among your men as long as they are good favourites—that is, worthy ones. Choose them with care. Trust them. Put them first in the line of honour and danger. Demand five times more of them than of others. A word about the method of choice in this matter: beware of all whisperers. Give several men a secret; see which of them takes longest to betray it; he will be the most trustworthy.

7. Always give prizes for practice marksmanship and work hard to be a marksman yourself. . . . Insist on silence and cohesion even when two men move off together on a fatigue. The Roman soldiers always moved as though they were near the enemy.

8. Be prepared in every detail, but remember that the best soldier is the one who travels with the fewest encumbrances. Minimum equipment: maximum speed in approach and in action. The same rule applies to your orders. Let your motto be: the minimum of orders; the maximum of enforcement.

9. The worst crime in your men is sleeping on sentry-go. Never fail to make a severe example in such a case.

10. Three determined soldiers are better than nine determined soldiers and one coward. For cowardice is as catching as the pest of the Indies. Remember that before his second attempt on Mexico's island capital, one of the hardest nuts ever cracked in war, Cortés sent back to Cuba all of his men who cared to go;

and in this he acted wisely—wisely even for Cortés, the greatest leader of men who ever threw a leg across a horse. . . . To know cowards, pretend to have a dangerous plan and most carefully observe which men feign sickness, which seem too talkatively ardent, and which remain firm.

11. Every move made under the enemy's observation must be smooth, competent, calm, and threatening.

12. He who attacks, conquers, and it is good tactics to attack, or appear to attack, at the enemy's point of strength.

13. Always fight when you choose if possible, and not when the enemy chooses.

14. There is a usual sequence for the speech to his men of any commanding officer before a battle. Remarking once more that how any speech is made is far more important than the content (see Rule 2 above), I give the sequence, which is as follows:

Remind your men of victories over similar enemies.

Point out any advantages of terrain or weapons.

List the enemy's weaknesses and absurdities.

Mention the shame of defeat.

Inspire them, for the honour of themselves, Spain, the King, etc., etc., to follow you.

Build competition between different arms—e.g., infantry and cavalry, crossbows and arquebuses.

Having helped your men to laugh at the enemy, list his insults and atrocities, for anger is stronger than wounds.

Exaggerate the enemy's riches, and the consequent profits of victory.

Emphasize the impossibility of retreat.

Remind them that Heaven will surely declare itself in their favour, and lastly,

With sincerity and deepest conviction, rather than humility, invoke the aid of the God of Battles; then, having done your best to bring them to the boil, call on Santiago, and have at the enemy.

15. Once battle is joined, cease to wonder when or how it will end. Go on killing, and when you have killed enough, the other side will fly or capitulate. But at the back of the commanding officer's mind must always be his objective, and if he sees that the fighting is lessening his chance of gaining his way, he must be prepared at the right moment, and still killing the enemy, to withdraw.

16. *All defeats must be turned into moral victories (see Rule 2 above).*

17. *It is good sense to pamper prisoners, and often to release them. In general your treatment of prisoners should be either very harsh or very lenient.*

18. *Always be ready to learn from your enemy. We Spaniards have been forged in the flames of seven hundred years of war against the Moors, from whom we learned much of value. When the Great Captain led us to Italy, where we faced the French iron-clad knights as well as the Swiss pikemen and the German infantry, we proved our tactics as swordsmen, crossbowmen, and light cavalry. We also improved them by copying what was best among the strangers. Even in Peru and Mexico, where our arms are so superior, we have not been too haughty to adopt the best of the Indians' weapons and stratagems. So it must be, as we go on to conquer the world, Enríquez. And I will end by repeating the valuable plagiarism: he who attacks, conquers.*

When I had written all that down, Enríquez took the parchment and begged Orellana to sign it. But he refused. He said that there was nothing original in it. It could all be read in the military manuals, and it had all been learned from experience by most of us who had suffered and enjoyed the conquest.

While we rested in that pleasant and shady place, we had opportunity to observe the regular rise and fall (of about a man's height) made by the tide, and to note that the weather was more squally than hitherto. The seamen computed that we had navigated 1,600 leagues,* one hundred of them in tidal water, yet observing the sky downriver, Bermúdez and the others said they thought we were still a long way from the sea. There was much discussion about the brigantines. Some were of the opinion that they should at once be got ready for seagoing. But Orellana thought it too soon to take down the bulwarks that had served us so well in the last fight.

* 5,870 miles.

Father Carvajal did the best of any of us from the rest in that place. One side of his face was still bandaged to give it protection from sun, wind, and insects, and his body wound was slow to dry up. Yet he showed ample signs of returning strength. This was of benefit to us, for he began to say Mass again, and he did it better than the other.

That halt among the oak trees, although we did not know it at the time, was to mark a geographical phase in our journey and was to be the end of what we had come to regard as normal voyaging.

CHAPTER NINETEEN

I HAVE TOLD YOU SOMETHING OF THE BANKS OF GREAT rivers, and particularly of the Marañón. I have spoken of the people we found on the banks and of their behaviour toward us. There will be no more of such talk, and for this reason: when we had rowed out into the stream and away from that grove where we had rested, we never saw either bank again. This was fate's doing. The river had become so immensely wide that it would have taken us days, I suppose, to get from one side to the other, and it was so set with shoals and islands that our navigation was always difficult and sometimes hazardous. In short, we could not *find* the banks.

We had experienced many squalls on the Marañón and the two upper tributaries, but with the exception of the one I described on the Canelos we had seldom been in serious difficulties with them. Now things were often different. We would be forced through narrow channels where the yellow water, suddenly compressed, would rise into breakers. Beyond the bar at the lower end of such a channel we were bedevilled by eddies and whirlpools. The wind daily became fiercer, and it was nearly always from the wrong direction, the east. When, as occasionally happened, it came from upstream, we would hoist our small sails on the jury masts and for a time would enjoy cascading down the river with the water frothing before and under our bluff bows and two men straining at the steering oar. But we were more prudent after one such romp, when the *Victoria* foundered. The wind aft grew stronger. The *San Pedro*'s sail was blown to pieces. Intoxicated by our own bustle and the scream of the wind, we in the *Victoria* did not know our danger until the river began to rush in through the rowing apertures in the bulwarks. The brigantine had developed such a yaw on the seas running under that it buried now one side, now the other. Most of us set to work with gourds, flinging the water overboard, and Bermúdez and Mangas used all their skill and brawn at the steering sweep. We tried to drop the sail, but the coarse lianas of which the halyard was made had swollen, and it would not come down. The heavy boat drew an even bigger stern wave after it, until we were pooped and the whole waist was flooded. Bermúdez, fearing this, had been making close to a spit of sand. Thanks to him, we sank in shallow water, and when the tide had gone down a little, we were able to refloat the brigantine.

Now we were navigating all the time on a fresh-water sea—as the first explorers had described it—a sea in which the many islands were so low that they were easily hidden by rain squalls or by distance. When we approached one, we would see the treetops first, then the land under, and if we were among islands in the early morning or the late evening we often saw only leaves, branches, and the graceful heads of palms, the land being swathed in mist. Many of those islands were uninhabited; others had Caribs on them, and they were cannibals. At one village where the inhabitants fled without fighting, we saw tender meat in the cooking pots—and among the pieces were human ears and hands. In another village we found a shoemaker's awl, complete with its sheath and thread. How had it got to that place? Had it been taken from Spaniards, or Frenchmen, or Portuguese, blown into the mouths of the Marañón? Had it perhaps come from the shipwreck of Juan Cornejo? In yet another village we picked up two toy brigantines, and these were added by Orellana to the King's store, together with an affidavit as to where they had been found. They might have been models of the *San Pedro* and the *Victoria*, and some of us were inclined to attribute them to necromancy. Yet from the workmanship of the carving, which was exceptionally good, and certain small but obvious errors in detail, it seemed likely that Caribs had made the models after seeing, and perhaps capturing, a brigantine or brigantines. These discoveries reminded us how easily we might yet disappear for ever, our belongings becoming the playthings of savages, our flesh softening in their cooking pots and dissolving in their stomachs. We were always short of food, but Orellana took care to send Robles and his men ashore only at small villages where the landing looked safe and resistance either weak or improbable.

The Captain went ashore a great deal himself, because the pottery, wooden dishes, and china of the Caribs would have excited the cupidity of the merchants of Spain. The decoration on these objects did not stop short at formal flowers and animals, but showed, often with astonishing success, such difficult subjects as the human figure in movement, fishes swimming, and the breaking waves of the river in a storm. Although they did not have fine materials to work with, those Caribs were probably the best craftsmen of the river peoples with whom we had contact. Yet they were cannibals, and for that we must condemn and hate them.

Despite all our precautions, the search for food eventually led us into a situation of great danger. At high water (this was an error in tactics, and one for which Orellana must accept the blame) we approached an island village set some little way up an estuary. A sea was running upriver, which was partly why we put in, hoping for shelter as well as food. The sea foamed on sandbanks to either side of us as we surged in, the *Victoria* leading the *San Pedro* by some forty lengths and both craft half out of control. When our keel grated, Robles and his foragers jumped into the surf and went up to the village, while Father Carvajal, the Negroes, and those of us in the brigantine's guard remained with Orellana, watching the *San Pedro* come through the surf. Within thirty paces of the beach the small brigantine lost way with a sudden jerk and instantly sank until only the rim of its raised bulwarks showed awash. The crew struggled ashore.

As though this was not bad enough, Robles and his men, who had cleared the village without difficulty, were at that moment furiously attacked by several hundred Caribs and, fighting every step, little doubting that all was well behind them, they retreated to the place where the *Victoria* lay beached. So well beached that she was high and dry. I said we had landed at the hour of high water. Already the tide had receded well down the sloping sands. All might have seemed lost to weaker spirits, and to make things even brighter it began to rain heavily.

In such emergencies a leader proves himself or otherwise. That cool one-eyed head once more served us. He rallied all the fighting men to form a human palisade across the strip of shore and protecting the *Victoria*. In the aggressively defensive cordon with the swordsmen and the pikes he put all the crossbowmen and his own two arquebusiers (for Maldonado's had had such a wetting that their pieces were useless and they fought as swordsmen).

When he saw that our line was ready and that the Caribs were coming to attack it, Orellana said: "Fate has brought you face to face with yet another foe—it is for you to do the rest. I must leave you for a little until the brigantines are both safe, but I shall be back among you, amigos, when and where the dogs press hardest." Then he waded out with Maldonado to the *San Pedro*.

With the important help of the two strong Negroes and such assistance as the friars could give, Orellana and Maldonado lifted out nearly all the *San Pedro*'s cargo and carried it to the water's edge. Orellana frequently left this work and ran to join the fighting at some hard-pressed point of the line. Maldonado, who would much rather have been fighting, but who had no intention of losing his brigantine (and his command) if he could help it, climbed into the sunken hull and, allowing the weight of his armour to hold him under water while he concentrated on holding his breath, he groped about to discover the location and extent of the damage. He found that the hull was resting on a sharpened stake that had penetrated the planking. There were many such stakes set firmly at the edge of deep water, and no doubt they were defences put there by the Caribs. Maldonado was able to stop the hole temporarily with blankets held down by chains and any other weights that came to hand. Then, with the Negroes and the friars, he bailed until they could lift the brigantine off the stake and float it ashore.

Orellana withdrew from the fighting line enough of us to turn the *San Pedro* on its side, and he set Mexía to repairing it, helped by the friars. Maldonado, water gushing from every crack in his harness, joined the fighting with a bellow of delight, and in such a scuffle he was worth five good men for his energy alone. He enjoyed himself; it was the only work that gave him honourable opportunity to rid body and spirit of the spleen that boiled within. There we were, all hard at it, and I was loosing off telling bolts while Hernández protected me most bravely with shield and sword, and on the other side of me was the crouching Illanes, very precise with his point and his footwork. Beyond him with his helmet back to front (for he had tried to dress himself like the rest of us) the Indian trumpeter was doing his best with a pike. While we fought those squat, dark, long-haired cannibals, our line waved like the body of a swimming serpent as this part advanced a little while that had temporarily to give way. It waved, but it did not waver. And behind us we rejoiced to hear the peaceful noises of the saw and the hammer. The surf pounded on the beach, and frigate birds sailed overhead in a sky washed clean by the passing rain.

At length, judging his moment, Orellana put his marksmen on either flank while the swordsmen tightened their line in the middle. Then he cried: "*¡Señores, Santiago!*" and we rolled them back, doing them great injury in the pursuit. They had fought well, and we could congratulate ourselves on our recovery, though for some time, as disaster seemed to pile on disaster, it had been shaky enough.

Mexía had finished his repairs and was worrying about their temporary nature. While the *San Pedro* was being reloaded and the *Victoria* hauled to the water on rollers, we ransacked the village and carried off maize, salt, and other food. It has not taken long to tell of this affair, but it lasted all of three hours. Darkness was touching the waves as we embarked.

We were on the water all night, and several of our crew suffered from the sickness of the sea. I cannot speak for those in the *San Pedro*, because I could not be in both brigantines at once, and since there was rivalry between the crews, we did not expect them to admit weakness of any kind. They readily admitted, however, to shipping much water when the weather blew up worse from the east before dawn. The boats then had to lie head to wind and sea, riding to Bermúdez's admirable drogues.

It was a calm and lovely morning. We rowed up a small creek in a densely wooded island, and we protected and partly hid the brigantines from the open water by felling two trees across the mouth of the creek. Orellana sent Robles and his men off to make sure that the island was uninhabited as we supposed, and when they came back they were all talking of the flowers and blossom they had seen.

"The whole island is alive with bees," Robles said. "And small wonder. Would you believe it? All those flowers are so high up that only the bees and monkeys and toucans can poke their noses into them, yet their scent lies in a cloud permeating everything, and if the fires were put out you would smell it too."

"What else did you notice?" Orellana asked. "Or did I send out a patrol to report on the flowers?"

Then Robles said that the woods were all but impassable, and that he had found no trace of Indians. And, calling a conference, Orellana said it was time to set about making the brigantines ready for a long voyage and stout enough to endure bad weather at sea. We would have to look to both hulls, then to deck the brigantines, rig them with masts and foremasts, and make sails, spars, rudders, and pumps. Since the *San Pedro* had shown itself to be the weaker of the two, we would work on it first.

The Captain said he would have to call upon blacksmiths again, surely for the last time, as we should need more nails and also iron fittings for the chain plates and the rudders. Because Juan de Alcántara had been killed, Orellana himself offered to work the forge. But Sebastián Rodríguez, who, you may remember, had been Alcántara's assistant, chose to take the Captain's suggestion as an affront, a personal and outrageous insult. He said he did not know what he had done to be so slighted, and declared that if his work had been unsatisfactory, he might have understood his being passed over; but he insisted that, on the contrary, he had been a better blacksmith and a stronger and neater worker than Alcántara, who seemed to have been given all the credit. So the Captain told Rodríguez that we would all be grateful to him if he would take charge, and name any among us to be his associate and assistant. And to show that the "insult" still rankled, Rodríguez chose Number Five, saying that the Negro was the strongest among us, even if he had the fewest brains, but that he (Rodríguez) would supply all of *those* that were needed.

That night, our first on the island, while fireflies shone in the dark, scented trees that sighed dolefully to the east wind, Alvár Gonzáles died. He had been wounded, though no more seriously than many of the rest of us, fighting the Caribs, and he had had a ducking when the *San Pedro* foundered. Apart from that, we could see no reason for his death. There was no question in his case of poison, for he died without fuss after lying unconscious for six hours.

We had thought something in the nature of a death was coming because that evening some of us had seen a large tree turn from green to white in a matter of five minutes. Márquez the Silent, a stubborn fellow who would not believe in portents, went to the tree although it was at some distance from our creek, and, belying his name, he made so much noise that as he got near the tree it turned green again, this time in a few seconds. The whiteness had flown away, for it was composed of hundreds of white herons. So, early the next evening, all five of us crossbowmen lay hidden within range of the tree, and we shot twelve of the herons. We used two-pronged bolts, but even if these carried the dead birds clear of that tree they could not fall to the ground because of the thicknesses of foliage and lianas. We picked up only four out of the twelve, and these with great difficulty.

Mexía complained—did he ever do anything else?—that there was no room to work, and that he was weak from lack of proper nourishment. But as he grumbled he set to work, and once more put us all in his debt by his ingenuity. We were indeed so short of food that the Captain rationed the maize each day at so many grains a man. The Indian trumpeter, who had played a manful part against the Caribs and who now sought to copy us in our clothes and our ways, remembered his pre-Spanish existence sufficiently to bring us in herbs and edible leaves and palm salads. He also fished as hard as any of us who could be spared from the other work. But the results of the fishing were meagre until one day the river made us a royal gift in the shape of a *gran bestia* * that came floating past the mouth of the creek. The Negro Panama swam out to it with a rope, and we hauled it inshore. It was still warm, and had no mark on it to show how or why it had died. In order that there should not be quarrels, and because meat will not keep in those places, Orellana ordered the skin and hoofs to be simmered to make a communal soup and the carcass to be di-

* A tapir.

vided into equal joints. The offal and entrails were likewise divided into forty-seven equal rations. Each man took his share and did what he liked with it according to his temperament, some eating it all as quickly as they could, others hoarding, and eating only a slice a day until it was in a state of rottenness. Most of us had plenty of good meat for four days, and as a result the work went well because the healthy grew stronger and the sick and wounded grew healthier. It was a blessing that we did not lack for salt.

You would have thought from the trouble he took that Diego Mexía was going to travel in the *San Pedro* and not the *Victoria.* He insisted on renewing all the planking, as well as many of the frames, and his demands put a heavy strain not only on himself but also on wood-cutters, carpenters, charcoal-burners, and blacksmiths. After eighteen days of it, the *San Pedro* was replanked, and Mexía refused to do any more work in that place. We say that there are fifty-nine different kinds of refusal, and that there is a way round all of them if it can only be found. Mexía's was the sixtieth—it was absolute. But he did compromise by suggesting that he would set up a workshop in the *Victoria* to make the pumps, rudders, and other things as we travelled on. Before consenting to move, Orellana made sure that we had forged more nails than we could possibly need, and that all the timber was cut and stowed in the brigantines that would be wanted for any conceivable work of rebuilding. It was well for us that he was strict in this matter, as you will learn. Then we cleared a way from the creek, hauling the felled trees round with tackles.

We rowed on and landed at every village we saw, being desperate for food. The foragers were unlucky. They got some fish, but no maize, none at all, and nothing in the way of meat.

On Sunday, August 6, the day of the Transfiguration of our Saviour, we came near a beach that even Mexía admitted would do very well for our shipbuilding. On the Monday we hauled out both brigantines.

Mexía found the *Victoria*'s hull to be in remarkably good order, but not so good that he did not renew a piece of planking here and there. Then he stripped off the arrowproof bulwarks and laid a deck in each brigantine. Hulls and decks were caulked with cotton taken from the Caribs upstream, and were paid with resin mixed with lampblack. From two lengths of the trunk of a small "oak" tree Mexía had devised bilge pumps. The interior of the trunk was hollow and smooth, and plungers with leather valves cut from old saddles and well greased with rancid turtle-fat fitted the apertures. The rudders were of Marañón oak strengthened with iron bands.

Our few seamen, under the orders of Diego Bermúdez, made the rigging. Most of the standing and running rigging was rove from those same lianas or tree-vines of which I have spoken so often. For the halyards we had enough of the palm-fibre rope made by the Indian women at Aparia, and they were treated with beeswax taken from my crossbow stores. Bermúdez saw to it that each vessel carried a quantity of spare "cordage" because, as he said, we would not find trees or their parasites on the sea, and we did not know how this peculiar natural fabric would withstand the chafe and the salt spray of a long sea passage. Each brigantine was given a mainmast and a foremast well smoothed and greased and strongly stepped and stayed. Each mast had a yard to carry a sail properly sewn sailor-fashion from the strong yet light and water-shedding Peruvian blankets that all of us Spaniards (perhaps I had better say "some of us") had been in the habit of pilfering from the Indians who originally set out from Quito with Gonzalo Pizarro.

We had chosen that smooth and sheltered beach because our object was to turn our river boats into ships. The beach nearly turned us into skeletons. We were left in peace there, but so hungry were we that we would dearly have liked to see Caribs, even if it meant fighting and more wounds. We found nothing to eat on that treeless island beyond some snails and small red crabs,* and on these we subsisted. The crabs were wary and swift, but if they were clever at eluding us, hunger made us cleverer at catching

* "We saw an immense number of crabs . . . on the water's edge. It was not easy to catch them. They would sit quietly . . . apparently waiting to be taken, but the moment we approached, however cautiously, they vanished like lightning under the water or into some crevice."—Mrs. Agassiz, on Marajó Island, at the mouths of the Amazon.

them. At noon the air lay trembling with heat on the sand and the rushes, and the mist would shut us in. We might have been a thousand miles from any other land. Vultures sometimes came to us though, creaking through the sky with drugged wingbeats. They also ate the crabs, and sometimes we remarked that we had other things in common, for we were so thin and ragged that we looked not unlike vultures.

Spurred on by the realization of our ebbing strength, we finished all that work in twelve days, days of famine that must be reckoned as among the hardest of this very long journey. But at last we were ready to reload the brigantines. We still had plenty of horseshoes, and these were stowed by the keels to act as ballast. The two awnings of woven palm fronds that had come with us from Aparia, an unconscionable distance upstream, were left forlorn on that deserted beach, where perhaps today wandering Carib canoemen use them as huts.

Orellana made some changes in the crews so that those men who had experience of the sea were equally shared between the two brigantines. He also said, laughing, that perhaps it would be wise to share out the one-eyed men, himself and Father Carvajal, but that he had no intention of doing so. Father Vera was upset by this harmless remark, and Orellana mollified him by giving him three crabs he had in his pocket. On the thirteenth morning, Mass was said, and all gave thanks to our Lord (who alone has the power to aid us in our struggles against odds and human weakness) that we were ready to leave that beach. I doubt if any of those who were there have ever wished to eat crab again. We sailed away, having done with rowing—thanks be to God—except in calms or in light head winds.

The river was now spread into countless wide channels, and we had expected the current to be gentler, but the opposite held because the water was constantly changing its mood according to the wind and to the tides. As the prevailing wind headed us, our greatest need was for good warps and heavy anchors. Mexía had done his best with the latter—they were somewhat in the shape of four-pronged grapnels, each fluke iron-tipped, with four hardwood shanks forming a pyramid, and a big stone lashed in the base of the pyramid—but even his best in that case was not good enough. So when the wind strengthened from the east, we had to seek out the shallows—which the wise navigator always shuns, when he has any choice in the matter. It often happened that we dragged, and thus lost much of the progress toward the sea that had been won at the cost of toil and hardship. Many times one or other of the brigantines was aground, with every man overboard and heaving with all his might, and a bit more added by desperation, to draw it into deeper water on a falling tide. I should tell you that Diego Bermúdez had been perfectly right when he had argued that the Marañón was stronger than the Northern Sea; for although the river rose and fell, and the islands grew larger or smaller, the current pushed relentlessly downstream.

If both brigantines had to withstand hard knocks, at least, having made every part of them ourselves, we knew their strengths and their failings; and if something was damaged or destroyed, we knew how to replace it. We had no need of chandlers. In that we might be said to be the superiors of ordinary sailors, though at the time we could have done with a greater proportion of ordinary sailors and a smaller one of expert blades—and even crossbowmen. There was continual mending and adjusting to be done on the rigging, and during this estuary passage, which lasted seven most uncomfortable days and nights, Bermúdez, Mangas, and the other seamen succeeded in improving the sailing qualities of both vessels.

We had good fortune in other ways, for we came fairly often upon small villages whose people were friendly. They were the first Indians of our journey who came to meet us unarmed, and we gratefully acknowledged their gentleness and humanity, though we would have preferred food to such estimable qualities. Either they were very short of food themselves or they concealed it from us, though they seemed eager enough to barter. In the majority of their humble villages we were able to buy yams—nothing else—with our gaudy beads.

Dawn found us becalmed off the last of our Marañón islands. To the east there was nothing but water as far and as wide as the eye could roam, and above the water a clear sky with a scurry of clouds high up. None of us doubted that this, at last, was the Northern Sea, though, to be sure, it was not grey, nor green, nor blue, but was the whitish-yellow colour of the river that we alone of all white men had come to know. There was a village on the island. We landed to spend our last day and to trade for smoked fish, or anything else the Caribs might offer. It was a busy day.

Orellana said that each man was to put aboard a jarful of drinking water. No man was to drink during the sea voyage from another man's jar, even if invited to do so. Before nightfall the Captain inspected both brigantines to make sure that the right number of jars was in each, and that every jar was full and had a name on it. Each man at sea was to be responsible for his own nourishment, though it was agreed that any fishes caught, or birds killed, or rainwater collected, were to be shared out equally among the crew. We were not famously off for stores. We had fish, yams, a certain root that was edible, and some maize. When I say "some," I do not mean "enough," because I had in my personal store half an almud * of maize roasted hard, and the man who thinks of that as plenty had better not invite me to dinner.

The arrangements concerning food that I have described to you annoyed certain worthy persons with whom I recently discussed our journey. They said it showed a spirit of selfish jealousy among us that each had to guard his own sustenance and was forbidden either to help his friends or to expect their generosity. I agree, of course, that such conduct is quite foreign to our nature, and all I can answer is that any man who has suffered hunger as we then suffered it will understand us, and will agree, as we did, that Orellana's orders were both just and wise. Nothing makes brutes of men more surely than the fear of starvation and the experience of its first pains. There is no greater leveller. Noble indeed is he who has the power to override the jealousy of hunger. I do not feel shame, I will not agree that I am defaming the compañeros, when I admit that since food had been scarce to the degree of nonexistence each of us had looked after himself, and there had been fights over a grain of maize or over a crab smaller than a frog. And if I appear to have talked too much about how and what we ate, Señores, let me remind you that eating is the most

* Less than one pint.

serious business of life. You do not so consider it? That is because your needs are cared for by cooks and servants three times a day, and in such blessed circumstances any of us, myself included, can scorn food.

If our stores could scarcely have been less impressive, they were on a par with the rest of our seagoing equipment. We had no compass, no chart, and no man among us trained to find his way by sun or stars. To set against these weaknesses, we had unbounded faith in each other and in our God; and faith, not unbounded, but a mixture of amusement, affection, and pious hope, that our brigantines would carry us through hard weather and boisterous seas. There were portents that God had our predicament very specially in mind and was helping us. For example, when we were struggling down the estuary, we had seen thunderstorms galore and rain squalls had blotted out whole islands from view, yet no rain had fallen upon us. Then again, we had the confidence of achievement. And if the sea did not look so wonderful and precious to us as—when it had seemed unattainable—we had expected it to look, we could not but admit that the Divine Power, having seen fit to bring us so far, would hardly consent to drown us in the final stage.

That last day spent on the Marañón was St. Louis's Day, Friday, August 25, 1542. Early the following morning the whole company, including even the Indian trumpeter and the Negroes, heard Mass beside the brigantines. A hundred naked Caribs stood round us, watching.

Father Carvajal did not forget at that moment those good compañeros whom we left behind, in and beside the river, and he named them: Arévalo the Horseman, Sebastián de Fuenterrabía, Diego Moreno, Juan de Aguilar, Baltasar Osorio, Juan de Arnalte, Alonso Gutiérrez, the two Alcántaras, Alvár Gonzáles, Mateo de Rebolloso, Pedro de Empudia, Antonio de Carranza, and García de Soria. May their souls rest in peace. Amen.

When the friar had finished, each of us said good-bye to everyone in the other crew, for though it had been arranged that we were to sail in company, we knew that we might well be separated. We had gained one man in the shape of an Indian and had lost fourteen Spaniards. Our total muster was therefore forty Spanish fighting men and two Portuguese, two friars, two Negro slaves, and one trumpeter who could blow a donkey's bray.

We climbed aboard our brigantines in good spirits, and after rowing out a little way from the island, trimmed our blanket sails to make the most of a light breeze from the south-east. Astern, the island smudged and disappeared. We saw only tumbling water, the sky with its myriad of small frisking clouds, and the other brigantine, which looked like half a walnut shell.

CHAPTER TWENTY

☼

THE SOUTH-EAST WIND SOON CAME GUSTY, AND AT TIMES strong. We had much more sea than the wind alone could account for. With sail reduced to the minimum—only the peaks of the foresails drawing—both brigantines were in difficulties, and some of us in the *Victoria,* assuming that the whole voyage was going to be made in similar circumstances, said that we should put back before it was too late, for otherwise we were sure to drown. Few fates at close view look worse than drowning, and this is very strange, since of all the methods of dying it must be nearly the least uncomfortable. There is an incongruity about it, however, that shocks the threatened victim without numbing him against the prospect of changing his own element for another and a wetter one. The brigantine now rolled in the narrow troughs, now perched on the peaked and breaking crests. Many of us were sick, while spray and worse than spray swept the deck, and none of us would believe Bermúdez when he shouted that these conditions were local and would pass off when we had won clear of the Marañón's outflow, with its battle of currents and its dangerously shoaling bottom.

Mangas, Lieutenant Robles, and—strangely enough—Hernández stayed aft with Bermúdez. It was they who did any work that had to be done, and Hernández, who was unaffected by the sea or our wild movement, looked after the bilge pump, which had to be used at short intervals, not because much water was coming through the hull planking, but because we were shipping a lot. The pump worked well, but Mexía was too ill to be pleased.

By late afternoon these conditions had so greatly abated that the stronger among us began to feel more lively. Both brigantines were still plunging and flinging up spray that came aboard, but with the easing of the sea we were making progress to the north-east, and we no longer thought that every pitch or lurch might be our last. We were alone, two very small boats on the sea. But the water was still fresh, and yellow, and we were still being pushed eastward by the power of the Marañón; and not only us, for we saw the weed islands and the tree trunks floating as during all those months we had seen them on the river itself. Here was a tree, dead, but carrying an abundance of life in the shape of flowers, grasses, and moss, moving splashily away from the New World that had given it birth, away from the setting sun, away from the Andes, whose canyons, volcanoes, and deep snows shed the water that fills the greatest of rivers. . . . Orellana reminded all of us to fill up our water jars while we still sailed in drinkable water.

Our helmsmen would turn more north when wind and sea allowed. They were anxious to sight the northern bank of the Marañón, the coast of *tierra firme,* since it was agreed among the seamen that the more we could hug that coast the shorter would be our passage to the island of Cubagua, which they said was our nearest Spanish settlement.

How near?

Some four hundred leagues,* they estimated, and it seemed too great a distance. But Diego Bermúdez laughed at the pessimists. He said that, once clear of the Marañón water, we would be able to steer north by west, and that as our distance up the coast increased, we would turn our bows more to the west. Thus, he said, we would bring the prevailing easterlies of the Northern Sea more aft, and the fresher they blew, within reason, the better progress would we make. Also, according to him, the currents of the sea would be in our favour all the way, and at times they would help us to the tune of as much as a league in the hour.

Orellana said it would be well if each man knew for how long he must spin out his meagre food supply, and he asked the seamen to calculate this. After much argument they put our likely run in the twenty-four hours at somewhere round thirty leagues, and they therefore said that if we did not get becalmed, or lose our way, or suffer any other disaster, we should make Cubagua in thirteen days, possibly less, possibly more.

* About 1,280 sea miles or 1,470 statute miles.

The *San Pedro*, being smaller and somewhat lower in the water, was even more uncomfortable than the *Victoria*, but Maldonado seemed in good fettle, and he said they were making little water and that the pump was more than capable of dealing with ten times the amount. Before nightfall we sailed very near them and the Captain once more reminded them that both vessels must do their utmost to remain in close company. Unfortunately we were without lanterns of any kind, but that night the helmsmen were able to see well enough to keep their stations. In any event, as Mangas remarked, there might be French privateers in those waters, and it would have been a dreary end to our voyage to be carted off in chains to Bordeaux.

With darkness the south-east wind dropped and became a light easterly that Bermúdez called a sea breeze, meaning a breeze sucked by the land off the sea, and in the morning some islands were in view on the port bow, and beyond them a low dark line that Bermúdez said was *tierra firme*. The sea was now salt and blue and was less confused. A steady breeze from south of east sent us foaming along heeled to port. The *San Pedro* had fallen some distance astern, and plainly we had the heels of her. Bermúdez and the other seamen were surprised. They admitted that they had given the smaller brigantine a good deal less sail area than ours, but said that they had done so because she had nearly the same waterline length as the *Victoria*, yet had a lighter and more easily driven hull. Orellana insisted that the speeds of both craft must be equalized, and that he was sure there must be some way of doing this without sacrificing our own speed. He suggested that the *San Pedro* carried too much ballast. We lowered the mainsail and allowed the other to come alongside. A line was thrown from one brigantine to the other, and the Captain and Bermúdez went aboard the *San Pedro*.

There was a good deal of cross-talk between crews. We of the *Victoria* called the others snails, tortoises, and other names. Some of them said that, given the right kind of weather, they would soon outstrip us, while others who were less optimistic accused us of having gained our places in the *Victoria* by toadying, favouritism, or even bribery. Looking back on this it seems absurd, but there was some ill feeling in it. Meanwhile Orellana,

"Everything."

"Then, man, compose yourself and listen, for I know nearly all the known places on this sea, and about Cubagua I can talk for a long time. . . ."

He said that he had put in there on a ship whose name now escapes me, and that it had been a bad landfall because their water casks were empty, they were carrying horses, and there was not a drop of water on the island.

"But there was plenty of wine," he said. "Dark wine shipped out from Spain and lighter stuff bought with pearls from a French ship, for Nueva Cádiz, which is the town on the island, was rich enough in all but water and fresh meat. When the wind veered and the first cargoes of drinking water were brought off from Cumaná, the nearest province on *tierra firme,* the inhabitants paid a pipe of good wine for an equal quantity of stale water, and thought it a fair exchange."

"Who discovered this island?" asked Orellana, whom we had wakened with our talk.

"Christopher Columbus got there in 1498, and he called it the Pearl Island," Bermúdez answered. "There were many Indian canoes fishing oysters, and the Almirante sailed his caravels about, looking for anchorage. The navigation is tricky on account of the reefs. The caravels were much admired by the Indians, but our Spaniards even more so. The Indians gave them all their oysters, and when our people opened them, to eat, they found many pearls in them. The canoes led them to a reasonable anchorage, and a party of Spaniards landed. There was nothing but friendliness on both sides, and the women of the island went naked save that they were garlanded with cables of pearls. Columbus said to his men: 'We have found the richest country in the world.' "

"He was mistaken, the Almirante?"

"Cubagua is nothing but a low slab of rock six leagues * out in the Gulf of Cumaná," Bermúdez answered. "If there were no pearls in the sea around it, there would be no people on the island, neither Indians nor Spaniards. They have salt there, also an abundance of fish and shellfish. Some rainwater is taken by catchment. And, perhaps because the island is treeless and dry, there

* 19 sea miles.

are no mosquitoes, though the same cannot be said for Santa Margarita, just to the north of it. Those are about all the natural advantages. Oh—I nearly forgot: there are plenty of wild rabbits, and these make good eating.

"News of the profusion of pearls drew many Spaniards to Cubagua, and the town, Nueva Cádiz, sprang up too quickly. Almost as quickly the island got a reputation for licentiousness nearly as bad (or as good, whichever way you look at it) as that of Cuba itself, and when the busybodies in Spain heard of this, they got His Majesty to declare Cubagua a prohibited area; no captain of any ship was allowed in theory to sail within fifty leagues of Cubagua or Cumaná. I say 'in theory' because it was not possible to control such comings and goings from the other side of the Northern Sea, and there was an immense and profitable trade with Nueva Cádiz, whose inhabitants were gluttons for supplies of all kinds from rice to muchachas, and paid handsomely in two of the best currencies, pearls and slaves.

"Some of the merchants in Spain laid their heads together and got the royal permission to equip a pearl-fishing venture to Cubagua. With their tongues in their cheeks and judicious leaks in their well-lined pockets, they persuaded the Office of the Indies that they would clean up Cubagua, and see that a generous share of the profits found its way home to Seville. They fitted out four caravels for the job, loading them, as merchants will, with profitable cargo rather than the means of defending themselves. And they added an invention of which they thought highly—a kind of dredge that could be dragged along the sea bottom to scoop out all the oysters lying there. In command of their enterprise they put a certain Don Luis de Lampoñano. Don Luis was probably a very fine gentleman; it would seem so, for he was said to have many debts in Spain. It is probable that he thought himself already vastly rich when he set sail for the Indies. He had no idea of the temper of the people of Cubagua. When I speak of the people I do not of course mean the Indians there, but the Spaniards who now ruled them.

"Don Luis arrived with his caravels and was told that if he dared to drop his iron contraption and damage the oyster beds, there would be serious consequences to himself and his ships. In vain did he show his royal permit. The local pearlers declared it to be worthless, and refused to admit that the King-Emperor would be so liberal with other people's property. They cowed Don Luis so thoroughly, and taunted him so unmercifully, that he went mad and died on Cubagua, or so the story goes. . . . I know another story—but perhaps I am talking too much?"

"Go on."

"You know how we are plagued on the route to the Indies and among the islands by French privateers. This is a disgrace to Spain, as we all know, and derives simply from the cupidity of our Seville merchants, who are mean about guns and gear because all they can think of is profit. The French ships, on the other hand, are well built, well found, and heavily gunned. . . . Well, to get back to the Pearl Island, one day a likely-looking Frenchman sailed into the gulf and dropped his hook off Nueva Cádiz. The Spaniards there got together fifty of the most picturesque Indians, hung them with splendid pearls, and put them in two war canoes, telling them that the white strangers in the privateer were so lustful and wanton that if a few of them were not killed within the next ten minutes, they would land and commit every kind of obscenity with all Indians of both sexes whom they could capture. The Indians paddled out to the ship, waving their ropes of pearls. The French sailors, thinking it was a question of barter, lined their rail, but instead of pearls they got a shower of poisoned arrows. They had no experience of such deadly poisons. And seeing several of their company gurgling in agony, they made sail at once and departed."

"Where do all the slaves come from, since the island is so small?"

"Raiding parties of Spaniards constantly go to and fro between Cubagua and Cumaná, where the people are hostile, and set in their evil ways. When I was in Nueva Cádiz, some six years ago, it was already getting difficult to obtain new slaves because the Indians on *tierra firme* were withdrawing more and more into the hinterland. This meant long marches inland led by Indian guides, who, as often as not, were treacherous. Then our soldiers would set a cordon round a village or encampment and seize all the men, women, and children whom they could take alive. They were untamed Indians who gave a lot of trouble on the march back to the sea, and who were prone to committing the sin of suicide in order to trick their captors. There might also be ambushes, and the Indians there fight with very unpleasant arrows made from poisoned reeds. . . . But it is the same with all pearling settlements, as you know. The pearling uses up Indians. More must be found. Those that are no longer useful for diving are sold, and so a slave trade begins. They say that Cubagua makes even more wealth from slaves than from pearls, but my guess is that both commodities must be running short, and that by the end of this century there will only be rabbits left on the island, while we Spaniards are developing other and more fertile places.* When I was in Nueva Cádiz, the soldiers were gambling as usual, dicing for slaves, and when our ship arrived they paid us in slaves for our linen, flour, and breeding swine."

We sailed on through the day until there was a cry from Hernán Gutiérrez de Celis:

"Land ho!"

Bermúdez was wakened, and when he saw the high land on the starboard bow he did not make a fuss, but merely said: "Amigos, that is the island of Trinidad, and it is evident that the currents, which are apt to be strong hereabouts, have drawn us too far in. As there is no wind, and what there is is from the worst direction, we must take to the oars, all of us, and do our best to get round the outside of that island. For if we go through between the island and *tierra firme* I warn you that you may never see Cubagua."

We took to the oars and worked hard with them, but it did no good. The current was too strong for us. It pulled us inexorably to the north-west and Trinidad was coming abeam as night fell. Bermúdez said we were being drawn at more than a league in the hour toward the gap known as the Serpent's Mouth, and that had we been in a big ship in such a situation, with night coming on and no way of stopping ourselves from being sucked

* "Isla Cubagua . . . is 100 feet high, parched, barren, and uninhabited. . . . Great caution is necessary when navigating in this vicinity as uncharted dangers may exist."—*West Indies Pilot*, 1941.

through, we would be as good as lost. There were several things in our favour, however: the small brigantine would pass over reefs that would impale any proper vessel; what wind there was was with the current; and the weather was very settled. There was, indeed, little we could do beyond going to sleep as usual. And when morning broke, we had passed easily and without effort through the Serpent's Mouth. We half wondered if Bermúdez and Mangas had not been pulling our legs and feigning anxiety where there was no call for it. Bermúdez detected our disbelief, and when Orellana asked how we were to get out of the great gulf in which we now sailed, Bermúdez said:

"We go round this island and come out at the top end, through a passage with several islands, and the passage is the Mouths of the Dragon."

"Is that a bad place?"

"It can be," Bermúdez answered dryly. "But since we came so easily through the Serpent's Mouth, let us say nothing about the Mouths of the Dragon until we have tried to get through them. I will add only this: where we are now, we are likely to have north-east winds, and once we have rounded the south-eastern point of the island, the Mouths of the Dragon will lie north-east of us; also we may or may not get contrary currents. You will excuse me for being a little vague in this matter. I have never been in this gulf, and only speak from hearsay, not experience. One thing is plain to me: we have a lot of rowing ahead of us, and rowing is a strain on empty stomachs."

The north-east wind came at nine in the morning, and blew until one hour before dusk. At three in the afternoon we had a violent thunderstorm and we filled our water jars and greatly refreshed ourselves with the rain. In the head wind Bermúdez soon proved that although our beamy and shallow-draft *Victoria* would sail on a reach, we could make nothing into the wind. By dint of experimenting with the sails and fitting a leeboard, the performance to windward was very slightly improved, and that day we sailed across the gulf until we were within sight of the land on the western side. Then the wind fell. We took the oars and cheerfully set to work, each man rowing for an hour and then taking an hour's rest. This went on through the night, and we were greatly helped, according to the seamen, by a north-going tidal stream. At dawn we sighted some islands ahead, and Bermúdez and Mangas agreed that they would be those of the Mouths of the Dragon. Just then, however, the current changed and headed us, and although we continued to row, we were losing ground. Two hours later the north-east wind came again, quite strong, and we again sailed north-west, glad of a rest from the oars. When we got near the shore, we anchored in shallows. The water was very dirty in this gulf, and the air was hot, but in the early afternoon it again rained heavily, and this was welcome. As soon as the tide turned in our favour we rowed north, carrying some sail. At five o'clock the wind dropped very light. We rowed on, keeping fairly near the coast of *tierra firme*. Night fell. For a while we anchored.

Dawn found us little more than a league from the Mouths of the Dragon, with a tidal stream in our favour and only a very light north-easterly against us. An hour later we were in a channel between two islands, and beyond them we saw the sea. But a sudden blast of wind from the north drove us back, and the best we could do was to get some sail on the brigantine and bear across to find shelter in the lee of a small island off the north-west coast of Trinidad. That was our third day in the gulf, and we were weary of it, weary in every way. That evening the north-east wind increased rather than falling. Getting up our wooden anchor, we pulled in to a beach, hauled out the brigantine, and slept ashore. In the morning the weather was still very bad. All that we found to eat were some plums, but they were ripe and sweet. We picked a great quantity of them. That afternoon we rowed north for six hours, but again had to shelter after making little progress. The next day the weather was even worse. We rowed until we could row no more, and were no nearer the open sea at the end of the day. The weather was bad all night, and continued so next morning, Friday, September 8.

That afternoon, however, there was a storm of rain that lasted several hours, and Bermúdez said the rain might kill the wind. We went to sleep with the brigantine sawing at its anchor warp and the wind whistling about us. But at midnight the lookouts wakened the rest of us, and we saw it was a flat calm. We did not know how long it would last, but all were determined to make a great effort to get out of the gulf. It might well be our last effort, for none of us had any maize or fish left, and we had nothing but plums inside us. The two Negroes rowed all night and were worth their weight in gold. The rest of us took turns. By dawn on Saturday we were in the heavy swell of a channel, and two hours later we were able to make sail and clear the Mouths of the Dragon.

If there is a more wonderful sensation than sailing in mild weather and in the chosen direction with a sufficient breeze on the quarter, then tell me of it. And our enjoyment of that sailing will be appreciated when I remind you that it followed seven days of rowing, days and nights of mingled hope, anxiety, and despair. We sailed with the mainland to port, mountains with trees right up to their summits. The only man among us who was not elated was the Indian trumpeter, who was also the only one who had not worked at the oars. He had eaten nothing since leaving the Marañón, and the farther we took him away from it, the weaker he became. Orellana was distressed. He had hoped to take the trumpeter with him to Spain, and had begun to teach him Castilian. It seemed that he would be more likely to need the language spoken in the place where Indians go when they die.

From the Mouths of the Dragon our progress was smooth and swift, and but for hunger, and the weakness of spirit that attends the ultimate stage of any voyage such as ours, would have seemed perfect.

Three hours past noon on Monday, September 11, 1542, we sighted the low outline of the Pearl Island, Cubagua. As men will at such times, we began to calculate our whole journey in terms of months, weeks, days, hours. It had taken me nineteen months and nine days to get from Puná Island, in the Southern Sea, to Cubagua, in the Northern Sea. Only eight and a half months had passed since our detachment left the expeditionary force of Gonzalo Pizarro at Christmas Camp, and as we had spent part of February, all March, and most of April in Aparia (our one long halt), and had wasted a week at the end between the Serpent's Mouth and the Mouths of the Dragon, we had not been sluggards. Nor could our thoughts fail to dwell with pride and gladness on our *Victoria,* the little ship of war that had served us so well. The *Victoria* had been launched one hundred and fifty-nine days before it fulfilled its purpose and we furled the sails at Nueva Cádiz.

It was four o'clock, and the town was asleep when we stole alongside a jetty, looking at the wooden houses above us and at the blessed symbol of the Cross. We stretched out our hands almost timidly and grasped the beams of the jetty, rejoicing in their slimy solidity that broke the apparent dream of our arrival. A few slaves, their faces branded with the letter "C"—standing for Don Carlos, the King—were there by the water. No Spaniards were to be seen. Our two Negro slaves lay sleeping in the bows. They were not excited, as we were, and so long as they were together, one place to them was much the same as another.

As we sat there by the jetty, a Spanish woman came from a house and passed slowly. She did not see us, but Blas de Medina, who was a lady's man, said that he had met her in Cuba, and that her name was Villegas the Open-Hearted. So he called out her name, and she came slowly toward the sea, shading her eyes.

When she saw us in our rags and nakedness, she showed no wonder, but only delight, and her first words (I had forgotten that the voice of woman could be both deep and sweet) were to ask if we were not Captain Orellana's party. She told us that the *San Pedro*, with all hands aboard, had arrived there two days earlier, and she bade us all follow a slave to her house and ask for wine and food; meanwhile she would tell the compañeros of the *San Pedro* and the whole town that Francisco de Orellana and his soldiers had by the grace of God arrived.

All but the Negroes and the Indian trumpeter left the brigantine and stood stiffly on the quay, striving to get the feel of the land underfoot. One bell rang, then another. Soon every bell in Nueva Cádiz was ringing, and we heard the noise of galloping hoofs. The caballero—it was the only horse on the island, and it had been borrowed from the Governor—came between the houses like a bullet, and we saw that it was Maldonado, very clean and splendid in new clothes. Across the open space toward us he galloped full stretch, twirling his lance, and yelling at the top of his voice: "Viva, viva, for the King-Emperor, our Lord, and Castile!"

APPENDIX

AND

BIBLIOGRAPHY

MECHANISM OF THE MILITARY CROSSBOW OF THE 15TH AND 16TH CENTURIES

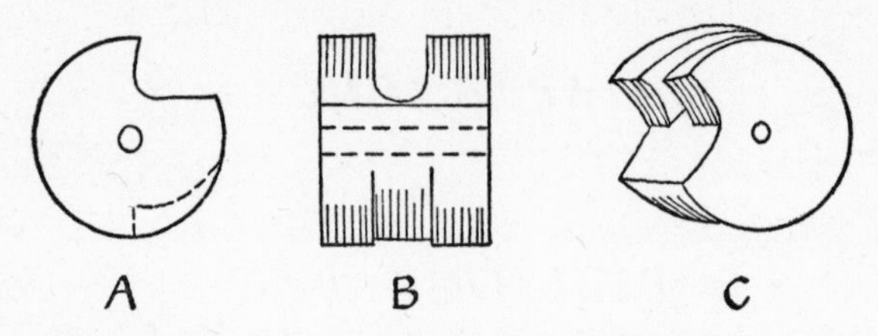

The revolving nut of the crossbow. Half full-size. Made of horn. A. *Side view.* B. *Rear.* C. *Perspective. The nut revolves in a horn socket.*

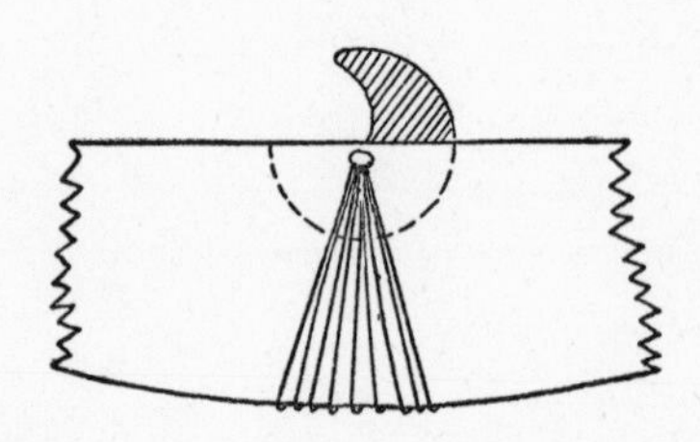

In many mediæval crossbows the pin through the nut was omitted, but sometimes, to prevent the loss of the nut, a thin length of catgut was passed through the hole and round the stock several times.

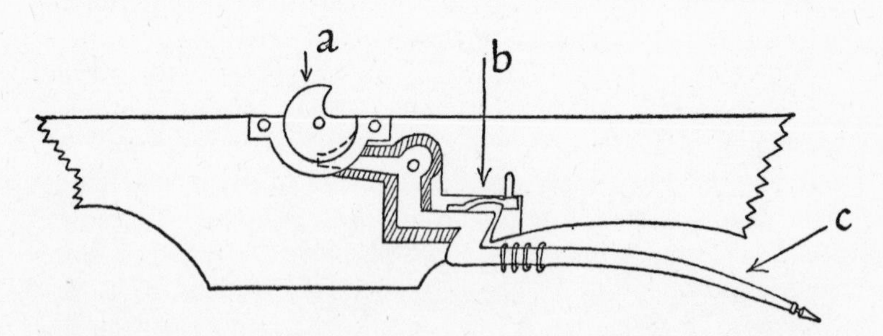

Section through the lock of crossbow to show how trigger works. (a) *Nut held in "fire" position by end of trigger.* (b) *Spring.* (c) *Trigger lever. Scale: 1/4-in. equals 1 in.*

(*From* The Crossbow *by Sir Ralph Payne-Gallwey, Bt., published by Longmans Green*).

APPENDIX

Being an Account of What Happened to Gonzalo Pizarro and His Men after Orellana's Detachment had Gone on down the River

WHEN THE BRIGANTINE AND CANOES WERE LOST TO SIGHT, Gonzalo Pizarro formed up his men and horses, chose a party of the youngest and strongest to be *macheteros,* and continued down the left bank of the Napo. It rained day and night. They marched on, famished and intolerably weary, until they were stopped by a swamp that seemed impassable. Near them was an island in the Napo, and Gonzalo thought that if only some food could be found, the island would make a good camp in which to build another brigantine, or brigantines. But food he must have, for without it his men could not rest, and without rest they must rot to death in those succulent places whose very greenness was awful.

In vain they looked downstream, hoping to see the brigantine *San Pedro* and its attendant canoes returning laden.

By this time they had acquired five canoes,[1] and when they had waited in vain for Orellana, Gonzalo ordered Captain Alonso de Mercadillo to take a dozen Spaniards downstream in canoes to look for food and for any traces of Orellana's detachment. After eight days'[2] absence, Mercadillo and his men paddled wearily back to the camp with neither news nor food. Gonzalo then sent another party, led this time by the experienced Gonzalo Díaz de

[1] Were these five canoes that Pizarro had asked Orellana to leave at places where they would be needed to ferry the land force across tributaries of the Napo? Pizarro denies this. He says in his *Letter to Charles V*: "By a miracle, I had personally captured five canoes."

[2] Pizarro (*Letter to Charles V*) says six days, other authorities eight.

Pineda, he who had led the first expedition to Canelas. Díaz de Pineda had instructions not to return empty-handed. They paddled downstream until they came to the mouth of a big tributary, which today, because of the gold in its sands, is known as the Aguarico. The small party landed at the junction of the two rivers, and there found a place on the bank where Orellana's men had made a clearing.[3] Díaz de Pineda decided, very wisely, to go up the tributary rather than down the Napo, arguing doubtless that Orellana must have led his men down the main stream and that had he found food there within a reasonable distance, he would long since have returned with it; further, it was better policy to paddle upstream, for then if and when he wished to return to the main body he would have the current with him as far as the Napo. Ten leagues up the Aguarico, they found thick plantations of yuca,[4] some of the plants grown so large that their stems looked like a young forest. They kneeled and gave thanks to God, and when they had eaten, they loaded their canoes and went back safely to Pizarro's camp, where Pizarro himself was the only man who had not given up hope of their return.[5]

For twenty-seven days the main body had been encamped by the swamp, eating nothing but saddles and stirrup leathers boiled and afterwards toasted over embers, "some palm shoots and fruit stems fallen from the trees, together with toads and serpents . . . because we had eaten in this wild country more than one thousand dogs and more than one hundred horses . . . and many were sick and others weak, while some died of hunger."[6] The

[3] Oviedo (*Historia general*) says they also found "huts," but this seems unlikely.

[4] This surely explains why Orellana's party did not find the yuca.

[5] This account of how the yuca was discovered is taken from Cieza de León: *Guerra de Chupas*. If it is true, and it rings true, Pizarro ill repaid Díaz de Pineda for his fortitude and his success, because in his *Letter to Charles V* Pizarro states that when the first party returned empty-handed, he (Pizarro) took "the canoes and seven or eight men" and found the food. It seems unlikely that Pizarro would have left the main body at this juncture, for there can be no doubt that his presence was the greatest single factor holding them together, and who would be more aware of that than he?

[6] Gonzalo Pizarro: *Letter to Charles V*.

yucas were divided out, cooked, and eaten. Then, lashing the canoes together, and swimming the surviving horses as often as they could, they made their way down to the Aguarico and across it to the far bank. This journey took them eight days, and the mouth of the Aguarico was so broad and deep that they lost some horses swimming it.

After a forced march they reached the yuca plantations, where they formed a camp and gorged themselves on the unappetizing roots. One man named Villarejo ate some other root, mistaking it for yuca, and went mad. They stayed eight days there "resting after a fashion" [7] and laying in supplies. Pizarro rallied his men, making them grate the yucas to mealy powder and bake bread of a kind. Two Spaniards died from eating a surfeit of the roots, while others swelled up so that they could not walk. Even those who were healthiest were sick, sore, and afflicted. From the presence of the yuca plantations run wild they deduced that the riverbank had at one time been populated by Indians who for some reason had moved elsewhere after planting stretches of the yuca extending for forty leagues.[8]

On the ninth day Pizarro ordered the swollen ones to be lashed in saddles, ropes joining their ankles under the horses' bellies. They complained of their sufferings, but others, who had to walk and to cut a path for men and horses, jeered at them, saying that there was nothing the matter with them, and that they were acting like rogues.[9] Pizarro marched with the rear guard, goading or encouraging stragglers, helping the sick. He had now renounced the possibility of finding El Dorado or other rich lands, for he marched his men *up* the Aguarico. The question now before them was one of survival. It is the strongest question that man can ask himself, unless there be a noble cause to die for, or great glory to be won.

As they marched, day after day, up the riverbank, they cut through yuca plantations until at last they came upon a small Indian village. Terrified by the sight of the strange men, and more

[7] Ibid.

[8] About 150 miles. Cieza de León: *Guerra de Chupas*.

[9] Ibid.

so by the miserable and foundering horses, the Indians leaped into canoes and abandoned their village. They were induced, however, to come back, close inshore, and they threw out some food from their canoes. They were paid with hawks' bells cut from the saddles, combs, and other trifles.

In another eight days of marching and cutting a way through the forest, they came on more small and impoverished villages, but on the eighth day the Indians explained in sign language that an uninhabited area lay upstream. Gonzalo had little idea where he was, nor which direction should be taken to get back to Peru. But he was on a river, and that offered more possibilities of transport and Indian cultivations than did the forests. Also the river was a big one. Surely its headwaters must be under or in the Andes? He held a council with the Quartermaster, Don Antonio de Rivera, Captain Sancho de Carvajal, Jerónimo de Villegas, Cristóbal de Funes, and Juan de Acosta. Their decision was that the invaluable Gonzalo Díaz de Pineda should be sent on ahead in two canoes lashed together, with a small force of Spaniards including a crossbowman and an arquebusier, and with Indian paddlers. Accordingly, the necessary Indians were press-ganged, and the village's stores were emptied. The two parties set out, that on the water making by far the better progress.

The way that now lay ahead would have tested, and might have defeated, the strongest and best-nourished of soldiers. The Spaniards marched on their courage and on the thoroughbred quality of men bred from generations of fighting stock, and seldom a coward in it. Even Gonzalo was anxious as he looked around him. The constant diet of yucas had "brought on a flux," the rain poured down, making their few pitiful rags cling to their nakedness. Some had made themselves sandals from saddle-leather, but the majority, their footgear long since worn to extinction, marched barefoot. Their bodies, but especially their feet and legs, were lacerated, for the way now led them through forest looped, twined, festooned with lianas whose spines were like the teeth of sharpened saws. They marched against hunger. It was a race to get somewhere before they died, and no means of keeping alive was too foul to contemplate. We know how the Spaniards prized, and even loved, their horses, yet it is said that at this time Pizarro's followers were reduced to cutting meat from the animals' quarters and plastering the resulting wounds with clay, and that they bled the horses to make soup, boiling the blood in their helmets together with herbs and peppers.[1] Gonzalo himself says:[2] "In the course of this uninhabited stretch all the remaining horses, more than eighty in number, were eaten. . . . There were many rivers and creeks of considerable size to be crossed. . . . There were days on this march when in an advance of two leagues twelve, thirteen, fifteen, and more bridges were built. . . . And there were days when we waded through swamps up to our knees in water, and for many stretches up to our waists and even higher."

Meanwhile the small party in two canoes was thrusting on upstream. Doubtless they knew how to get the most out of their Indian paddlers. As arranged, they made a smoke signal every evening, in the hope that Pizarro's party might see it and have some notion of their progress, and that they still lived.

One evening "at the hour of compline" (nine p.m.) they landed and sat down on the trunk of a great tree stranded by the river's edge. As they were ruminating sadly on their hardships and those of the expedition enmeshed in the forest far behind them, one of the party, Don Pedro de Bustamente, stood up and saw in the moonlight at the bend of the river fourteen or fifteen canoes with eight or nine Indians in each, all carrying arms and shields. Gonzalo Díaz de Pineda struck flint and steel to light the match of the party's single arquebus, while Don Pedro wound the crossbow and set a bolt in the groove. The Indians advanced confidently. Díaz de Pineda shot one in the chest. Bustamente hit another in the arm. The Indians attacked with darts and arrows. Two more were killed, and they turned away, but the Spaniards at once embarked, managed to get among them, and captured some of their canoes, the occupants taking to the river. In the canoes they found food. . . . It is astonishing to reflect that the fate of Gonzalo Pizarro's expedition certainly rested during those few moonlit moments on the courage and good luck of Díaz de Pineda and his handful of men.

[1] Toribio de Ortiguera: *Jornada del Río Marañón. . . .*

[2] *Letter to Charles V.*

After they had eaten, they cut crosses in the bark of trees on the bank to show those behind that they had been there, and for the rest of that night they paddled on upstream. The dawn for once was clear and bright, without rain. Looking to the south, they saw a range of great mountains, at which sight they gave thanks to God. They took the mountains to be "the Cordillera of Quito, or that which lies near Popayán and Cali." Presently they came to some rapids, and there, "for the first time in three hundred leagues," [3] they saw stones.[4]

Díaz de Pineda, loyal soldier, decided that it was time to turn back and take his commander this sustaining news. It was well that he did so. He had travelled against the current for eleven days; now with it in a day and a half he covered nearly the same distance, and as he passed his marks and the sodden embers of his signal fires he began to lose hope. Then one of his men heard the noise of the *macheteros* painfully slashing the road some way in from the bank. Joyfully the small party landed and met the main body of scarecrows, wild-eyed, gaunt, and wretched. Gonzalo Pizarro was with the rear guard. Díaz de Pineda hurried back to him, and Pizarro flung his arms about the caballero, who represented life itself—or at least renewed hope of it.

We can be sure that Pineda's news lost nothing in the telling when Pizarro spoke to his men, who were all but overwhelmed by the back-breaking work of the march. He increased the number of Spaniards cutting with axes and machetes and helped them to some degree of lustiness by his own example. They had to wade more swamps, and it took them ten days of marching to reach the crosses cut by Díaz de Pineda's party after their skirmish with the Indians. At that place they took an Indian prisoner, who told them of a village and agreed to lead them there. Pizarro or-

[3] 1,100 miles.

[4] Díaz de Pineda's party's adventures are described by Cieza de León (*Guerra de Chupas*), and Herrera (*Historia general*) gives a brief account of them. On certain of those rivers, stones are a great rarity. De la Condamine (*Relation d'un voyage*) writes: "The savages of those countries do not know what a stone is, for a stone, a single stone, is as rare as a diamond. When they get to Borja, it is amusing to see them run and pick up stones as rare objects, then throw them away when they find so many more."

dered Juan de Acosta to go on ahead with eighteen swordsmen, while the main body followed at the best speed it could now muster.

After a long march, Acosta and his men saw the village, a strong position on a hilltop. The Indians gathered to defend it. Although footsore, utterly exhausted, and starving, the nineteen Spaniards formed up and advanced proudly. Acosta and two others were wounded, but they fought their way into the village, and the Indians fled, leaving a plentiful supply of food in their huts. Following in the tracks of Acosta's detachment, Gonzalo lost eight Spaniards, who died in the swamps.

From that village their way lay across yet another great uninhabited region. After another infernal march, when many had died of hunger and fatigue, they reached the village of Coca. They were so emaciated and so altered by suffering that they could scarcely recognize one another. The Indians at Coca received them kindly, however, and, when they were well enough to continue their march, told them of a shorter route back to Quito, more northerly than that which they had followed on leaving the City above the Clouds some sixteen months earlier.

On the new route they also had many rivers to cross, and at length they came to one so difficult that it took them four days to build a bridge. While they were doing this, those on sentry-go one night saw a comet blaze its way across the sky. And the following morning Gonzalo Pizarro said that in his dreams a dragon had attacked him and plucked out his heart. Jerónimo de Villegas, who was known as an interpreter of dreams, said that Pizarro's meant that he would soon learn of the death of the person nearest to his heart.

What can have been Gonzalo Pizarro's thoughts as they crossed the Cordillera, stumbling along, so many skeletons covered with sores, cuts, and bruises, some of them naked, some wearing the uncured skins of animals, each man carrying his sword and leaning on a staff? There were only eighty of them all told and, as they said themselves, it was a miracle that so many had survived. Indeed, as we look on things today, it was more than a miracle, for the survival of those eighty (about half of Gonzalo Pizarro's complement of Spaniards) showed that *men,* not Gods, not saints, but men, can do the impossible if they be determined and well led. But Pizarro, as they struggled over the high places in June 1542, must have reflected sourly on the array that he had led in January 1541 through those same mountains, a confident army with its invincible Captain General, its armour, its lances, its pennants, its cavalry, its four thousand Indian slaves, its meat on the hoof, and its more-than-high hopes of El Dorado.[5]

News of their coming preceded them to Quito, and Spaniards with their wives and children came out from the town to meet them. They brought with them horses, that Gonzalo Pizarro and his caballeros might ride into the town as they had ridden out. But Gonzalo refused to ride, for they had also brought him terrible news.

He learned that: ". . . the Licentiate Vaca de Castro . . . had taken from me that city of Quito, together with La Culata and Puerto Viejo . . . and had caused himself to be received as Governor of all that territory. . . ." And worse, far worse: "How Don Diego de Almagro[6] and other persons had murdered the Marquis my brother and had taken possession of the land."[7]

When his men and the softer, cleaner, fatter Spaniards of Quito had "mingled their tears of joy," the young Pizarro led the way to the gates of the city, his mind already seething with plans to win back Peru, which had been his brother's "in the name of the King" and which was shortly to be his, though not for long, in defiance of the King himself.

For those of us who admire boldness and stamina, Gonzalo Pizarro was a very great man.

[5] "Pizarro's expedition was a disaster of such magnitude that none like it in America could be recalled."—Toribio Medina: *Descubrimiento.*

[6] Known as "the Lad," the son of Diego de Almagro, Francisco Pizarro's first and most important confederate in the conquest of Peru, the confederate whom he had fought, defeated, and executed.

[7] *Letter to Charles V.*

BIBLIOGRAPHY

I

ALCEDO, ANTONIO DE: *Geographical and Historical Dictionary of America. . . .* Translated by G. A. Thompson (London, 1812–15).

AMERICAN GEOGRAPHICAL SOCIETY, THE: *The Discovery of the Amazon.* Special Publication no. 17 (New York, 1934).

BENZONI, GIROLAMO: *La Historia del mondo nuouo* (Venice, 1565). Translated by Rear-Admiral W. H. Smyth for the Hakluyt Society (London, 1857).

BRY, THEODOR DE: *America* (Frankfurt: Oppenheim; 1602–34).

CASTELLANOS, JUAN DE: *Elegías de varones illustres de Indias* (Madrid, 1850).

CIEZA DE LEÓN, PEDRO DE: *La Cronica del Peru* (Antwerp, 1534). Translated in part by Sir Clements R. Markham for the Hakluyt Society (London, 1864).—*Guerras Civiles del Peru: I. Guerra de las Salinas; II. Guerra de Chupas.* Edited by Marcos Jiménez de la Espada (Madrid, 1842). Both parts translated by Sir Clements R. Markham for the Hakluyt Society: *The War of Chupas* (London, 1918) and *The War of Las Salinas* (London, 1923).

CONQUISTADOR ANÓNIMO, EL (Mexico, 1938).

CORTÉS, HERNANDO: *Letters of Cortés* (*The Five Cartas de Relación*). Translated by F. A. McNutt (London, New York, 1908).

CUNNINGHAME GRAHAM, R. B.: *Hernando de Soto* (London, 1912).—*Bernal Díaz del Castillo* (London, 1915).—*The Conquest of New Granada* (London, 1922).—*Pedro de Valdivia, Conqueror of Chile* (London, 1926).—*The Horses of the Conquest* (London, 1930).

D., H. P. [Henry Peter Dunster]: *Conquest of Mexico and Peru by Hernando Cortés and Francisco Pizarro* (London, 1860).

DÍAZ DEL CASTILLO, BERNAL: *Historia verdadera de la conquista de la Nueva España* (Madrid, 1632). Translated by A. P. Maudslay for the Hakluyt Society (London, 1908–16).

ERCILLA Y ZUNIGA: *La Araucana,* with English translation by Walter Owen (Buenos Aires, 1945).

ESPADA, MARCOS JIMÉNEZ DE LA: "*La Traición de un tuerto*" (series of articles in *Illustración Española y Americana,* 1893–4). See also CIEZA DE LEÓN.

GARCILASO DE LA VEGA, INCA: *Comentarios reales de los Incas* (Lisbon, 1609).—*Historia general del Peru* (Córdoba, 1617). Both the above translated by Sir Paul Rycaut (London, 1688), and *Com. Real.* by Sir Clements R. Markham for the Hakluyt Society (London, 1859, 1871).

GÓMARA, FRANCISCO LÓPEZ DE: *Historia general de las Indias* (Saragossa, 1552).

HARLOW, VINCENT TODD: *Voyages of the Great Pioneers* (London, 1929).

HERRERA, ANTONIO DE: *Historia general de los hechos de los Castellanos en las islas y tierra firme del Mar Oceano* (Madrid, 1601–15). Sixth Decade translated by Sir Clements R. Markham for the Hakluyt Society (London, 1859).

KERR, ROBERT: *General History, and Collection of Voyages and Travels* (Edinburgh, 1812).

MEDINA, JOSÉ TORIBIO: *Descubrimiento del Río de las Amazonas* (Seville, 1894). Translated by Bertram T. Lee for the American Geographical Society (New York, 1934).

MELÉNDEZ, JUAN: *Tesoros verdaderos de las Indias* (Rome, 1681).

MULLER, DR. RICHARD: *Orellana's Discovery of the Amazon River* (Guayaquil, 1937).

ORTIGUERA, TORÍBIO DE: *Jornada del Río Marañón, con todo lo acaecido en ella y otras cosas notables dignas de ser sabidas acaecidas en las Indias Occidentales del Pirú* (Madrid, 1909). Translated by Bertram T. Lee for the American Geographical Society (New York, 1934).

OVIEDO Y VALDÉS, GONZALO FERNÁNDEZ DE: *Historia general*

y natural de las Indias (Madrid, 1851–5). Translated in part by Bertram T. Lee for the American Geographical Society (New York, 1934).

PIZARRO, GONZALO: *Letter to Charles V* (Archivo General de Indias, Seville. "Patronato" case 1, shelf 1, bundle 1/6, no. 2, div. 11). Translation by Bertram T. Lee for the American Geographical Society (New York, 1934).

PRESCOTT, WILLIAM HICKLING: *Conquest of Peru* (New York, 1847).—*Conquest of Mexico* (New York, 1843).

RALEIGH, SIR WALTER: *The Discoverie of the large and bewtiful Empire of Guiana*, with preface by V. T. Harlow (London, 1928).

RAMUSIO, GIOVANNI BATTISTA: *Delle navigationi e viaggi* (Rome, 1605).

ROBERTSON, WILLIAM, D. D.: *The History of America* (Edinburgh, 1777).

SOUTHEY, ROBERT: *History of Brazil* (London, 1810–19).

VELASCO, JUAN DE: *Historia del Reino de Quito* (Quito, 1844).

XERES, FRANCISCO DE: *Verdadera relación del conquista del Perú y provincia del Cuzco . . .* (Seville, 1534). Translated by Sir Clements R. Markham for the Hakluyt Society (London, 1874).

ZÁRATE, AGUSTÍN DE: *Historia del descubrimiento y conquista de la provincia del Perú* (Madrid, 1853).

II

ACUÑA, FR. CRISTÓBAL DE: see RODRÍGUEZ below.

ADMIRALTY, HYDROGRAPHIC DEPARTMENT OF THE: *South America Pilot*, Part 1 (London, 1945).—*West Indies Pilot*, Vol. I (London, 1941); Vol. II (London, 1942).

AGASSIZ, PROFESSOR and MRS. LOUIS: *A Journey in Brazil* (London, 1868).

BATES, HENRY WALTER: *The Naturalist on the River Amazons* (London, 1910).

CONDAMINE, C. M. DE LA: *Relation abrégée d'un voyage fait dans l'intérieur de l'Amérique Méridionale* (Maestricht, 1778).

DARWIN, CHARLES ROBERT: *Journal of Researches into the Geology and Natural History of the Various Countries visited by H.M.S.* Beagle *1832–1836* (London, 1839).

EDWARDS, WILLIAM HENRY: *A Voyage up the River Amazon* (New York, 1847).

GRUBB, KENNETH GEORGE: *Amazon and Andes* (London, 1930).

HERNDON, LT. WILLIAM LEWIS, U.S.N., and GIBBON, LT. LARDNER, U.S.N.: *Exploration of the Valley of the Amazon* (Washington, 1854).

HUMBOLDT, BARON FRIEDRICH H. A. VON: *Vues des Cordillères* (Paris, 1816).—*Personal Narrative of Travels to the Equinoctial Regions of America,* translated by Thomasina Ross (London, 1814–29).

MARCOY, PAUL (being the pseudonym of LAURENT SAINT CRICQ): *A Journey across South America from the Pacific Ocean to the Atlantic Ocean,* translated by E. Rich (London, 1873).

MAW, LT. H. L., R.N.: *Journal of a Passage from the Pacific to the Atlantic* (London, 1829).

ORTON, PROFESSOR JAMES: *The Andes and the Amazon* (New York, 1870).

OSCULATI, GAETANO: *Esplorazioni nell'America equatoriale* (Milan, 1929).

POEPPIG, EDUARD: *Reise in Chile, Peru, und auf dem Amazonenströme* (Leipzig, 1835).

RODRÍGUEZ, MANUEL: *El Marañón y Amazonas* (Madrid, 1684); incorporating Fr. Cristóbal de Acuña's *Nuevo descubrimiento del gran río de las Amazonas.* Father Acuña's work was translated by Sir Clements R. Markham for the Hakluyt Society (London, 1859).

ROOSEVELT, THEODORE: *Through the Brazilian Wilderness* (New York, 1914).

ROYAL GEOGRAPHICAL SOCIETY, *Journal of the*: Hamilton Rice: *From Quito to the Amazon via the River Napo* (1903).—Dr. William Jameson: *Excursions Made from Quito to the River Napo* (1858); *Journey from Quito to Cayambe* (1861).—George James Pritchett: *Explorations in Ecuador* (1860).—Richard Spruce: *On the Mountains of the Llanganati . . .* (1861).

SMYTH, LT. W., R.N., and LOWE, F., R.N.: *Narrative of a Journey from Lima to Pará* (London, 1836).

SPRUCE, RICHARD: *Notes of a Botanist on the Amazon and Andes* (New York, 1908). *See also* ROYAL GEOGRAPHICAL SOCIETY above.

TSCHUDI, JOHAN JAKOB VON: *Travels in Peru,* translated by Thomasina Ross (London, 1847).

ULLOA, ADMIRAL ANTONIO DE: *Relación historica del viage á la America meridional hecho de orden de S. Mag . . .* (Madrid, 1748). Translated by J. Adams (London, 1758). —*Naticias Americanas* (Madrid, 1772).

WALLACE, ALFRED R.: *A Narrative of Travels on the Amazon and Rio Negro* (London, 1853).

WHYMPER, EDWARD: *Travels among the Great Andes of the Equator* (London, 1908).

III

ARGOTE DE MOLINA, GONZALO: *Libro de la Monteria* (Seville, 1582).

ASENJO BARBIERI, FRANCISCO: *Cancionero musical de los siglos XV y XVI* (Madrid, 1890).

BARADO Y FONT, FRANCISCO: *Armas y Armaduras* (Madrid, 1895).

CALVERT, ALBERT F.: *Spanish Arms and Armour* (London, 1907).

GALVAM D'ANDRADE, ANTONIO: *Arte da Cavalleria* (Lisbon, 1678).

JAL, A.: *Glossaire Nautique* (Paris, 1848).

LAKING, SIR GUY FRANCIS, BT.: *A Record of European Armour and Arms through seven centuries* (London, 1920–2).

MARTÍNEZ DE ESPINAR, ALONSO: *Arte de ballesteria y monteria* (Madrid, 1644).

NAVIA OSORIO Y VIGIL ARGÜELLES DE LA RUA: *Réflexions militaires et politiques* (Paris, 1735–8).

PAYNE-GALLWEY, SIR RALPH, BT.: *The Crossbow* (London, 1903).

Pollard, Major H. B. C.: *A History of Firearms* (London, 1926).

Soto, Serafin Maria de, Conde de Clonard: *Historia organica de las armas de infanteria y caballeria españolas* (Madrid, 1851–62).

Tenorio, José Maria: *La Aviceptologia* (Madrid, 1861).

Ufano, Diego: *Artilleria* (Brussels, 1612).

A NOTE ON THE TYPE

This book was set on the Linotype in a face called *Eldorado,* so named by its designer, WILLIAM ADDISON DWIGGINS, as an echo of Spanish adventures in the Western World. The series of experiments that culminated in this type-face began in 1942; the designer was trying a page more "brunette" than the usual book type. "One wanted a face that should be sturdy, and yet not too mechanical. . . . Another desideratum was that the face should be narrowish, compact, and close fitted, for reasons of economy of materials." The specimen that started Dwiggins on his way was a type design used by the Spanish printer A. de Sancha at Madrid about 1774. Eldorado, however, is in no direct way a copy of that letter, though it does reflect the Madrid specimen in the anatomy of its arches, curves, and junctions. Of special interest in the lower-case letters are the stresses of color in the blunt, sturdy serifs, subtly counterbalanced by the emphatic weight of some of the terminal curves and finials. The roman capitals are relatively open, and winged with liberal serifs and an occasional festive touch.

The title page and binding of this book were designed by the creator of its typeface—W. A. Dwiggins. It was composed, printed, and bound by The Plimpton Press, Norwood, Massachusetts.